DESALINATION
BY REVERSE OSMOSIS

edited by

Ulrich Merten

THE M.I.T. PRESS

Massachusetts Institute of Technology
Cambridge, Massachusetts, and London, England

Copyright © 1966 by
The Massachusetts Institute of Technology

Set in Monotype Modern No. 8 with Twentieth Century
by The Colonial Press
and printed in the United States of America by
The Riverside Press.

Library of Congress catalog card number: 67-12088

Preface

In this country, economic desalting of sea- and brackish water is now a national goal that has attracted widespread governmental and public attention.

On signing the Saline Water Conversion Act of 1965, President Johnson remarked, "We have lingered too long under the impression that desalting sea water is a far out and a far distant goal. Since the dawn of time, every drop of water that man has drunk or used has been desalted in Nature's own still." [1] He could have added that even before man drank of that water, Nature had devised other processes — including membrane processes — for accomplishing the same task. At the recent First International Symposium on Water Desalination, Professor A. Katchalsky commented that "the slow invasion of the fresh waters of rivers by sea animals and plants must have been accompanied by the development of a series of mechanisms which, by maintaining a constant internal osmotic pressure, prevented the organisms from swelling to [the] bursting point." [2]

In 1952, when the United States began its formal desalting program, thermal distillation was the only one of Nature's approaches which had been transformed into a well-established desalting technique. Since that time electrodialysis — a membrane process — has proved itself in installations of significant size, and several other potentially attractive processes have been brought to a pilot-plant or prepilot-plant stage of development. There is little question that among these newer processes reverse osmosis stands out as the one attracting the most world-wide attention among desalting enthusiasts at this time.

[1] Press Release, Office of the White House Secretary, "Remarks of the President at the Signing Ceremony of the Saline Water Conversion Act (in the Rose Garden)," August 11, 1965.

[2] Katchalsky, A., B. Z. Ginzburg, and M. Ginzburg, "Biological Desalination," a paper presented by Professor Katchalsky at the First International Symposium on Water Desalination, October 5, 1965, Washington, D. C.

The basic principles underlying reverse osmosis have been understood for decades, and considerable work was done in the early part of this century with membranes that showed some ability to differentiate between water and dissolved salts. But no serious effort was directed at developing reverse osmosis as a desalination process until shortly after the federal desalination program was established. In early 1953, Professor C. E. Reid[3] of the University of Florida proposed to the Department of the Interior that a part of the national program be directed toward the study of this process.

During the 1950's the University of Florida group and, independently, a group at the University of California at Los Angeles did the exploratory work which showed that reverse osmosis is a technically feasible process. Their work led to the present flurry of interest which Secretary of the Interior Udall referred to at the Symposium on Water Desalination when he commented that "among the new ideas, reverse osmosis has particularly attracted the attention of our technicians." [4]

This book is, then, an effort by one group of interested technicians to share some of the things they have learned with others who may have developed their interest more recently. It is intended as an introduction to a rapidly changing field, and not as a text. We hope it will prove useful in this role.

A few words about the content and arrangement of the chapters and about their authors may be helpful at this point. Professor Reid's pioneering work introduced us all to reverse osmosis, and he has the introductory assignment again in Chapter 1. This chapter lays the thermodynamic groundwork for understanding the process and discusses the membrane phenomena as well as the engineering problems in a preliminary way.

Chapters 2 through 4 are concerned with the membranes on which the reverse-osmosis technology is based. Chapter 2 outlines some current theoretical approaches to describing membranes and transport through them. In Chapter 3, Dr. S. Loeb describes the preparation of high-flux cellulose acetate membranes and reviews their properties. Dr. Loeb was one of the authors of UCLA Engineering Department Report No. 60-60 which must by now be considered a classic in the field, and has continued to be a leader of the UCLA group in the ensuing years. Chapter 4 is a further discussion of cellulose acetate membrane properties, with emphasis on the quantitative interpretation of experimental results. The chapter was prepared by Dr. H. K. Lonsdale, who has been a

---

[3] Breton, E. J., Jr., and C. E. Reid, Office of Saline Water Research and Development Progress Report No. 16, April 1957.

[4] Address of Stewart L. Udall, Secretary of the Interior and Honorary Chairman of the First International Symposium on Water Desalination, Washington, D. C., October 4, 1965.

member of our research group since we first began to look at the reverse-osmosis problem some five years ago.

Beyond casual mention in Chapters 2, 3, and 4, there is nothing in this volume about any specific membrane material other than cellulose acetate. The reason is that the literature on membranes with some of the properties of interest is too voluminous, and that concerning reverse osmosis measurements *per se* too unrewarding, to justify extensive coverage. Reports by Drs. Reid, Loeb, and Lonsdale and their co-workers[3],[5—9] record some of the attempts that have been made to find alternates to cellulose acetate.

In Chapters 5 through 7 the emphasis of our discussion shifts from the membrane itself to the complete reverse-osmosis system. The design of such systems is largely determined by the membrane properties and the mass-transport problems inherent in this approach to desalination. The Chemical Engineering Department at M.I.T. is well known for its work in heat- and mass-transfer, and its work in the past few years has included the reverse-osmosis problem. Professor P. L. T. Brian summarizes the results in Chapter 5. In Chapter 6, Mr. D. T. Bray, who led the reverse-osmosis engineering effort in our laboratory while many of our present engineering concepts were evolved, brings together the membrane properties and mass-transport considerations with the economic factors, to arrive at some general guidelines to systems engineering for reverse osmosis. Then, in Chapter 7, comes the proof of the pudding, insofar as it has been proved. Mr. E. H. Sieveka, who authors this section on pilot-plant experience, gives it the perspective gained from long association with desalination pilot-plant work, first in electrodialysis and then in reverse osmosis, at the Office of Saline Water.

Finally, this nation's research and development in desalination, and particularly in reverse osmosis, is reviewed from a programmatic point of view in Chapter 8. Much of the past and present work in the field has been sponsored by the federal government, and Dr. G. F. Mangan, Jr., has had a particularly good vantage point for observing the rapid growth of the field from his positions in the Office of Saline Water, and more recently in the Office of Water Resources Research, both in the Department of the Interior.

I wish to thank all the contributors to this volume for their hard work in preparing their chapters, and Dr. H. K. Lonsdale and Mrs. K. M. McIntosh for their assistance in the editorial tasks. Several of

[5] Reid, C. E., and J. R. Kuppers, J. Appl. Polymer Sci. *2*, 264 (1959).

[6] Reid, C. E., and H. G. Spencer, J. Appl. Polymer Sci. *4*, 354 (1960).

[7] Loeb, S., UCLA Department of Engineering Report No. 61-42 (1961).

[8] Manjikian, S., UCLA Department of Engineering Report No. 65-13 (1965).

[9] Lonsdale, H. K., U. Merten, R. L. Riley, and K. D. Vos, Annual Report, April 16, 1964 through April 15, 1965, Contract No. 14-01-0001-250, U.S. Department of the Interior, Office of Saline Water.

us (D. T. B., P. L. T. B., H. K. L., U. M.) are indebted to the Office of Saline Water of the United States Department of the Interior for current support of research in the areas about which we have written. The support of this Office has been an essential factor in the rapid development of reverse osmosis during the last several years.

ULRICH MERTEN

San Diego, California
October 1966

Contents

DESALINATION
BY REVERSE OSMOSIS

1. Principles of Reverse Osmosis

Charles E. Reid

Knowledge of osmotic phenomena dates back more than two centuries — the experiments of the Abbé Nollet on diffusion through animal membranes were published in 1748. It was over a hundred years later, however, that experiments with artificially prepared membranes were successful (by Traube in 1867). In 1877 Pfeffer made the first quantitative measurements, using a membrane consisting of copper ferrocyanide precipitated in the pores of porcelain. This type of membrane was widely exploited in the late nineteenth and early twentieth centuries and led to highly accurate results even at high osmotic pressures. Though most of this work involved solutions of organic molecules, especially sugars, solutions of electrolytes, including sodium chloride, were successfully studied. A major part of this work, including the perfecting of the difficult techniques for preparing and handling the membranes, was done by H. N. Morse and his co-workers at Johns Hopkins University, and the Earl of Berkeley and E. G. J. Hartley[1] in England. A good review of early work on osmosis was written by Findlay.[2]

Meanwhile theoretical developments had started with van't Hoff, who used Pfeffer's results as the starting point for building up a comprehensive theory of dilute solutions. As thermodynamics developed into a mature scientific discipline, largely through the work of J. W. Gibbs, it provided a sound theoretical understanding of the phenomenon of osmotic pressure and of its relation to other thermodynamic properties. These developments had been largely completed by 1920, and interest in osmosis as a field of research waned. It had been shown that the same

1

information on the thermodynamic properties of solutions could be obtained by less difficult techniques, and, except for its biological importance, osmosis appeared to be only a curiosity, interesting primarily as an illustration of the power of thermodynamic reasoning.

This attitude has been changed by two very different developments: One is the realization that for solutions of polymers, in contrast to those of low-molecular-weight solutes, osmotic-pressure measurements furnish the easiest means of determining the molecular weight of the solute and the thermodynamic properties of the solutions. The other, which forms the purpose of this book, is the prospect that reversal of osmotic flow may prove a commercially feasible method of obtaining fresh water from saline sources. Though the interest here is in the production of fresh water, developments in this process are practically certain to be important in other processes also, wherever a pure solvent must be removed from a solution, either to recover the solvent or to concentrate the solution.

This chapter will contain a description of the phenomenon of osmosis, a development of the thermodynamic theory, a discussion of mechanisms of membrane selectivity, and some general considerations of how these principles will affect the large-scale application of reverse osmosis.

1.1   Description of Osmosis

Osmosis depends on the existence of a membrane that is selective in the sense that certain components of a solution (ordinarily the solvent) can pass through the membrane, while one or more of the other components cannot do so. Such a selective device is called a *semipermeable membrane;* it is usually, though not always, in the physical form suggested by the word *membrane.* If a semipermeable membrane separates a solution from a pure solvent, or two solutions of different concentrations, the tendency to equalize concentrations will result in a flow of solvent from the less concentrated phase — that is, the phase richer in solvent — to the other one (Fig. 1–1). It is this flow of solvent that is termed *osmosis.* If an attempt is made to impede the flow by exerting pressure on the solution (assuming for simplicity that the other phase is pure solvent), the rate of flow will be decreased. As the pressure is increased, a point will be found at which the flow is brought to a complete stop, the tendency to flow being in equilibrium with the opposing pressure. This equilibrium pressure (actually, the equilibrium-pressure difference between the solvent and solution phases) is called the *osmotic pressure;* as will be shown later, it is a property of the solution and cannot depend in any way on the membrane, so long as the latter has the necessary property of semipermeability. Further increase of the pressure on the solution causes reversal of the osmotic flow, and pure

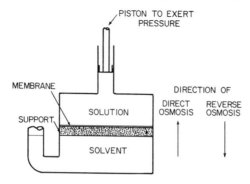

Fig. 1—1   Schematic diagram of osmotic apparatus.

solvent passes from the solution, through the membrane, into the solvent phase. This last phenomenon is the basis of the reverse-osmosis method of desalination.

It will be noticed that reverse osmosis bears some resemblance to filtration, in that both involve removing a liquid from a mixture by passing it through a device that holds back other substances. For this reason the reverse osmosis method is sometimes called "ultrafiltration." Despite this similarity, there are important differences between reverse osmosis and any kind of filtration, and discussion of some of the more striking ones is appropriate here.

The most obvious difference is the osmotic pressure itself. There is no reason to doubt that this exists and must be overcome in any filtration but it is easy to calculate that in ordinary filtration it is undetectably small. To illustrate this, consider a suspension containing 60 g/l of a solid with a particle size of one nanogram (10^{-9} g). Since there are 6×10^{10} particles per liter, the molar concentration of these particles is $6 \times 10^{10}/6 \times 10^{23} = 10^{-13}$ mole/l. Substitution into van't Hoff's equation (Eq. 1.20) leads to an osmotic pressure of 2.5×10^{-12} atm, or less than 2×10^{-6} micron of mercury. By contrast, the osmotic pressure of seawater is about 25 atm. Thus osmotic pressure has no detectable effect on ordinary filtration but is one of the major influences determining the characteristics of reverse osmosis.

A second difference, really a corollary of the first, is that in filtration the removal of liquid is usually continued until the cake of solid is substantially free of it. In reverse osmosis, however, removal of solvent increases the concentration, and therefore the osmotic pressure, of the remaining solution. Because of this increase in osmotic pressure, it is necessary or at least practically desirable to discard the concentrated solution while it still contains much of its original solvent.

Finally, in ordinary filtration the filter acts as a sieve; that is, the separation is based simply on the relative sizes of the pores and the particles that are held back. Such a mechanism is possible for an osmotic membrane, and some of them do function in just this manner. Those of interest for the desalination of water, however, are not of this type (see Section 1.3).

Most osmotic membranes have little mechanical strength and must be supported if they are to withstand large pressure differences. The development of supporting media to provide the necessary strength without seriously impeding flow is essential to the practical application of reverse osmosis.

1.2   The Thermodynamics of Osmosis

In this section it will be assumed that the reader is acquainted with the fundamental ideas of thermodynamics, but the principal ones needed are listed and discussed briefly here. Derivations may be found in practically any standard textbook of chemical thermodynamics.[3]

Flow of matter from one region to another is determined by a property called the *chemical potential*. Any kind of matter, such as water, flows in the direction in which its chemical potential decreases, exactly as heat flows in the direction of decreasing temperature. The chemical potential is defined by Gibbs's equation,

$$dU = T\,dS - p\,dV + \sum_i \mu_i\,dN_i, \tag{1.1}$$

where U is the energy, T the temperature, S the entropy, p the pressure, V the volume, and μ_i and N_i are the chemical potential and number of moles, respectively, of component i. Alternatively, the chemical potential may be related to the differentials of other properties; in terms of the Gibbs free energy G, the relation is

$$dG = -S\,dT + V\,dp + \sum_i \mu_i\,dN_i. \tag{1.2}$$

This leads immediately to the relations

$$\mu_i = \left(\frac{\partial G}{\partial N_i}\right)_{T,p,N} \tag{1.3}$$

and

$$V = \left(\frac{\partial G}{\partial p}\right)_{T,N}, \tag{1.4}$$

where the subscripts outside the parentheses mean, as is usual in thermodynamic discussions, that these variables are held constant during the differentiation; N is used to mean the entire set of N's, while N_j is used for all N's other than N_i. Differentiating the second equation with respect to N_i gives

$$\left(\frac{\partial^2 G}{\partial N_i\,\partial p}\right)_{T,N_j} = \left(\frac{\partial V}{\partial N_i}\right)_{T,p,N_j}. \tag{1.5}$$

The derivative on the right is the quantity called the *partial molar volume* of component i; it will be denoted by v_i, and it is usually interpreted as the increase in volume, per mole of component i added, when an infinitesimal amount of this component is added to the system, or as the increase in volume when one mole of i is added to a system so large that no appreciable change in composition occurs. For a system of only one component, it becomes simply the molar volume. The derivative on the left can be expressed in terms of the chemical potential by reversing the order of differentiation and applying Eq. 1.3. This gives

$$\left(\frac{\partial \mu_i}{\partial p}\right)_{T,N} = v_i. \tag{1.6}$$

In actual calculations it is customary to use not the chemical potential itself but a quantity called the activity a_i and related to the chemical potential by

$$\mu_i = \mu_i^0 + RT \ln a_i \tag{1.7}$$

where R is the gas constant, a_i the activity of component i, and μ_i^0, called the *standard chemical potential* of i, is dependent on temperature and pressure only,[*] not on concentration. Various conventions are available for defining μ_i^0, but for the solvent in the treatment of solutions it is always taken to be the chemical potential of pure solvent, μ_1^*; this means that the activity of pure solvent is unity.

The thermodynamic requirement for osmotic equilibrium is that the chemical potential of the solvent should be the same on both sides of the membrane; no such condition is imposed on the solute, since the membrane prevents its passage. If we start with pure solvent at pressure p'' on both sides of the membrane, the two phases will of course be in equilibrium, both having chemical potential μ_1^*. If we now add solute to the solvent on one side, its chemical potential is reduced to

$$\mu_1(p'') = \mu_1^*(p'') + RT \ln a_1(p''), \tag{1.8}$$

where the p'' in parentheses indicates that the corresponding property is evaluated at the pressure p''. We propose to restore equilibrium by increasing the pressure on the solution until the chemical potential of the solvent in the solution is raised back up to that of pure solvent, $\mu_1^*(p'')$. From Eq. 1.6 it can be seen that the increase in the chemical potential of the solvent in the solution as the pressure is increased from p'' to p' is

$$\int_{p''}^{p'} \left(\frac{\partial \mu_1}{\partial p}\right)_{T,N} dp = \int_{p''}^{p'} v_1 \, dp. \tag{1.9}$$

Since this increase, added to the chemical potential given by Eq. 1.8,

---

[*] Some authors define it at a fixed pressure, so that it is dependent on temperature only.

must restore the chemical potential of the solvent in solution to that of the pure solvent, $\mu_1^*(p'')$, we find

$$-RT \ln a_1(p'') = \int_{p''}^{p'} v_1 \, dp. \tag{1.10}$$

This equation is exact, and in principle it makes possible the calculation of the osmotic pressure, which is simply $p' - p''$, if a_1 can be measured independently at the pressure p'', and v_1 is known as a function of p. Actually, this equation is very unwieldy, and simplifying approximations are always made in it.

Before we take up these approximations, however, it is instructive to derive another form of Eq. 1.10. Starting as before with pure solvent at pressure p'' on both sides of the membrane, we first increase the pressure on one side to p'. Since only pure solvent is involved, the increase in chemical potential is

$$\int_{p''}^{p'} v_1^* \, dp$$

the asterisk indicating that this is the molar volume of the pure solvent. Then solute is added; since this addition takes place at the high pressure p', the change in chemical potential is

$$\mu_1(p') - \mu_1^*(p') = RT \ln a_1(p'). \tag{1.11}$$

In order that these two changes add to zero, we must have

$$-RT \ln a_1(p') = \int_{p''}^{p'} v_1^* \, dp. \tag{1.12}$$

Equations 1.10 and 1.12 leave us with a choice of experimental difficulties; we may avoid the need for determining the partial molar volume and use the molar volume of the pure solvent, but only at the cost of having to know the activity of the solvent in the solution at the high pressure.

The first approximation usually made in Eq. 1.10 is to assume some simple expression for v_1 as a function of p; thus the compressibility may be assumed constant; or, with only slightly less accuracy, it may be neglected altogether and the volume treated as constant. This last approximation leads to

$$-RT \ln a_1(p'') = (p' - p'')v_1 = \pi v_1, \tag{1.13}$$

where π is the osmotic pressure. The activity is often determined from vapor-pressure measurements by the equation

$$a_1 = \frac{P_1}{P_1^*}, \tag{1.14}$$

the numerator and denominator on the right referring to the vapor pressures of the solution and pure solvent, respectively; if the solute is volatile, partial vapor pressures of the solvent must be used. This gives the activity at the pressure P_1, but since P_1 and p'' are usually both rather low and activity varies only slowly with total pressure, it is accurate enough to identify this activity with that of Eq. 1.13 and write

$$\pi v_1 = RT \ln \left(\frac{P_1^*}{P_1} \right). \tag{1.15}$$

Despite the approximations that have been introduced in deriving it, this equation gives excellent results in most cases. Experimental osmotic pressures for sucrose solutions are compared to values calculated using Eq. 1.15 in Table 1–1; the agreement is seen to be quite good.

Table 1–1   Osmotic Pressure of Aqueous Sucrose Solutions at 30°C
(Interpolated from data in Ref. 16.)

| | Osmotic pressure/atm | | |
Molality	van't Hoff's Eq.	Eq. 1.15*	Experimental
0.991	20.3	26.8	27.2
1.646	30.3	47.3	47.5
2.366	39.0	72.6	72.5
3.263	47.8	107.6	105.9
4.108	54.2	143.3	144.0
5.332	61.5	199.0	204.3

* From Ref. 15.

Further simplification of Eq. 1.13, however, requires approximations that for many solutions are rather gross, except at very low concentrations. The first of these is *Raoult's law*, according to which the activity of the solvent can be identified with its mole fraction Z_1. Then

$$\ln a_1 \approx \ln Z_1 = \ln (1 - Z_2) \approx -Z_2, \tag{1.16}$$

the second approximation being justified because the first one has already restricted this treatment to very small values of Z_2. Substitution into Eq. 1.13 gives

$$\pi v_1 = RTZ_2. \tag{1.17}$$

The smallness of Z_2 also justifies the approximation $Z_2 \approx N_2/N_1$, and so

$$\pi(N_1 v_1) = N_2 RT \tag{1.18}$$

or

$$\pi V = N_2 RT, \tag{1.19}$$

where $V = N_1 v_1$ is, roughly, the volume of the solvent or, even more roughly, the volume of the solution. Van't Hoff first deduced this equation empirically from the data of Pfeffer, and it is called *van't Hoff's Equation*. Another version of it is

$$\pi = n_2 RT, \tag{1.20}$$

where n_2 is the molar concentration of the solute. Because of the many approximations made in deriving it, it is not surprising that it gives reasonably accurate results only at very low osmotic pressures — usually below 2 atm (see Table 1–1).

The resemblance of Eq. 1.19 to the ideal-gas law led van't Hoff to speculate that osmotic pressure might be caused, in analogy to gas pressure, by the collisions of the solute molecules with the membrane. Such ideas were widely held for many years but are now mainly historical curiosities.

This treatment has largely ignored the character of the solute, or has tacitly assumed that it is a single species. Actually, the treatment must be modified if the solute dissociates or associates in solutions. In either case those equations that relate osmotic pressure to activity or vapor pressure are still valid, but not those that relate it to concentration. For electrolytic solutions, it was at first assumed that if the formula unit of the salt dissociates into ν ions, the osmotic pressure should be ν times as great as that of a nonelectrolytic solution of the same molar concentration. Actually, the ratio is greater than 1 but less than ν, and it approaches ν as the concentration approaches zero. Arrhenius regarded this as evidence of partial dissociation, which tended toward completeness with increasing dilution. For strong electrolytes this view soon became untenable and was replaced by the idea that in dilute solutions of strong electrolytes dissociation is complete, but the chemical potentials of the ions are reduced by their electrostatic interactions. The mathematical treatment of this idea by Debye and Hückel in 1923 forms the basis of current theories of electrolytic solutions; a discussion of this, however, is beyond the scope of this chapter.

Finally, osmotic pressure, being a property that measures the activity of the solvent in a solution, can be related thermodynamically to other properties likewise dependent on the activity of the solvent — for example, the freezing-point depression.

If the solid that separates out of a solution on freezing is pure solvent, a simple thermodynamic expression can be derived for the freezing-point depression. Consider the equilibria between pure solid solvent and pure liquid solvent at the freezing point, T_f^*, on the one hand, and between pure solid solvent and liquid solution at the freezing point of the solution, T_f, on the other. For both equilibria μ_1/T must be the same for both phases, and so the change in this quantity, in going from one set of conditions to the other, must be the same for both phases. According to the Gibbs-Helmholtz equation, which is derived in most thermodynamics textbooks,

$$\left(\frac{\partial(\mu_1/T)}{\partial T}\right)_p = -\frac{h_1}{T^2}, \tag{1.21}$$

where h_1 is the partial molar enthalpy of the solvent. It follows that the change in μ_1/T as the temperature of the solid solvent changes from T_f^* to T_f is given by

$$\frac{\mu_1^{s*}(T_f)}{T_f} - \frac{\mu_1^{s*}(T_f^*)}{T_f^*} = \int_{T_f}^{T_f^*} \frac{h_1^{s*}}{T^2} dT, \tag{1.22}$$

the superscript s referring to the solid. For the process of cooling pure liquid solvent from T_f^* to T_f an analogous equation holds. The equilibrium condition must then be reached by adding solute at the temperature T_f, and this changes μ_1/T by the amount $R \ln a_1$. Thus the total change is

$$\frac{\mu_1^{l}(T_f)}{T_f} - \frac{\mu_1^{l*}(T_f^*)}{T_f^*} = \int_{T_f}^{T_f^*} \frac{h_1^{l*}}{T^2} dT + R \ln a_1(T_f), \tag{1.23}$$

where the superscript l refers to the liquid and the T_f in parentheses after a is to emphasize that the activity must be evaluated at the temperature T_f, not at T_f^*. Since the left sides of Eqs. 1.22 and 1.23 must be equal, we find that

$$R \ln a_1(T_f) = -\int_{T_f}^{T_f^*} \frac{\Delta h_f}{T^2} dT, \tag{1.24}$$

where $\Delta h_f \equiv h_1^{l*} - h_1^{s*}$ is the molar heat of fusion. This gives the activity of the solvent in the solution at the temperature T_f; however, since the variation of the activity with temperature is usually not great, a good approximation may often be obtained by identifying this activity with that of Eq. 1.13, resulting in

$$\pi v_1 = T \int_{T_f}^{T_f^*} \frac{\Delta h_f}{T^2} dT. \tag{1.25}$$

Since the range of integration is usually rather small, Δh_f varies little over this range; the approximation of constant Δh_f may then be introduced to yield

$$\pi v_1 = \frac{\theta \Delta h_f}{T_f T_f^*} T, \tag{1.26}$$

where $\theta = T_f^* - T_f$ is the freezing-point depression. Thus seawater with a freezing point of $-1.9°C$ has an osmotic pressure at 25°C of 25.1 atm, taking Δh_f as 143.5 cal/mole and v_1 as 18.05 ml/mole. Unfortunately, reliably accurate experimental data with which this result may be compared appear to be lacking. Stoughton and Lietzke[4] have recently published very useful tables of calculated values for the osmotic pressure of sea-salt solutions as a function of concentration and temperature.

1.3 Mechanism of Membrane Function

Although the mechanism by which the membrane exercises its property of semipermeability cannot affect the osmotic pressure, an understanding of it is not only of interest in itself but is essential in any rational program of membrane development. Several possible means of membrane function have been proposed, and probably each of them is valid for some systems.

The simplest type of membrane, at least in concept, is one that functions merely as a sieve. If such a membrane is to be effective, the solvent molecules must be much smaller than the molecules or ions of the solute, and the pore size of the membrane must be intermediate. This condition is easily attainable with cellophane membranes and polymer solutions; thus the important use of osmotic measurements in the study of polymers depends on sieve-type membranes. However, the likelihood of making a sharp distinction between water molecules and small inorganic ions by this means appears remote.

Callendar[5] suggested that osmotic transport might proceed by distillation in cases where the solute is not volatile; the liquid-vapor interface, or the vapor space between two liquid surfaces, could then be regarded as the membrane. Porous films could act as osmotic membranes if the liquid is kept out of the pores by surface tension, the solvent alone passing through them as vapor. While it is uncertain whether any of the usual osmotic membranes work in this manner, Townsend[6] has made measurements of osmotic pressure that unequivocally depends on setting up osmotic equilibrium by distillation. The apparatus is shown in Fig. 1–2; the pure solvent in the central tube is under tension but is held by

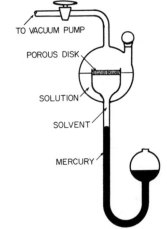

TO VACUUM PUMP

POROUS DISK

SOLUTION

SOLVENT

MERCURY

Fig. 1–2 Apparatus for osmotic-pressure measurement with vapor membrane.

surface tension in the pores of the disk. When the tension is adjusted so that no flow occurs (as observed by the mercury-solvent meniscus), the solution and solvent are in equilibrium. The osmotic pressure is then the pressure difference between the solution and the solvent, with the tension on the latter considered as a negative pressure. An inert gas, introduced into the apparatus under pressure, may make it possible to reach equilibrium without having the solvent under tension. Since this type of membrane has no mechanical strength except that provided by surface tension, it appears difficult to use at large pressure differences. Nevertheless, Hassler[7] proposed, and actually constructed on a small scale, membranes that can accomplish the desalination of water by this principle.

Solubility of the solvent in the membrane has been suggested as a possible mechanism of semipermeability; systems in which a liquid membrane is used to demonstrate this mechanism are known as curiosities. But generally the concept of solubility of the solvent in the membrane is introduced into treatments in a formal way without reference to the chemical nature of the solution formed. Unless the latter is adequately treated, this idea may evade the question of how the membrane functions, rather than answer it.

If the membrane is viewed as a porous body in which solvent but not solute is adsorbed on the pore walls, this adsorbed solvent may so fill the pores that there is no room for the passage of solute molecules. Solvent molecules can pass through by successive transfer from one adsorption site to the next; since the association of the solvent molecules with the adsorbing surface need not be completely broken during this process, it requires relatively little energy, compared to that required for a solute molecule, to invade the mass of adsorbed solvent. A mechanism similar to this was proposed by the author[8] and his co-workers for cellulose acetate, the most widely studied material for desalination membranes. In this case the adsorption forces arise from hydrogen bonding, and solutes with hydrogen-bonding tendencies similar to those of water (e.g., ammonia) are only weakly rejected. As originally proposed, this mechanism also incorporated the feature, previously suggested by several other workers,[9] that the sorbed water is held in a quasi-crystalline arrangement, which excludes most ions in the same manner as ice does. Recently, however, measurement of diffusion coefficients has provided evidence against this feature.[10]

Finally, a permselective membrane (that is, a membrane that permits cations to pass through but not anions, or vice versa) can in principle act as an osmotic membrane, since the need to maintain electrical neutrality will prevent the passage of cations if anions are blocked, and vice versa. Examples exist both among membranes synthesized primarily as permselective membranes but shown to act as osmotic membranes also,[11] and among those made primarily as osmotic membranes but later shown to function at least partly by a permselective mechanism.[12]

Membranes for thermodynamic studies must not be "leaky," in the sense of being slightly permeable to solute. For desalination, however, leaky membranes may be useful; reduction of salt content by 99% will bring seawater into the concentration range of excellent potable waters. Leaky membranes tend to show better reduction of salt content at higher pressure differences.[8,13] This has been explained on the basis of a decrease in pore size as the membrane is compressed, with resulting decrease in leakiness.[13] An alternative explanation has been given by Clark,[14] who calculated that for the solute the principal chemical potential difference across the membrane is due to concentration difference, while for the solvent it is due mainly to pressure difference. Thus increase of pressure should increase the flow rate of the solvent approximately in proportion to the excess pressure (above the osmotic pressure), while it should have little effect on the solute flow rate.

1.4 Application of Principles to Plant Design

Before taking up the detailed research described in the succeeding chapters, one may find it interesting and instructive to consider how much the principles described in this chapter can tell us about a reverse-osmosis plant.

It will be assumed that the plant will consist of (1) a pump for raising the pressure of the feed water to the chosen operating pressure; (2) the reverse-osmosis unit, in which the feed water is separated into fresh water ("product water") and concentrated solution ("brine"), the latter to be discarded; and (3) a turbine for recovering energy from the rejected brine.

The minimum energy requirement can be calculated thermodynamically; it is simply πv_1. This can be seen from the fact that no work is necessary merely to maintain the pressure on a fixed volume of solution; however, when a mole of water in this solution passes through the membrane, the volume of the solution is decreased by v_1 at the constant pressure π; thus work in the amount πv_1 must be done on the solution. For typical seawater with osmotic pressure 24.8 atm and partial molar volume 18.0 ml/mole, this gives 446 ml·atm/mole; in more familiar units, this amounts to 2.63 kw-hr per thousand gallons. Since this calculation is based on the assumption that no extra pressure beyond the osmotic pressure will be used, it corresponds to a thermodynamically reversible process. It follows that this is the minimum energy for the separation, regardless of the method used.

In actual use all processes, including reverse osmosis, use much more energy than this. There are several reasons for the extra energy needed in reverse osmosis. In the first place, although any pressure exceeding the osmotic pressure will cause reverse osmotic flow, achieving a practical rate of flow may require a much higher pressure, perhaps several times as high as the osmotic pressure. Second, as fresh water is removed from the saline solution, the concentration, and therefore the osmotic pressure, of the remaining solution is increased; moreover, this increase takes place where it is most effective: immediately adjacent to the membrane surface. Finally, the process of pumping the feed water to high pressure and recovering energy from the rejected brine are subject to the inevitable mechanical losses in pumps and turbines.

Even without the economic incentive to minimize plant size by increasing flow rates, these considerations would lead to a practical energy requirement much higher than the thermodynamic minimum. If pumping of the feed water to high pressure and recovery of pumping energy from the rejected brine could be carried out without loss, it would be desirable to make the stream of fresh product water very small in relation to the feed, since this would largely obviate the loss resulting from the increase in concentration. Actually, the energy invested in the feed water cannot be fully recovered, and the less efficient the recovery the more important it is to make the best possible use of the feed by removing a relatively large product stream from it. Requirements for minimizing these two losses are, then, contradictory; the best compromise between them may lead to an energy requirement several times the thermodynamic minimum. (Actually, an entirely different problem — the precipitation of salts on the membrane surface — may prove to be the limiting factor in the amount of product water removed, particularly in the treatment of brackish waters.)

Complicating these considerations is the relation of plant cost to operating pressure. A high pressure will increase the flow rate and so reduce the membrane area. This will reduce the cost of the reverse-osmosis unit (though not in proportion to the decrease in membrane area, since higher pressure will necessitate more massive construction). Against this saving will be the increased cost of energy and pumping equipment.

Still another consideration is the fact that the build-up of concentration takes place at the membrane surface. The resulting excess of solute near the surface must be removed by diffusion back into the bulk of the solution; this can be done much more effectively, however, if diffusion is aided by mechanical stirring. It is known experimentally that rapid flow of the solution across the membrane increases the rate of flow through it. Providing this crossflow without inordinately increasing the mechanical complexity of the reverse-osmosis unit is a task awaiting the designer's ingenuity.

Reasoning of this sort could continue indefinitely, though with increasingly doubtful value. The aim of this section has not been to tell how a plant should be designed but only to relate the principles of reverse osmosis to the questions that must be answered in laboratories and pilot plants by the kind of research reported in the subsequent chapters.

14   C. E. Reid

References

1. Morse, H. N., *The Osmotic Pressure of Aqueous Solutions*, The Carnegie Institute of Washington, Washington (1914); Berkeley, Earl of, and E. G. J. Hartley, *Proc. Roy. Soc. (London)* **A73**, 436 (1903); **A78**, 68 (1906).
2. Findlay, A., *Osmotic Pressure*, Longmans, Green & Co., New York (1913).
3. The following books treat thermodynamic principles in notation similar to that used here:
    Reid, C. E., *Principles of Chemical Thermodynamics*, Reinhold Publishing Corp., New York (1960).
    Guggenheim, E. A., *Thermodynamics — An Advanced Treatment for Chemists and Physicists*, Interscience Publishers, New York, 4th ed. (1959), or earlier editions.
    Caldin, E. F., *An Introduction to Chemical Thermodynamics*, Clarendon Press, Oxford (1958).
    Zemansky, M. W., *Heat and Thermodynamics*, McGraw-Hill Book Company, Inc., New York (1957).
4. Stoughton, R. W., and M. H. Lietzke, *J. Chem. Eng. Data* **10**, 254 (1965).
5. Callendar, H. C., *Proc. Roy. Soc. (London)* **80**, 466 (1908).
6. Townsend, R. V., *J. Am. Chem. Soc.* **50**, 2598 (1928).
7. Hassler, G. L., and J. W. McCutchan, *Saline Water Conversion (Advances in Chemistry* series, No. 27), American Chemical Society, Washington (1960) pp. 192ff.
8. Reid, C. E., and E. J. Breton, *J. Appl. Polymer Sci.* **1**, 133 (1959); Reid, C. E., and J. R. Kuppers, *ibid.* **2**, 264 (1959).
9. Stamm, A. J., and W. K. Loughborough, *J. Phys. Chem.* **39**, 121 (1935); Neale, S. M., and G. R. Williamson, *ibid.* **60**, 741 (1956).
10. Lonsdale, H. K., U. Merten, and R. L. Riley, *J. Appl. Polymer Sci.* **9**, 1341 (1965).
11. McKelvey, K. S. Spiegler, and M. R. J. Wyllie, *J. Phys. Chem.* **61**, 174 (1957).
12. Reid, C. E., and H. G. Spencer, *J. Appl. Polymer Sci.* **4**, 354 (1960).
13. Reid, C. E., and H. G. Spencer, *J. Phys. Chem.* **64**, 1587 (1960).
14. Clark, W. E., *Science*, **138**, 148 (1962).
15. Berkeley, Earl of, E. G. J. Hartley, and C. V. Burton, *Phil. Trans. Roy. Soc. London* **A218**, 295 (1919).
16. Frazer, J. C. W., and R. T. Myrick, *J. Am. Chem. Soc.*, **38**, 1907 (1916).

2. Transport Properties of Osmotic Membranes

Ulrich Merten

Osmotic processes are of current technical interest in two widely separated fields: in the biological sciences, because of the importance of selective transport through cell membranes to life processes; and in chemical processing, where desalination is the most publicized but by no means the only proposed use of membrane permeation as a unit process in chemical separations.[1,2]

The study of membrane properties in living systems is made more difficult by the chemical complexity of the membranes encountered and by the fact that metabolic processes serve as a source of the energy required to cause transport against what appears to be large chemical potential gradients. The study of the synthetic membranes of interest in desalination is more straightforward, and it is with such membranes that we will be concerned here.

As of this writing, the cellulose acetate membranes described in Chapters 3 and 4 are the only membranes generally recognized as having practical value in reverse-osmosis applications. For this reason they are the only ones discussed in detail in this volume. While they are rather well suited to their purpose, their properties leave something to be desired in several important respects, and much research is currently in progress to find superior materials. For this reason it seems worthwhile to discuss transport in osmotic membranes somewhat more generally here.

The literature concerning membrane transport is voluminous and varied. Tuwiner's volume[3] on membrane technology includes a general

15

historical review; Helfferich,[4] Schlögl,[5] and Bergsma and Kruissink[6] include extensive references to the literature of ion-exchange membranes in their discussions; Rogers[7] gives a very complete discussion of diffusion in membranes; and Ferry's 1936 paper[8] on ultrafiltration remains a most useful review of the early literature on porous membranes. A wide variety of membrane phenomena has been examined, and a body of theory has gradually evolved to explain particular phenomena and to relate the phenomena to one another.

Some parts of the theoretical treatment of membrane phenomena are described in this chapter. We have attempted to select those aspects that are apt to be most useful in interpreting reverse-osmosis experiments, predicting membrane performance on the basis of limited data, and selecting candidate membrane materials for further study. We have included a somewhat more lengthy discussion of water sorption in polymer materials than might otherwise seem appropriate, because an understanding of water sorption provides a most important link between the physical models used in discussions of membrane transport phenomena, and the chemistry of membrane materials.

2.1 General Considerations

The most generally applicable description of transport across membranes uses the language of irreversible thermodynamics. The flow of the ith component of the external solutions is written

$$F_i = L_{ii}X_i + \sum_j L_{ij}X_j. \tag{2.1}$$

Here the L's are so-called phenomenological coefficients whose magnitude determines the relationship between the fluxes F of the several components and the forces X that the several components experience. The first term on the right side of the equation states that the ith component will move in the direction of a force applied to it; and the L_{ii} are always positive. The remaining terms express the relationship between the flux of one component and the forces acting on others. The coefficients of these terms, the L_{ij}, are subject to two restrictions of importance in our considerations. First, Onsager's reciprocal relations require that $L_{ij} = L_{ji}$; i.e., the coupling between species i and j is the same whether we refer to a flux of i related to a force on j, or vice versa. Second, thermodynamic considerations require that $L_{ii}L_{jj} - L_{ij}^2 \geq 0$; thus thermodynamically, the L_{ij} can have either sign, but their absolute magnitude is limited by the magnitudes of the L_{ii}. In particular, this condition states, as Schlögl[5] has indicated, that if L_{ii} for any species is zero, then all the L_{ij} for that species are also zero: If a component of the solution will not move through the membrane under the influence of forces acting directly upon that component, then it will not pass through the membrane at all.

The validity of these statements concerning the phenomenological coefficients depends on a proper choice of the forces X_i by methods described, for instance, by de Groot.[9] Using the fluxes of the individual components as we have here, the appropriate choice under isothermal conditions is

$$X_i = - \operatorname{grad} \mu_i + Y_i, \qquad (2.2)$$

where μ_i is the chemical potential of species i, and Y_i is the external force, composed of electrical and mechanical forces in particular, acting on component i.

If no external forces act on a component, and if there is no coupling of flows (i.e., if all $L_{ij} = 0$), then Eq. 2.1 reduces to a simple diffusion equation,

$$F_i = -L_{ii} \operatorname{grad} \mu_i. \qquad (2.3)$$

Cases in which the Y or the L_{ij} are nonzero are, however, often encountered in studies of membrane processes.

The coupling of two components flowing through a membrane most commonly occurs because each carries the other along. In this case, the L_{ij} in question is positive, since the flow of component i is in the direction of the force acting on component j. Schlögl[10] states that he has found no example of the observation of a negative L_{ij}, and Kedem and Katchalsky[11] speculate that such values may only be observed in multicomponent biological systems, in which carriers for certain solutes are present. In our simple inanimate systems, we can probably safely concern ourselves only with positive coupling coefficients.

In isothermal osmosis and reverse-osmosis procedures, the only forces commonly applied externally to cause flow are concentration gradients and pressure gradients. Both appear explicitly in the chemical potential part of the X_i when it is expanded as

$$\operatorname{grad} \mu_i = \left(\frac{\partial \mu_i}{\partial c_i}\right)_{p,T} \operatorname{grad} c_i + v_i \operatorname{grad} p, \qquad (2.4)$$

with c_i the concentration and v_i the partial molar volume of the ith component (Eq. 1.6). Hence, in this case the Y_i are zero. If an electric field ϕ is also impressed across the membrane, an external force of magnitude $(-\mathfrak{F} z_i \operatorname{grad} \phi)$ must be added, where z_i is the ionic charge of the ith component and $\mathfrak{F}$ the Faraday constant; or, equivalently, the electrochemical potential can be used in place of the chemical potential of Eq. 2.4.

An integrated form of Eq. 2.4 will be useful to us in our subsequent discussions. Using subscript 1 to designate solvent (water) and subscript 2 to designate solute in a two-component system, we may write

$$\Delta \mu_1 = \int \left(\frac{\partial \mu_1}{\partial c_1}\right)_{p,T} dc_1 + \int v_1 \, dp = \int \left(\frac{\partial \mu_1}{\partial c_2}\right)_{p,T} dc_2 + \int v_1 \, dp. \qquad (2.5)$$

The osmotic pressure difference $\Delta\pi$ between two solutions of different concentration, is the pressure difference that exists when $\Delta\mu_1 = 0$. Thus, for v_1 constant,

$$v_1 \Delta\pi = - \int \left(\frac{\partial\mu_1}{\partial c_2}\right)_{p,T} dc_2 \tag{2.6}$$

and

$$\Delta\mu_1 = v_1(\Delta p - \Delta\pi), \tag{2.7}$$

where $\Delta\pi$ is the difference in osmotic pressures of the two solutions as defined by Eq. 1.13. We may also write this as

$$\Delta\mu_1 = -\frac{\alpha R T v_1}{M_2} \Delta c_2 + v_1 \Delta p, \tag{2.8}$$

where α is the osmotic coefficient of the solute and is unity where van't Hoff's equation applies in the form given in Eq. 1.20.

For the solute,

$$\Delta\mu_2 = \int \left(\frac{\partial\mu_2}{\partial c_2}\right)_{p,T} dc_2 + \int v_2 \, dp, \tag{2.9}$$

or, if we assume dilute solution behavior (i.e., activity proportional to concentration) and v_2 constant,

$$\Delta\mu_2 = RT\Delta \ln c_2 + v_2 \Delta p \tag{2.10}$$

from Eq. 1.7.

It is possible to show, as Clark[12] has pointed out, that $v_2 \Delta p$ is generally small compared to $RT\Delta \ln c_2$ under the conditions of greatest interest in reverse osmosis. Using 20 cm³/mole as the partial molar volume of the solute in the solution, at room temperature we require,

$$\left| \ln \frac{c_2'}{c_2''} \right| \gg |8 \times 10^{-4} \Delta p| \text{ for } \Delta p \text{ in atm} \tag{2.11}$$

where $'$ and $''$ refer to the high- and low-concentration membrane-solution interfaces, respectively.

The pressures of interest in reverse osmosis are generally less than 100 atm, so the pressure term in Eq. 2.10 is negligible for $(c_2'/c_2'') \gg 1.1$. In general, we are interested in solute concentration ratios in the external solutions, c_2'/c_2'', of 5 to 100, so that

$$\Delta\mu_2 = RT\Delta \ln c_2 \tag{2.12}$$

is a good approximation.

The results of membrane experiments can be formally expressed in terms of phenomenological coefficients for the membrane, replacing the gradient terms in Eq. 2.4 by finite differences across the membrane thickness. Staverman[13] discusses the relations between observable membrane properties and the phenomenological coefficients of Eq. 2.1. If the interpretation of the coefficients is to be other than formal, however, it is generally necessary to distinguish between effects taking place at the membrane-solution interfaces and those taking place within the membrane itself. Thus, the relative concentrations of solution constituents frequently change abruptly at membrane-solution interfaces, and the pressure and electrostatic potential differences existing across the membrane proper differ from those measured between the two solutions because of pressure and potential changes at the interfaces.

The interface effects are commonly calculated on the assumption that the external solutions and the membrane are in chemical equilibrium at the membrane surfaces; we shall adopt this approximation here. The distribution of water and of salt between the membrane and the external solution can then be characterized by equilibrium distribution coefficients K_1 and K_2, respectively, at each interface; and certain pressure and electrostatic potential changes at the interfaces can be calculated from requirements of electrochemical equilibrium. We will define K_1 and K_2 in terms of mass of component 1 (or 2) per unit volume of membrane, divided by mass of component 1 (or 2) per unit volume of solution.

2.2 Membrane Models

Semipermeable membranes are most commonly discussed as porous materials through which solutions pass by viscous flow and selectivity is obtained by a sieving mechanism; or as solution-diffusion barriers in which each component is dissolved and in which each component diffuses independently of the other. We shall discuss the viscous flow and solution-diffusion models briefly, then describe one method of discussing the properties of membranes which have an intermediate character, and finally touch on one description of charged membranes.

In all cases we shall consider the isothermal steady state only, with transport through the membrane occurring in one direction. We shall visualize a reverse-osmosis apparatus like that of Fig. 1-1, with reverse osmotic water flow occurring in the negative y direction. The boundary conditions in our equations will be the solute concentrations c_2' and c_2'' in the solutions in contact with the upper and lower surfaces of the membrane, respectively. If stirring in the system is inadequate, these concentrations, in particular c_2', will differ from the bulk solution concentrations by an amount that may be calculated by methods discussed in Chapter 5.

Solution-Diffusion Membranes

Ferry[8] credits L'Hermite[14] with suggesting in 1855 that ultrafiltration may occur by a solution-diffusion mechanism. We shall regard as barriers of the solution-diffusion type those membranes in which the movement of each species can be described as solution of that species in the membrane substance and diffusion through the membrane material. Our definition will be restricted to cases in which there is no coupling of the diffusive flows of the solution components within the membrane. Rogers[7] gives a comprehensive treatment of diffusion in solution-diffusion membranes; in it he pays particular attention to cases in which some of the simplifying assumptions made here fail, e.g., those in which the diffusion coefficient is concentration dependent.

In principle, sorption-desorption rates at the membrane surface could be rate limiting in membranes of this type, and Laidler and Schuler,[15] and Zwolinski, Eyring, and Reese[16] have treated cases where these rate effects must be included. It will be assumed that the solution processes are sufficiently rapid so that an equilibrium distribution of solute and solvent between the solution immediately adjacent to the membrane and the membrane surface is maintained. The rate-limiting step in the transport process, then, is the diffusion of each species in its own chemical potential gradient, $d\mu_1/dy$ for water and $d\mu_2/dy$ for the solute. For water in our systems, the activity difference across the membrane is always small (e.g., the activity of water in a 5% NaCl solution at room temperature is 0.97 times the activity of pure water[17]) so that we may reasonably replace $d\mu_1/dy$ by the chemical potential difference across the membrane $\Delta\mu_1$ divided by the membrane thickness λ.

Equation 2.3 relates flux to the chemical potential gradient, through a phenomenological coefficient L_{ii}. In our model discussions, it will be more useful to replace L_{ii} by terms having a more concrete physical significance. Thus we will write

$$F_1 = -c_{1m}m_{1m}\frac{d\mu_1}{dy} = -c_{1m}m_{1m}\frac{\Delta\mu_1}{\lambda}, \qquad (2.13)$$

where c_{1m} is the concentration of water within the membrane material, m_{1m} is its mobility, and both have been assumed constant over the small μ_1 range of interest. (The use of mobilities and their relation to diffusion coefficients are discussed, for example, by Shewmon[18] and by Jost.[19] For convenience, we have chosen to use a mobility defined as velocity per unit force on one mole of particles, rather than per particle. Numerically, it is the particle mobility divided by Avogadro's number.) The chemical potential difference across the membrane is given by Eq. 2.7, so that Eq. 2.13 becomes

$$F_1 = -c_{1m}m_{1m}v_1\frac{\Delta p - \Delta\pi}{\lambda}. \qquad (2.14)$$

If the water–membrane-material solution obeys dilute-solution laws, i.e., if $(\partial\mu_1/\partial c_{1m})_{p,T} = RT/c_{1m}$, then the mobility may be identified with a Fick's law diffusion coefficient for water in the membrane material through the relationship $D_{1m} = m_{1m}RT$.

The diffusion of solute through the membrane may be similarly described. Thus,

$$F_2 = -m_{2m}c_{2m}\left[\left(\frac{\partial \mu_2}{\partial c_{2m}}\right)_{p,T}\frac{dc_{2m}}{dy} + v_2\frac{dp}{dy}\right],\qquad(2.15)$$

where c_{2m} is the solute concentration within the membrane, and m_{2m} and v_2 are the solute mobility and partial molar volume, respectively, and are both assumed constant. We have already indicated that at reasonable concentration differences across the membrane the pressure gradient term is not important in solute diffusion. For a constant distribution coefficient K_2 and Fick's law diffusion, Eq. 2.15 reduces to

$$F_2 = -D_{2m}\frac{\Delta c_{2m}}{\lambda} = -D_{2m}K_2\frac{\Delta c_2}{\lambda},\qquad(2.16)$$

where D_{2m} is the diffusion coefficient for the solute in the membrane material. Concentration profiles in a solution-diffusion membrane in a reverse-osmosis situation are shown in Fig. 2-1.

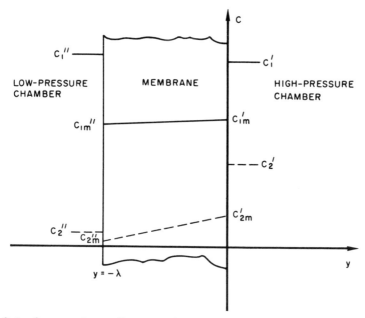

Fig. 2–1 Concentration profiles in a solution-diffusion membrane. The concentration ratios c'_{1m}/c'_1, c''_{1m}/c''_1, c'_{2m}/c'_2, and c''_{2m}/c''_2 are the distribution coefficients for water (subscript 1) and solute (subscript 2) at the interfaces $'$ and $''$.

Because the solute flux in the reverse-osmosis situation is essentially pressure independent while the water flux varies linearly with $(\Delta p - \Delta \pi)$, the salt-concentration reduction factor for solution-diffusion membranes can become very large as Δp increases. In the limit of very high pressures, of course, the assumption that the effect of pressure on membrane properties and on $\Delta\mu_2$ can be ignored fails, but for $c_2' \gg c_2''$ and where Eqs. 2.14 and 2.16 are valid, the salt-concentration reduction factor becomes

$$\frac{c_2'}{c_2''} = \frac{c_2' F_1}{F_2 c_1''} = \frac{c_{1m} D_{1m} v_1 (\Delta p - \pi')}{D_{2m} K_2 RT c_1''} = \frac{D_{1m} K_1}{D_{2m} K_2} \frac{v_1 (\Delta p - \pi')}{RT}, \quad (2.17)$$

where π' is the osmotic pressure of the solution in the high-pressure chamber.

Viscous-Flow Membranes

The solution-diffusion membranes just discussed represent one extreme among possible membranes, in that we have assumed no coupling of solvent and solute flows. A porous membrane with sufficiently large pores represents the other extreme, in which coupling is that characteristic of viscous flow.

The total volumetric flux through a highly porous membrane can generally be described using Poiseuille's law, so that

$$\epsilon u = -H \frac{dp}{dy} = -\frac{\epsilon r^2}{8\eta} \frac{dp}{dy} \approx -\frac{\epsilon r^2}{8\eta} \frac{\Delta p_m}{t\lambda}. \quad (2.18)$$

Here u is the center-of-mass velocity of the pore fluid, ϵ the fractional open area of the membrane, H its hydrodynamic permeability, η the viscosity of the pore fluid, and r an equivalent cylindrical pore radius. We shall assume that r is constant through the membrane, equate ϵ with the fractional pore volume of the membrane, and neglect solution density changes with concentration. Then u must be constant through the membrane, and we are justified in replacing the pressure gradient by $\Delta p_m/t\lambda$, where t is a tortuosity factor included to indicate that the effective pore length may be greater than the measured membrane thickness.

In a membrane of this type the salt flux can be represented as the sum of a contribution due to center-of-mass motion of the fluid and another due to diffusion of the solute with respect to the center of mass. Thus, the flux of solute may be written

$$F_2 = c_{2m} u + J_2, \quad (2.19)$$

where c_{2m} is the solute concentration (still expressed as mass per unit total membrane volume), u the center-of-mass velocity, and J_2 the diffusive flow of solute per unit membrane area at any point. If the diffusive flux is given by Fick's law, we may write

$$J_2 = -D_{21} \frac{dc_{2m}}{dy}, \quad (2.20)$$

with D_{21} the diffusion coefficient for the solute in the center-of-mass system. Combining Eqs. 2.19 and 2.20 gives

$$F_2 = -D_{21} \frac{dc_{2m}}{dy} + c_{2m}u. \tag{2.21}$$

The complete expression for diffusion in the center-of-mass system for a binary solution is given by de Groot.[20] In the absence of external forces one obtains

$$J_2 = -D_{21} \frac{dc_{2m}}{dy} + D_{21} \frac{c_{1m}}{\rho_m \epsilon} \left(\frac{\partial \mu_2}{\partial c_{2m}}\right)^{-1}_{p,T} \left(\frac{M_2}{M_1} v_1 - v_2\right) \frac{dp_m}{dy}, \tag{2.22}$$

where ρ_m is the density of the pore fluid and has been assumed constant. Combining with Eqs. 2.18 and 2.19 gives

$$F_2 = -D_{21} \frac{dc_{2m}}{dy} - \left[c_{2m} \frac{H}{\epsilon} - D_{21} \frac{c_{1m}}{\rho_m \epsilon} \left(\frac{\partial \mu_2}{\partial c_{2m}}\right)^{-1}_{p,T} \left(\frac{M_2}{M_1} v_1 - v_2\right)\right] \frac{dp_m}{dy}. \tag{2.23}$$

In dilute solutions, $(\partial \mu_2 / \partial c_{2m})_{p,T} = RT/c_{2m}$, $c_{1m} = \rho_m \epsilon$, and

$$F_2 = -D_{21} \frac{dc_{2m}}{dy} - c_{2m} \left[\frac{H}{\epsilon} - \frac{D_{21}}{RT} \left(\frac{M_2}{M_1} v_1 - v_2\right)\right] \frac{dp_m}{dy}. \tag{2.24}$$

With the assumptions discussed for Eq. 2.18, the pressure gradient through the membrane is constant, and we may use

$$F_2 = -D_{21} \frac{dc_{2m}}{dy} + c_{2m}u^0, \tag{2.25}$$

where

$$u^0 = -\left[\frac{H}{\epsilon} - \frac{D_{21}}{RT} \left(\frac{M_2}{M_1} v_1 - v_2\right)\right] \frac{\Delta p_m}{t\lambda} = u \left[1 - \frac{D_{21}\epsilon}{RTH} \left(\frac{M_2}{M_1} v_1 - v_2\right)\right]. \tag{2.26}$$

Thus an equation of the form 2.21 can be used for all dilute-solution cases, but for very small membrane permeabilities H the term $(D_{21}/RT)[(M_2/M_1)v_1 - v_2]$ can become comparable to H/ϵ; then u must be replaced by u^0.

The relation of center-of-mass diffusion coefficients to the coefficients normally measured in the laboratory has been discussed by Hartley and Crank.[21] In dilute solutions they are equal.

A porous membrane of this kind can effect a separation of solvent and solute in reverse osmosis only if the solute concentration in the pore liquid differs from that in the external solution in contact with the membrane. Assuming chemical equilibrium across the interface, we relate the internal concentration at each interface to the external concentration through the equilibrium constants

$$c'_{2m} = K'_2 c'_2; \qquad c''_{2m} = K''_2 c''_2. \tag{2.27}$$

(With c_{2m} as defined here, mass of solute per unit total membrane volume, the pore-liquid concentration is equal to the external concentration when $K_2 = \epsilon$, where ϵ is the fractional pore volume of the membrane.)

Integrating Eq. 2.21 we have

$$c_{2m} = \frac{F_2}{u} + B \exp\left(\frac{u}{D_{21}} y\right), \tag{2.28}$$

with B a constant of integration. The appropriate boundary conditions in a reverse-osmosis experiment are that Eqs. 2.27 are satisfied at $y = 0$ and $y = -t\lambda$, and that

$$\frac{F_2}{\epsilon u} = c_2'', \tag{2.29}$$

where the latter condition simply expresses the fact that the concentration of the solution on the exit side of the membrane is determined by the relative magnitudes of the salt and water flows through it. Thus Eq. 2.28 becomes

$$c_2'' = \frac{K_2' c_2' \exp\left(-ut\lambda/D_{21}\right)}{K_2'' - \epsilon + \epsilon \exp\left(-ut\lambda/D_{21}\right)}. \tag{2.30}$$

Equation 2.28 shows the shape of the solute concentration profile at various flow rates; several cases are illustrated in Fig. 2–2.

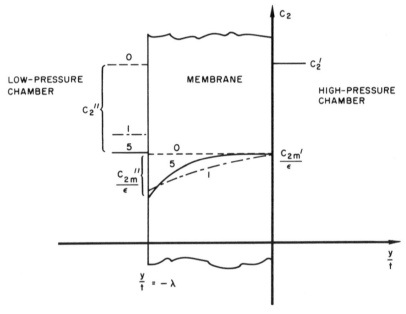

Fig. 2–2   Concentration profiles in a viscous-flow membrane. The three curves are for values of $(ut\lambda/D_{21})$ equal 0, 1, and 5 as labeled. The distribution coefficient for the solute c_{2m}/c_2 has been chosen equal to 0.5ϵ at both interfaces.

It is apparent from Eq. 2.30 that the lowest outlet solute concentration is achieved at the highest (in the negative y direction) linear velocities, and that in the limit

$$\frac{c_2'}{c_2''} = \frac{\epsilon}{K_2'} \approx \frac{K_1}{K_2'}. \tag{2.31}$$

The last expression is strictly valid only for dilute pore liquids.

The assumption of chemical equilibrium across the interface requires the chemical potential for water as well as that for salt to be continuous across the interfaces. Since we have chosen to treat the water-salt mixture within the membrane as a separate phase, it is a two-component system, and this condition becomes

$$\Delta\mu_1' = \int_{p'}^{p_m'} v_1 \, dp + \int_{c_2'}^{c_{2m}'} \left(\frac{\partial\mu_1}{\partial c_2}\right)_{p,T} dc_2, \tag{2.32}$$

where $\Delta\mu_1'$ is the chemical potential change for water across the interface. We may identify the second integral with the osmotic pressure change across the interface as we did for the entire membrane in Eq. 2.7, so that

$$\Delta\mu_1' = v_1(\Delta p' - \Delta\pi') = 0, \tag{2.33}$$

and similarly for the other interface. Thus,

$$\Delta p_m = \Delta p - \Delta p' + \Delta p''$$
$$= \Delta p - \Delta\pi' + \Delta\pi'', \tag{2.34}$$

with the difference in each case being the pressure (or osmotic pressure) outside the membrane adjacent to the interface less the pressure (or osmotic pressure) within the membrane adjacent to the interface. It is noteworthy that in general $(\Delta\pi' - \Delta\pi'') \neq \Delta\pi$, and the effective pressure driving solution through the membrane in this case is not simply the excess of the hydrostatic pressure over the osmotic pressure difference. With the use of a dilute-solution approximation for an undissociated solute,

$$\Delta\pi' = \frac{RT}{M_2}\left(\frac{c_{2m}'}{\epsilon} - c_2'\right) = \frac{RT}{M_2} c_2'\left(\frac{K_2'}{\epsilon} - 1\right) \tag{2.35}$$

and similarly for $\Delta\pi''$, so that

$$\Delta p_m = \Delta p - \frac{RT}{M_2}\left[c_2'\left(\frac{K_2'}{\epsilon} - 1\right) - c_2''\left(\frac{K_2''}{\epsilon} - 1\right)\right]; \tag{2.36}$$

it is this value of the pressure drop across the membrane that is to be used in Eq. 2.18.

This picture of the highly porous membrane which excludes a solute but allows viscous flow within the pores may not be realized in practice and may be useful only as a limiting case; we have discussed it here as an introduction to some more realistic models. We might remark in this connection that the use of a cylindrical pore model, while extremely useful, can be deceiving in some respects. In particular, real membranes in general have a rather heterogeneous porosity and, at least where relatively large pores and somewhat larger molecules are in question, a membrane may act essentially as a "depth filter": i.e., molecules or particles slightly too large to pass through the membrane can be carried deep enough into it so that they cannot readily escape again. This may lead to a decrease in permeability due to pore blocking, an effect well documented in ultrafiltration.[7] In osmotic phenomena involving small ions and molecules, and membranes appropriate thereto, such effects appear to be less important.

Finely Porous Membranes

From a practical point of view, solution-diffusion membranes are of great interest because of the high degree of selectivity which they can, in principle, provide, while viscous flow membranes are attractive because of their high permeabilities. The existence of a solute distribution coefficient K_2 different from ϵ in a porous membrane in which Eqs. 2.18 and 2.20 are obeyed, implies an effect of the membrane on the equilibrium properties of the pore fluid, with no effect on transport within the pore. In reality, one would expect any mechanical and electrostatic forces that affect the equilibrium to influence transport as well. Such effects on transport will affect the coupling terms in the flux equations, and it seems likely that many useful membranes will fall into a category intermediate between the two just described: a class of materials in which coupling of flows exists, but to a substantially lesser degree than in viscous-flow membranes.

A number of different models might be suggested for such intermediate membranes, but we deal in detail only with one suggested by experiments on cellulose acetate membranes, for instance those reported by Sourirajan.[22] It is well established that initially quite porous membranes of cellulose acetate can be progressively modified by heat treatment to become more and more selective until their properties approach those of a solution-diffusion membrane. It seems reasonable to regard the membranes of intermediate properties as porous structures with a pore size too small to permit unrestricted flow of solute molecules, but with all the solvent and solute within the membrane contained in these small pores.

We may, then, begin with the same solute-flow equation which we used in describing porous membranes (Eq. 2.19), except that we will now write the diffusive flux of salt as

$$J_2 = m_{21}c_{2m}\left[-\left(\frac{\partial \mu_2}{\partial c_{2m}}\right)_{p,T}\frac{dc_{2m}}{dy} + Y_2\right], \qquad (2.37)$$

where m_{21} is the mobility of the solute in water and Y_2 the frictional force acting on each mole of solute as a result of its interaction with the membrane material; it is introduced here as an external force in the sense of Eq. 2.2.

Extensive treatments of frictional membrane models have been presented by Spiegler[23] and by Kedem and Katchalsky.[11] In this very elementary approach we assume, with the earlier workers, a linear relation between the frictional force per mole of solute and the solute velocity within the pore u_2, so that

$$Y_2 = -f_{23}u_2 = -\frac{f_{23}F_2}{c_{2m}}, \qquad (2.38)$$

where f_{23} is an appropriate friction coefficient representing the interaction of the solute with the membrane. The mobility of solute in water m_{21} may also be restated as a friction coefficient for solute interacting with water, $m_{21} = 1/f_{21}$.

Inserting Eqs. 2.37 and 2.38 into Eq. 2.19, and defining the term

$$b \equiv 1 + \frac{f_{23}}{f_{21}}, \tag{2.39}$$

we have

$$F_2 = -\frac{c_{2m}}{f_{21}b}\left(\frac{\partial\mu_2}{\partial c_{2m}}\right)_{p,T}\frac{dc_{2m}}{dy} + \frac{c_{2m}}{b}u. \tag{2.40}$$

With dilute-solution behavior $[(\partial\mu_2/\partial c_{2m})_{p,T} = RT/c_{2m}]$,

$$F_2 = -\frac{RT}{f_{21}b}\frac{dc_{2m}}{dy} + \frac{c_{2m}}{b}u, \tag{2.41}$$

identical with Eq. 2.21 for the highly porous case (if $m_{21}RT \equiv D_{21}$) except for the introduction of b.

Examination of Eq. 2.41 for the case where u approaches zero shows that the apparent diffusion coefficient for the salt within the membrane is reduced by a factor of $1/b$ from its free-solution value by interaction with the membrane. Thus $1/b$ is the equivalent of the drag factor in membrane dialysis. Faxen[24] has proposed a method for calculating this drag factor on geometrical grounds, which has been used in the interpretation of dialysis measurements by Lane and Riggle,[25] for example. It seems unlikely, however, that only geometric factors are involved.[26]

Spiegler[23] discussed the relation between a friction factor, analogous to our f_{21}, and the diffusion coefficient for the solute in dilute free solutions, D_{21}. Since in each case it is the interaction between the solute and water which is determining, one might assume that the interactions are identical within and without the membrane, and that $f_{21} = RT/D_{21}$. However, Spiegler argues that in his homogeneous model the dilute solution value of the friction factor should be multiplied by that volume fraction of the membrane which is water, to reflect the smaller number of encounters between water and solute within the membrane. In the present model, where water and solute are both assumed confined to pores, the argument for reducing the interaction in this way is less strong. In any case, f_{21} can be assumed to be of the order of magnitude of RT/D_{21} in membranes of reasonably high water content, and Spiegler indeed finds this to be the case in an analysis of data for a cation-exchange resin; but exact numerical agreement is not necessarily to be expected.

It is interesting to examine the limits in which Eq. 2.41 approaches the two cases discussed previously. For negligible solute-membrane interactions, $f_{23} \ll f_{21}$; therefore, $b \approx 1$, and the highly porous membrane case is obtained. For $f_{21} = 0$,

$$F_2 = -\frac{RT}{f_{23}} \frac{dc_{2m}}{dy}, \tag{2.42}$$

the solution-diffusion case.

If we solve Eq. 2.41 as before for Eq. 2.21, the final result in a reverse-osmosis situation is

$$c_2'' = \frac{K_2' c_2' \exp\left(-ut\lambda f_{21}/RT\right)}{K_2'' - b\epsilon + b\epsilon \exp\left(-ut\lambda f_{21}/RT\right)}. \tag{2.43}$$

This simple solution is possible only, of course, if b and f_{21} are independent of c_{2m}.

In the limit of high negative flow velocities, the salt-concentration reduction factor from Eq. 2.43 approaches

$$\frac{c_2'}{c_2''} = \frac{b\epsilon}{K_2'} \approx \frac{bK_1}{K_2'} \tag{2.44}$$

with the last equality strictly valid only for very dilute solutions. Again the two limiting cases are apparent. For $b = 1$, the maximum achievable concentration reduction is K_1/K_2', while for b large, correspondingly large reductions are achievable.

The frictional forces between solute and membrane postulated here affect not only the solute permeability of the membrane, but its apparent hydrodynamic permeability as well. The force per unit volume of pore fluid due to the interaction of the solute and the membrane is just the force per mole multiplied by the molar concentration in the pore fluid, $c_{2m}/\epsilon M_2$, where M_2 is the molecular weight of component 2. This force must be added to the pressure gradient to obtain the total force acting on unit volume of pore fluid. Using Eq. 2.38, we may write for dilute solutions

$$u = -\frac{H}{\epsilon} \left[\frac{dp}{dy} + \frac{f_{23}F_2}{\epsilon M_2}\right], \tag{2.45}$$

where H is the hydrodynamic permeability of the membrane to the solvent.

The volumetric flow can be calculated as a function of the pressure drop through the membrane from Eq. 2.45 with the help of Eq. 2.29 if the exit concentration c_2'' is known. Thus

$$u = -\frac{H}{\epsilon} \left[\frac{1}{1 + (Hf_{23}/M_2\epsilon)c_2''}\right] \frac{\Delta p_m}{t\lambda}. \tag{2.46}$$

Combining with Eq. 2.43 yields an expression for u in terms of Δp_m and the inlet concentration c_2'. Since we have again treated the pore fluid as a separate phase, Δp_m can be related through Eq. 2.34 to the total pressure difference across the membrane. Unfortunately the validity of treating the pore fluid as a two-component system in which the membrane material has no direct effect on solvent chemical potential becomes increasingly questionable as the pore diameter becomes smaller. The behavior of sucrose solutions filtered through cellophane may be sufficiently simple to permit analysis with the help of a model of this kind. Henderson and Sliepcevich[27] have conducted a series of such experiments. In Figure 2–3 we compare some representative points from

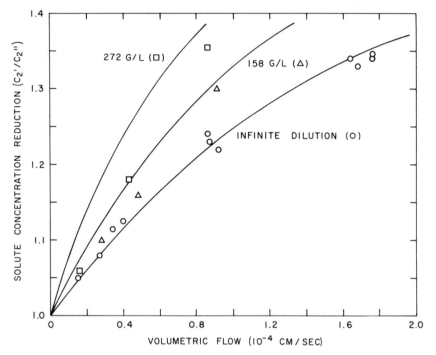

Fig. 2–3   Data of Henderson and Sliepcevich[27] for ultrafiltration of sucrose solutions through cellophane. Solid lines are from Eq. 2.43 with an appropriate choice of distribution coefficient and tortuosity.

their "infinite dilution" results to the predictions of Eq. 2.43, assuming $K_2' = K_2''$ and assigning the values $K_2'/b\epsilon = 0.65$ and $t\lambda f_{21}/RT = 6.0 \times 10^3$ sec/cm. The linear velocity in the pore u has been calculated from the volumetric flow ϵu, using $\epsilon = 0.67$ from the original data. It is apparent that the fit is quite satisfactory; and the value of $t\lambda f_{21}/RT$ required is also reasonable. The free-solution diffusion coefficient for sucrose[28] is $RT/f_{21} = 5.2 \times 10^{-6}$ cm²/sec at 25°C, and the reported membrane thickness[27] is 4.9×10^{-3} cm. Thus, this value for the exponential expression corresponds to $t = 6.4$, somewhat higher than is generally thought reasonable but certainly of the right order.

Equation 2.43 predicts concentration factors that depend only on the volumetric flow rate if K_2, b, and f_{21} are independent of concentration. The concentration dependence of f_{21} can be estimated from available data on the viscosity of sucrose solutions.[29] Assuming that f_{21} is inversely proportional to solution viscosity, we find $RT/f_{21} \approx 3.3 \times 10^{-6}$ cm²/sec at 158 g sucrose/l and $RT/f_{21} \approx 2.1 \times 10^{-6}$ cm²/sec at 272 g sucrose/l. Keeping $K_2'/b\epsilon = 0.65$, we can now calculate the higher concentration curves of Fig. 2-3. Although the experimental points fall somewhat below the predicted curves, the agreement is not too bad, and the deviations are at least in a predictable direction; f_{21} changes less than is predicted from the solution viscosities, and this is to be expected if the pore fluid is less concentrated than the external solution — i.e., if $K_2'/\epsilon < 1$.

In principle, the data of Henderson and Sliepcevich permit an evaluation of b (or f_{23}) through a comparison of the volumetric flow rates observed to the predictions of Eq. 2.46. Unfortunately, the analysis is complicated by the dependence of the viscosity (which appears in H) on pore-fluid concentration and uncertainty concerning the relation of Δp_m to Δp. Rough calculations can be made, however, which indicate that b is indeed greater than 1.0, and that the sucrose removal is therefore not entirely due to exclusion ($K_2'/\epsilon < 1$) but also involves kinetic interaction. A separate equilibrium evaluation of K_2 would greatly facilitate this kind of analysis.

Charged Membranes

The most studied selective membranes are the ion-exchange membranes. Early observations and theories of electrokinetic phenomena in these materials are summarized by Sollner[30] and also in more modern reviews.[4,5] Model theories generally deal with one of three cases: The first is the case of pore diameters large enough so that the fixed charges must be viewed as attached to well-defined pore walls, and the radial distribution of mobile charges must be more or less explicitly accounted for. The first theory of this kind was apparently due to Helmholtz, and more recent discussions include those of Dresner[31] and of Läuger.[32] The second case is that of pores small enough (and charge densities low enough) so that the membrane can be considered an essentially homogeneous mixture of fixed and mobile charges, but too large to interfere mechanically with ion migration. This model has its origins in the work of Teorell,[33,34] and Meyer and Sievers,[35] and has been developed more recently by Schmid,[36] Läuger and Kuhn,[37] and Schlögl.[5] The third case, developed by Kedem and Katchalsky,[11] and Spiegler,[23] permits inclusion of mechanical "friction" effects. We will here consider the second case, since it is mathematically simplest and contains most of the new features which the existence of a fixed charge adds to the membrane problem.

In reverse-osmosis experiments, external potential gradients are generally not measured, nor is an effective external electrical connection provided between the two sides of the membrane. (Such a connection could be provided by placing reversible electrodes on both sides of the membrane and connecting them through an external circuit.) Therefore, any potential gradient that exists within the membrane is the result of the transport processes themselves.

The solution to the charged-membrane problem is complicated by the fact that the concentrations of cations and anions within the membrane, c_{+m} and c_{-m}, are not equal, and we must therefore write flux equations for each separately. Dealing only with the case of no net electrical current flow (no external connection), the molar anion and cation flows must be equal, so that

$$\frac{F_+}{M_+} = \frac{F_-}{M_-},\qquad(2.47)$$

where the subscripts $+$ and $-$ refer to the cations and anions, respectively. As in Eq. 2.19,

$$F_+ = J_+ + c_{+m}u; \qquad F_- = J_- + c_{-m}u. \qquad(2.48)$$

We then have two equations like Eq. 2.37, and assuming $(\partial\mu/\partial c_{+m})_{p,T,\psi} = RT/c_{+m}$ and similarly for the anions,

$$J_+ = m_+\left[-RT\frac{dc_{+m}}{dy} + c_{+m}Y_+\right];$$

$$J_- = m_-\left[-RT\frac{dc_{-m}}{dy} + c_{-m}Y_-\right]. \qquad(2.49)$$

The forces Y in a pore too large for mechanical effects to be important are due to the interaction of the charged particles with the electrostatic potential gradient $d\psi/dy$; thus, for a uni-univalent electrolyte

$$Y_+ = -\mathfrak{F}\frac{d\psi}{dy}; \qquad Y_- = \mathfrak{F}\frac{d\psi}{dy}. \qquad(2.50)$$

Inserting these results into Eq. 2.48, we obtain

$$F_+ = -m_+RT\frac{dc_{+m}}{dy} - m_+c_{+m}\mathfrak{F}\frac{d\psi}{dy} + c_{+m}u \qquad(2.51)$$

and a similar result for F_-. Charge neutrality within the membrane requires

$$\frac{c_{-m}}{M_-} = \chi + \frac{c_{+m}}{M_+} \qquad(2.52)$$

where χ is the molar concentration of fixed positive charges in the membrane. (In cation exchangers, χ is negative.) Hence,

$$dc_{-m} = \frac{M_-}{M_+}dc_{+m}, \qquad(2.53)$$

and this, together with the condition of Eq. 2.47, permits us to eliminate $d\psi/dy$ from Eq. 2.51 and its F_- counterpart and obtain

$$F_+ = -RT \frac{m_+m_-(M_-c_{+m} + M_+c_{-m})}{M_-m_+c_{+m} + M_+m_-c_{-m}} \frac{dc_{+m}}{dy} + \frac{M_+c_{+m}c_{-m}(m_+ + m_-)}{M_-m_+c_{+m} + M_+m_-c_{-m}} u.$$

$$(2.54)$$

Placing Eq. 2.52 into Eq. 2.54 yields

$$F_+ = -m_+RT \left[1 - \frac{(m_+ - m_-)c_{+m}}{(m_+ + m_-)c_{+m} + m_-M_+\chi} \right] \frac{dc_{+m}}{dy}$$

$$+ c_{+m} \left[1 + \frac{m_+M_+\chi}{(m_+ + m_-)c_{+m} + m_-M_+\chi} \right] u. \qquad (2.55)$$

This is the equivalent of Eq. 2.41 in our earlier considerations but differs from that expression in at least two important respects: First, the quantity in brackets is not the same in each term, while in Eq. 2.41 the quantity $1/b$ appeared in both. Second, the quantities in brackets are not independent of c_{2m}, whereas our integration of Eq. 2.41 assumed independence for $1/b$.

The significance of Eqs. 2.54 and 2.55 is perhaps best indicated by examining certain limits and comparing these with Eqs. 2.21 and 2.41 for uncharged membranes. If the cation and anion mobilities are equal, then Eq. 2.54 reduces to

$$F_+ = -m_+RT \frac{dc_{2m}}{dy} + \frac{2M_+c_{+m}c_{-m}}{M_-c_{+m} + M_+c_{-m}} u. \qquad (2.56)$$

One way to express this result is that the salt diffuses through the pore at its normal diffusion rate, but the concentration which must be used in the viscous flow term is an appropriate average of the cation and anion concentrations.

If the mobilities of the two ions are comparable (though not necessarily equal) and one ion is present in the pore to the virtual exclusion of the other [e.g., $(c_{+m}/M_+) \gg (c_{-m}/M_-)$], then Eq. 2.54 becomes

$$F_+ = -m_-RT \frac{dc_{+m}}{dy} + \frac{M_+}{M_-} c_{-m} \frac{m_+ + m_-}{m_+} u. \qquad (2.57)$$

Thus, in this case the mobility of the minority ion is determining in the diffusion term, and the minority ion concentration, divided by the transference number of the majority ion, is the appropriate concentration in the viscous flow term.

We have already alluded to the fact that the integration of Eq. 2.55 is complicated by the fact that the dependent variable c_{+m} appears in a somewhat inconvenient manner in the coefficients of both terms. For this and similar reasons many authors, in particular Läuger and Kuhn,[37] have chosen to solve analytically only the case where c_{+m} is in equilibrium with essentially equal concentrations c_2' and c_2'' on either side of the membrane.

This restriction makes such treatments relatively uninteresting in the usual reverse-osmosis situation, since we are interested in large concentration differences. It is perhaps worth noting, therefore, that Eq. 2.55 can, in fact, be integrated by standard methods to obtain an expression that contains y and c_{+m} explicitly, but it is not a very convenient one. More important, Eq. 2.55 is readily solved by numerical methods. To complete the solution in a particular case, we replace c_{+m} at $y = 0$ and $y = -t\lambda$ by $K'_+ c'_2 (M_+/M_2)$, and $K''_+ c''_2 (M_+/M_2)$, where the distribution coefficients are those for the cation (or, equivalently, we could have carried out the whole procedure for the anion). This will, then, allow us to calculate c''_2, knowing c'_2 plus the significant membrane and ion-mobility parameters, just as Eqs. 2.30 and 2.43 permit such a calculation in the cases to which they are appropriate.

Very large salt-concentration reduction factors will be obtained with ion-exchange membranes, in general, only when there is good exclusion of one ion, and when Eq. 2.57 (or its anion exchanger equivalent) obtains. Under these circumstances, analogously to Eq. 2.30, we get

$$c''_2 = \frac{K'_- c'_2 \exp\{-[(m_+ + m_-)/m_+ m_- RT] ut\lambda\}}{K''_- - \epsilon[m_+/(m_+ + m_-)](1 - \exp\{-[(m_+ + m_-)/m_+ m_- RT] ut\lambda\})},$$
(2.58)

and at the highest flow rate (in the negative y direction),

$$\frac{c'_2}{c''_2} = \frac{\epsilon}{K'_-} \frac{m_+}{(m_+ + m_-)} \approx \frac{K_1}{K'_-} \frac{m_+}{(m_+ + m_-)}.$$
(2.59)

Finally, we must modify Eq. 2.18 to obtain an expression for the center-of-mass velocity u. In the present case there is an electrostatic force acting on the pore fluid of $-\mathfrak{F}(d\psi/dy)$ multiplied by the molar concentration of excess positive charge in the pore fluid, $-\chi/\epsilon$. Thus,

$$u = -H \left(\frac{dp_m}{dy} - \frac{\chi}{\epsilon} \mathfrak{F} \frac{d\psi}{dy} \right).$$
(2.60)

Simultaneous solution of Eq. 2.51 and its anion-flux equivalent permit a calculation of $d\psi/dy$ with the result

$$\mathfrak{F} \frac{d\psi}{dy} = -\frac{M_- RT(m_+ - m_-)}{M_- m_+ c_{+m} + M_+ m_- c_{-m}} \frac{dc_{+m}}{dy} + \frac{M_- c_{+m} - M_+ c_{-m}}{M_- m_+ c_{+m} + M_+ m_- c_{-m}} u.$$
(2.61)

In the special case of good exclusion and the co-ion mobility smaller or not too greatly larger than the counter-ion mobility, a simple result is obtained. For instance in a cation exchanger, if $c_{+m}/M_+ \gg c_{-m}/M_-$, then $c_{+m} \approx -\chi M_+$ and $dc_{+m}/dy \approx 0$, so that

$$\mathfrak{F} \frac{d\psi}{dy} = \frac{u}{m_+}$$
(2.62)

and

$$u = -\left[\frac{H}{1 - (\chi H/\epsilon m_+)} \right] \frac{\Delta p_m}{\lambda t}.$$
(2.63)

Again, as in the pore models discussed in the preceding sections, Δp_m differs from Δp by an amount equal to the difference in the osmotic pressure changes at the two interfaces. This has been discussed for the present case by Schlögl[38] and by Läuger and Kuhn.[37] Making the dilute-solution approximation for the osmotic pressure, and taking into account the effects of the anions and cations separately, we can write Eq. 2.35 as

$$\Delta \pi' = RT \left(\frac{c'_{+m}}{M_{+\epsilon}} + \frac{c'_{-m}}{M_{-\epsilon}} - \frac{2c'_2}{M_2} \right) \qquad (2.64)$$

or, with Eq. 2.52, as

$$\Delta \pi' = RT \left[\frac{\chi}{\epsilon} + \frac{2c'_2}{M_2} \left(\frac{K'_+}{\epsilon} - 1 \right) \right] \qquad (2.65)$$

and similarly for $\Delta \pi''$. The resulting expressions are inserted in Eq. 2.34 to obtain Δp_m.

Potential changes also arise at the interfaces in the case of a charged membrane. However, with the restriction which we have imposed, i.e., no external current flow, the potential gradient within the membrane can be treated as a dependent variable and we need no explicit knowledge of the total potential difference between the solutions.

Experimental studies of reverse osmosis using membranes containing fixed charge groups have been fragmentary. Baldwin, Holcomb, and Johnson[39] have reported results obtained on polyacrylate-cellophane membranes. Most of the measurements were carried out with sodium chloride solutions at an applied pressure of 170 atm, and flow rates through the 0.001-inch-thick membranes were of the order of 5×10^{-4} g/cm²-sec. If the ion mobilities in these membranes are those character-istic of the free ions in solution ($D \approx 1.5 \times 10^{-5}$ cm²/sec), then the exponential term in Eq. 2.43 is of the order of exp (0.1), and little salt rejection is to be expected. In fact, salt-concentration reduction factors as high as 5 were observed, probably indicating that there was an effect of the pore walls on ion mobility in addition to the coulomb exclusion. That this was indeed the case is further indicated by the observation of Baldwin, et al.,[39] that salt rejection did not vary as rapidly with concen-tration as one would predict on a purely coulombic basis; indeed, their calculated pore radius of 5 Å is so small that one might well expect that direct interaction between ions and pore walls would be important.

McKelvey, Spiegler, and Wylie[40] reported a series of reverse-osmosis measurements on commercially available ion-exchange membranes. Their Nalfilm-2 anion-exchange membranes were the most extensively studied, and these had flow rates such that the exponential term in Eq. 2.43 is about exp (2×10^{-3}) if free-solution mobilities are assumed, again implying very little salt rejection. In fact, salt-concentration reduction factors of 10 were observed for 0.01 and 0.1 normal sodium chloride solutions. Assuming simple Donnan theory to calculate K'_+ (as will be discussed in the section on salt sorption), one can estimate maximum salt-concentration reduction factors for these two cases of 30 and 3, respectively, according to the anion-exchanger equivalent of Eq. 2.59. Again, the observed dependence on salt concentration is much smaller than one might expect, and salt rejection is much better in the more concentrated case than the maximum predicted by the simple coulomb picture.

A model incorporating at least features of both the charged-membrane and finely porous models is required to account for these experimental results; and far more extensive data will be required to test models of sufficient complexity to include both effects.

2.3 Sorption Properties

The importance of sorption in determining transport rates in membranes is apparent in the preceding model discussion. For example, in the solution-diffusion model, the water content c_{1m} and the solute distribution coefficient K_2, together with the respective diffusion coefficients, determine membrane permeability to water and salt.

Aside from this obvious connection to transport properties, water sorption is important because of its close relation to membrane structure. In particular, the applicability of the solution-diffusion model depends on the water being essentially molecularly dispersed in the membrane, and the applicability of the various pore models depends in large measure on the size of the water aggregates.

Water Sorption

The extent of water sorption in a polymer film depends upon the chemical compatibility of water and the polymeric material and upon the nature and strength of the forces holding the polymer chains together. The importance of chemical compatibility is perhaps obvious: Linear polyethylene and polystyrene are highly insoluble in water and sorb little water, while their highly substituted derivatives polyvinyl alcohol and linear polyvinyl benzene sulfonate are highly soluble in water. The importance of forces between chains is illustrated by the latter two polymers, which are readily made water insoluble by cross-linking; also by cellulose, which is typically partially crystalline and sorbs much more water in its amorphous regions than in the more strongly bound crystalline regions. A theory of water sorption which is to be generally applicable to osmotic membrane materials must take both these factors into account.

The most common experimental observation of water sorption is the sorption isotherm obtained by measuring the water content of a polymer sample as a function of ambient relative humidity (or water activity referred to liquid water as the standard state). Theoretical approaches must seek first to account for the isotherms observed.

In the diffusive theories of water transport through membranes, the water is viewed as molecularly dispersed in the polymer, and in the simplest case the isotherm is given by Henry's law, i.e., $a_1 = kZ_1$, where a_1 is the activity of water, Z_1 the mole fraction of water in the membrane material, and k a constant. Henry's law is a limiting law, valid in dilute solutions. Its validity in a particular system implies random distribution of water molecules on equivalent sites whose number is large compared with the number of sorbed molecules, and no interaction between sorbed molecules. It is necessarily valid at sufficiently low water activities. Validity of Henry's law at high water activities is the exception rather than the rule in polymer-water systems, however. Myers, et al.,[41] found Henry's law to be valid from 0 to 100% relative humidity for their samples of polyethylene and polypropylene, and Yasuda and Stannett[42] obtained the same result with polyethylene terephthalate.

The best-known attempts to modify simple solution theory to make it more generally applicable to polymer solutions are those of Flory[43] and of Huggins.[44] These authors pictured a typical polymer chain as being composed of many flexibly connected segments whose size is equal to that of a solvent molecule, and calculated the configurational entropy of the solutions on statistical grounds.

This approach has been notably useful in interpreting the results of experiments on nonpolar polymer–solvent systems, but less successful in the case of the polar systems of interest here. Nevertheless, it does account for polymer solution behavior much more adequately than does ideal solution theory, and it has been applied in some cases, for example to dextran-water solutions at high relative humidities by Taylor, Cluskey, and Senti.[45]

In viscous-flow models of membrane transport the water is viewed as contained in small pores. On this model, the water content of a material with pores of uniform diameter changes abruptly at the water activity equal to that given by[46]

$$\ln a_1 = -\frac{2\sigma v_1 \cos \omega}{rRT}, \tag{2.66}$$

where σ and v_1 are the surface tension and molar volume of water, r is the pore radius, and ω is the contact angle, measured through the liquid phase, between liquid water and the pore wall when the ambient gas, containing water vapor at activity a_1, is the third phase. Below this activity the only water in the pore is water vapor. Above this activity, the pore is filled with liquid water.

While not very useful quantitatively in our case, Eq. 2.66 does serve to illustrate the importance of water-membrane interactions to the problem: If water does not wet the membrane material (i.e., if $\omega < 90°$), then liquid water will not enter the pore at water activities near (or less than) unity.

The capillary condensation equation (Eq. 2.66) cannot be expected to be valid for very-small-diameter pores in hydrophilic membrane materials, because the same water-membrane interactions which cause water to wet the pore walls will lead to adsorption on the walls. If the quantity of water adsorbed in the first few molecular layers is comparable to the pore volume, then the discontinuous behavior predicted by Eq. 2.66 will not be observed. Instead, there will be a gradual increase in water content of the pores as the water activity is increased, as a direct result of adsorption on the pore walls. One might therefore expect that adsorption theory would be useful in discussing this portion of the isotherm.

The most widely used theory of physical adsorption is the multilayer theory of Brunauer, Emmett, and Teller.[47] The B-E-T theory extends the earlier monolayer theory of Langmuir[48] to account for the adsorption of additional layers on the first adsorbed monolayer and has been applied with good success to many cases of physical adsorption.

As most frequently used, the theory assumes that an infinite number of additional layers are possible and gives, for the relationship between the quantity adsorbed and the ambient water activity, the relation

$$\frac{c_{1m}}{c_{1m}^0} = \frac{Ca_1}{(1 - a_1)[1 + (C - 1)a_1]}, \qquad (2.67)$$

where c_{1m}^0 is the amount of adsorbed water needed to form a complete monolayer and the parameter C is a constant given approximately by $\exp[(E_a - E_1)/RT]$, in which E_a is the heat of adsorption of the first monolayer and E_1 the heat of liquefaction of the gas.

Brunauer, Emmett, and Teller suggested that the same approach can be used to calculate gas adsorption in pores, if one assumes not an infinite number of possible layers but a finite number, determined by the pore dimensions. In a later article, Brunauer, Deming, Deming, and Teller[49] extended the original B-E-T theory and compared the results obtained for two different pore sizes with those calculated from the capillary condensation equation. They found that the modified B-E-T theory failed to predict complete filling of large pores at saturation pressure and was therefore unsatisfactory in that case; but in the case of small pores, a few molecular dimensions in diameter, the theory fitted available data well and accounted for the continuous variation of adsorption with ambient adsorbate pressure in a more satisfactory way than is possible with the capillary condensation equation. Hill,[50] using a statistical mechanical theory of multilayer adsorption which under certain circumstances leads to the B-E-T equation, was able to predict complete filling of pores under certain conditions and concluded that the multilayer adsorption and capillary condensation theories can be reconciled.

The B-E-T theory was originally applied to solids with reasonably well defined porosity, such as charcoal and silica gel, and one of its strengths lies in the fact that for such materials the surface area available for adsorption is generally found to be independent of the nature of the adsorbate. For these rigid adsorbents, the principal variations in apparent surface area which are observed can be attributed to exclusion of adsorbate molecules from pores too small to accept them.

It has also been recognized, however, that adsorption theory can provide useful insight into the behavior of materials in which the available surface area and the pore size depend upon the nature of the sorbate and the quantity sorbed. For example, Hendricks, Nelson, and Alexander[51] showed that the sorption of water by the mineral montmorillonite could be understood as adsorption on the silicate sheets that make up the crystallites. The spacing between these sheets was found to increase as the water sorption increased, and the surface area apparently available to water was found to be 50 times that determined by nitrogen-adsorption techniques. Similarly, Shaw[52] found that a B-E-T analysis of water sorption in native egg albumen indicated a specific surface area almost 100 times as large as that found with nitrogen, and associated this with water adsorption in intermolecular polar interfaces within the albumen crystallites.

The use of the B-E-T theory to interpret the results of water-sorption measurements in organic materials was greatly extended by Bull,[53] who studied a series of purified proteins and found that the theory described the results obtained in most of these cases very satisfactorily. But the significance of the monolayer areas calculated for various proteins remained obscure until Pauling[54] pointed out that the experimental value obtained could be accounted for if one assumed an initial adsorption of one molecule of water on each polar side chain. (Most of the carbonyl and imide groups of the peptide bonds apparently do not sorb water in the primary sorption step because the hydrogen-bonding capacity of the groups is satisfied in bonds between them.)

More recent theoretical and experimental studies of water sorption in polymer systems have shown that this concept of multilayer adsorption on polar sites capable of binding a single molecule in the primary sorption step is somewhat oversimplified but nevertheless extremely useful. Thus, White and Eyring[55] recognized that since the polymer network is not rigid, the energetics of polymer swelling are important in determining the shape of the sorption isotherm, and attempted to include this effect in a revised isotherm equation. Similarly, Dole[56] has generalized the theory to take into account variable heats of adsorption in successive layers and interactions between adsorbed molecules in the same layer. Both used the statistical derivation of the B-E-T isotherm given by Hill[57] as a starting point. Much of this work has been summarized by McLaren and Rowen[58] and by Housman.[59]

A more recent and highly informative theory of polymer-solvent systems is the cluster theory of Zimm and Lundberg,[60,61] which states that it is quite possible to calculate a clustering function from isotherm data that will indicate the degree to which the solvent distribution in the polymer deviates from randomness. Thus, if the clustering function for the solvent is strongly negative, the solvent molecules are widely spaced and presumably attached to isolated sorption sites; if the clustering function is positive, the average solvent molecule has more nearest neighbors of its own kind than would be expected in a random distribution. The theory does not attempt to distinguish between the solution and adsorption theories already discussed nor to predict results to be obtained in a particular system, but it does provide a useful picture of the way in which solvent is distributed in systems for which isotherm data are available.

Zimm and Lundberg calculated values for the clustering function of the solvent from experimental data on several systems. They found small positive values at all concentrations for the systems benzene-rubber and toluene-polystyrene, but strongly negative ones for the system water-collagen at low relative humidities. These values increased rapidly with increasing relative humidity and were somewhat positive at saturation. Thus, initial sorption on specific sites, followed by some positive clustering at high water concentrations, was indicated. Some positive clustering is necessarily present in high-solvent-content systems, because the solvent is excluded from the volume occupied by the polymer.

Starkweather[62] used the same technique to examine water sorption in a series of polymeric materials and found positive values in all cases studied at saturation water-vapor pressure, but negative values below 70 to 90% relative humidity for several hydrophilic polymers, including cellulose and certain proteins. He found positive clustering at all relative humidities in the case of annealed nylon, polyvinyl acetate, and polymethyl methacrylate.

To our knowledge, water-sorption data for cellulose acetates have not previously been examined in the light of the Zimm-Lundberg theory. In Fig. 2–4 we present the clustering function $c_1 G_{11}$[62] for 39.8 wt-% acetyl cellulose acetate, calculated from the data of Lonsdale, et al.,[63] and compare it to Starkweather's values for annealed nylon 66,[62,64] Zimm and Lundberg's values for collagen,[60] and Starkweather's interpretation[62] of Thompson's polyvinyl acetate data.[65] All the curves are terminated at their high-water-content ends, at a water content corresponding to satu-

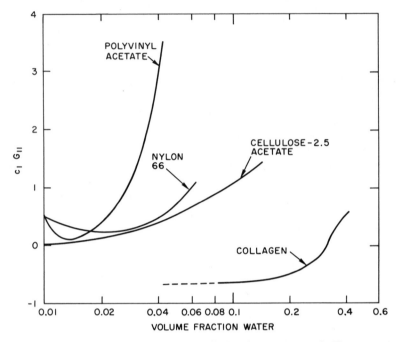

Fig. 2–4   Clustering of sorbed water in several polymeric materials. The parameter c_1G_{11} is a clustering function in the Zimm-Lundberg[60] theory. Positive values indicate that each water molecule has more other water molecules as nearest neighbors than would be expected in a random solution.

ration at 95% relative humidity. The figure thus presents a comparison of total water contents, together with the comparison of degree of clustering.

The behavior of cellulose acetate contrasts interestingly with that of the other three polymers, particularly at low water contents. In this region the protein, collagen, shows strong negative clustering of water, indicating sorption on specific sites, each apparently occupied by only one water molecule. Nylon and polyvinyl acetate, on the other hand, show positive clustering, indicating a strong preference on the part of additional water molecules for sites already occupied by one or more of their own kind. Cellulose acetate shows little clustering of either sign, suggesting a much more nearly random distribution of the water molecules.

It is probably fruitless to speculate on the detailed significance of these results until an analysis of more data has been made and direct comparisons between water sorption and transport properties are possible. It is evident, however, that polymers with similar total water sorptions at saturation can differ markedly in clustering properties, and it seems likely that these differences will be reflected in transport properties.

Salt Sorption

The problem of salt sorption in selective membranes has received detailed consideration only in the case of ion-exchange membranes. Here the principal effect is an electrostatic one.

The Donnan theory, originally used to explain electrolyte distributions between solutions separated by a selective membrane, forms the basis for treating quasi-homogeneous models like that used earlier in discussing transport through charged membranes. In this model, the fixed and mobile ion distributions within the membrane are assumed to be uniform. Writing the sorption equilibrium of a uni-univalent salt and using sodium chloride as an example,

$$\text{Na}^+ + \text{Cl}^- = \text{Na}_m^+ + \text{Cl}_m^-, \tag{2.68}$$

where the subscript m signifies that these are ionic species within the membrane. At equilibrium the product of the activities on the two sides of the equation must be equal:

$$\gamma_\pm^2 \left(\frac{c_2}{M_2}\right)^2 = \gamma_{\pm m}^2 \frac{c_{+m}}{M_+} \frac{c_{-m}}{M_-}, \tag{2.69}$$

where $\gamma_\pm$ and $\gamma_{\pm m}$ are the mean molar activity coefficients for the uni-univalent salt in the external solution and within the membrane, respectively. Charge neutrality within the membrane requires that Eq. 2.52 be satisfied. Combining Eqs. 2.52 and 2.69 we obtain

$$\frac{c_{+m}}{M_+} = -\frac{\chi}{2} + \left[\left(\frac{\chi}{2}\right)^2 + \left(\frac{\gamma_\pm}{\gamma_{\pm m}} \frac{c_2}{M_2}\right)^2\right]^{\frac{1}{2}} \tag{2.70}$$

and

$$\frac{c_{-m}}{M_-} = \frac{\chi}{2} + \left[\left(\frac{\chi}{2}\right)^2 + \left(\frac{\gamma_\pm}{\gamma_{\pm m}} \frac{c_2}{M_2}\right)^2\right]^{\frac{1}{2}}. \tag{2.71}$$

Thus the ion whose sign is the same as the sign of the fixed charge (the co-ion) tends to be excluded from the membrane, while the ion of opposite sign (the counter-ion) is preferentially sorbed. At high external salt concentrations the effect is minimal and

$$\frac{c_{+m}}{M_+} \approx \frac{c_{-m}}{M_-} \approx \frac{\gamma_\pm}{\gamma_{\pm m}} \frac{c_2}{M_2}, \tag{2.72}$$

while at very low external concentrations and with χ positive, $c_{-m}/M_- = \chi$ and $c_{+m}/M_+ \approx 0$, and vice versa for negative χ. Examples of the behavior of K_+ and K_- as a function of salt concentration are given in Fig. 2–5.

The simplest useful assumption one can make concerning the activity coefficients of Eq. 2.69 is that $\gamma_{\pm m} = \gamma_\pm/\epsilon$. This is the result obtained if the water and salt are collected in pores and the mean molar activity

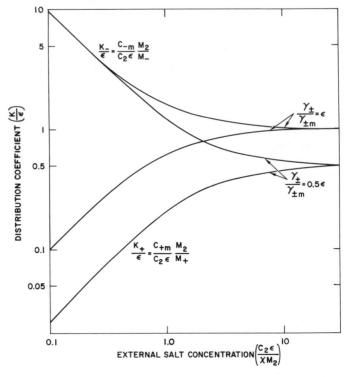

Fig. 2–5   Distribution of ions of a uni-univalent salt between an anion exchanger and an external solution. The upper curves represent the Donnan equilibrium. The lower curves assume a further exclusion of the salt for nonelectrostatic reasons, which can be accounted for with the help of an activity coefficient within the membrane $\epsilon\gamma_{\pm m}$, which is different from the activity coefficient in the external solution $\gamma_{\pm}$.

coefficient in the pore liquid is the same as that in the external solution. We have included the possibility of other activity coefficients in order to emphasize that exclusion from charged membranes need not be due to coulomb forces alone. For example, ion activities in the pore model of an ion-exchange resin are affected by the swelling pressure within the pores, as has been pointed out by Gregor.[66] This pressure arises because of the tendency for water from the relatively dilute external solution to enter the pores to dilute the more concentrated pore fluid. We have already encountered this effect in discussing interface pressure changes in connection with porous membrane models. Helfferich[67] reports that this pressure effect can be either treated explicitly or simply included in the activity coefficients. Helfferich also discusses a number of other effects that may influence activity coefficients within ion-exchange membranes.

Donnan equilibrium calculations are valid, of course, only when the assumption of uniform ion concentration is valid. For this to be the case, the distance between fixed charges must be large compared to the pore diameter (so that we need not treat the fixed charges as localized on pore walls) and the Debye length (the effective range of coulomb forces) in the pore fluid must be large compared with the pore diameter. The Debye length[68] in a uni-univalent salt solution having the molarity of seawater is 4 Å. Thus, only extremely finely porous membranes can be treated as quasi-homogeneous in the presence of such a concentrated salt solution.

The problem of calculating ion distributions in charged membranes where the quasi-homogeneous approach fails has recently been treated by Dresner and Kraus,[69] and by Dresner.[70]

Some clues to the distribution behavior of salts in aqueous solution-membrane systems where Donnan exclusion plays no role may be obtainable from known properties of water-organic liquid extraction systems. Diamond and Tuck[71] reviewed knowledge in this area in 1960. Kraus, Raridon, and Baldwin[72] have exploited the membrane-organic liquid analogy by measuring distribution coefficients for simple salts between their aqueous solutions and liquid esters which they selected as model systems. The agreement between the results of Lonsdale, et al.,[63] for sodium chloride in cellulose acetate and those of Kraus, et al.,[72] in their most closely analogous liquid is encouragingly good.[73]

Salt sorption in membranes that are of the solution-diffusion type and have no appreciable fixed ion content has been touched on recently by Scatchard,[74] whose principal interest was the spatial distribution of ions near the interface between a membrane of this type and water. The most important factors in determining this distribution are the interionic effects treated by the Debye-Hückel theory.

If these effects alone would determine the gross distribution coefficients, it would be possible to estimate salt-distribution coefficients between aqueous solutions and a polymer membrane from a knowledge of the dielectric constant of the membrane material. A comparison of such a prediction with the results available for salts in cellulose acetate shows, however, that this procedure can be highly misleading.

Thus, Scatchard calculates for sodium chloride, considering dielectric effects only,

$$\ln \frac{K_2}{K_1} = -1.15 \frac{d - d_m}{d_m}, \qquad (2.73)$$

where d and d_m are the dielectric constants of the aqueous solution and of the membrane material, respectively. The dielectric constant of wet, 39.8 wt-% acetyl cellulose acetate can be estimated using the rule suggested by Scatchard on the basis of Åkerlöf's data for organic liquids,[75] i.e., that the dielectric constant of a water-organic liquid mixture is a linear function of the volume fraction. Published values for cellulose ester dielectric constants are 2 to 6, and the membranes in question are 16 vol-% water. Thus, $d_m \simeq 0.2d$, and

$$\frac{K_2}{K_1} = 2.5 \times 10^{-5}, \qquad (2.74)$$

as compared to experimental values of $K_2 = 0.035$, $K_1 = 0.16$; therefore $K_2/K_1 = 0.22$. It is apparent from this calculation, and certainly not surprising, that this particular membrane material and probably many others differ from water in properties, other than dielectric constant, that are important in determining salt sorption.

Ferry[76] calculated "entrance factors" for porous membranes on geometrical grounds. While these factors are not presented as distribution coefficients in the sense used here, they affect the osmotic process in the same way; i.e., they represent an exclusion of the solute from the membrane pore, and the extent of this exclusion is not dependent on flow rates through the membrane.

Glueckauf[77] has recently suggested the use of a treatment similar to Scatchard's[74] for estimating salt-distribution coefficients in the case of finely porous membranes. The salt in this case is assumed to reside in the water phase but to be partially excluded by the presence of low-dielectric-constant material forming the pore walls. The validity of this model, like that of many of the others described here, is yet to be investigated in detail; the concept deserves special mention, however, because it relates salt distribution to water distribution within the membrane. Thus, water distribution appears as a peculiarly important property of osmotic membrane materials: high water content is important to high water permeability; the extent to which water is clustered within the membrane material will determine whether flow through it is essentially diffusive or viscous in nature; and the same parameter may be an important factor in determining salt distribution between the membrane and the external salt solution.

2.4   Membrane Characteristics

The mathematical treatments already developed are primarily of interest in bringing about an understanding of transport phenomena in specific membrane materials. They can also be useful in providing a basis for predicting membrane performance from limited data and indicating what are reasonable performance objectives.

Membrane Evaluation

Most of the past work on membranes for desalination purposes has consisted simply of reverse-osmosis measurements on candidate materials. While such measurements are obviously of interest, they have two important limitations: their execution requires high-pressure equipment not readily available in many laboratories; and such measurements are subject to major errors, particularly as regards salt permeability, because of slight membrane imperfections.

An evaluation of the reverse-osmosis performance of membranes can be made from the results of zero-pressure, direct-osmosis measurements, if it is assumed that the membrane is homogeneous across its thickness and that its transport properties are independent of pressure and solution concentration. These assumptions must, of course, be checked in further experiments in the case of materials whose properties appear to be of real interest.

Since the measurements in question are gross measurements of membrane permeability, their first interpretation can be in terms of the general considerations discussed in Section 2.2.

From Eqs. 2.1, 2.2, 2.8, and 2.10,

$$F_1 = -\frac{L_{11}}{\lambda}\left(-\frac{\alpha RTv_1}{M_2}\Delta c_2 + v_1\,\Delta p\right) - \frac{L_{12}}{\lambda}(RT\Delta\ln c_2 + v_2\,\Delta p), \qquad (2.75)$$

$$F_2 = -\frac{L_{12}}{\lambda}\left(-\frac{\alpha RTv_1}{M_2}\Delta c_2 + v_1\,\Delta p\right) - \frac{L_{22}}{\lambda}(RT\Delta\ln c_2 + v_2\,\Delta p). \qquad (2.76)$$

In direct-osmosis experiments, $\Delta p = 0$, and

$$F_1 = \frac{L_{11}}{\lambda}\frac{\alpha RTv_1}{M_2}\Delta c_2 - \frac{L_{12}}{\lambda}RT\Delta\ln c_2 \equiv \mathcal{O}_1^d\frac{\alpha v_1}{M_2}\frac{\Delta c_2}{\lambda} = \mathcal{O}_1^d\frac{v_1}{RT}\frac{\Delta\pi}{\lambda}, \qquad (2.77)$$

$$F_2 = \frac{L_{12}}{\lambda}\frac{\alpha RTv_1}{M_2}\Delta c_2 - \frac{L_{22}}{\lambda}RT\Delta\ln c_2 \equiv -\mathcal{O}_2^d\frac{\Delta c_2}{\lambda}, \qquad (2.78)$$

where $\mathcal{O}_1^d$ and $\mathcal{O}_2^d$ are the apparent water and salt permeabilities, respectively, measured in direct osmosis. Solving Eqs. 2.77 and 2.78 for L_{11} and L_{22} in terms of $\mathcal{O}_1^d$, $\mathcal{O}_2^d$, and L_{12} and using the results in Eqs. 2.75 and 2.76 yield

$$F_1 = \frac{\mathcal{O}_1^d}{\lambda}\left(\frac{\alpha v_1}{M_2}\Delta c_2 - \frac{v_1}{RT}\Delta p\right) - \frac{L_{12}}{\lambda}\left(\frac{M_2}{\alpha}\frac{\Delta\ln c_2}{\Delta c_2} + v_2\right)\Delta p \qquad (2.79)$$

and

$$F_2 = -\frac{\mathcal{O}_2^d}{\lambda}\left(\Delta c_2 + \frac{v_2}{RT}\frac{\Delta c_2}{\Delta\ln c_2}\Delta p\right) - \frac{L_{12}}{\lambda}\left(\frac{\alpha v_1 v_2}{M_2}\frac{\Delta c_2}{\Delta\ln c_2} + v_1\right)\Delta p. \qquad (2.80)$$

Since the direct-osmosis experiments do not provide an evaluation of the cross coefficient L_{12}, it is not possible to predict performance at elevated Δp quantitatively from these expressions. Furthermore, while direct-osmosis experiments are much less subject to errors due to imperfections than are reverse-osmosis measurements, and good water permeabilities can generally be obtained by this technique, the fact remains that in membranes highly impermeable to salt the small amount of leakage that occurs by diffusion through a pinhole can still invalidate measurements of salt permeability. For these two reasons, a second type of zero-pressure experiment is useful. In these "immersion experiments" a wet membrane sample is immersed in a salt solution, and the rate of salt sorption is determined as a measure of the salt permeability of the material.

Owing to the relatively high ratio of water to salt permeability in most of the materials of interest, equilibrium water distribution is obtained in a membrane after immersion much more rapidly than is equilibrium salt distribution. Therefore, an analysis of the salt absorption after immersion can be based on the assumption that grad $\mu_1 = 0$. Since, in addition, no pressure gradients exist, Eq. 2.1, provided there is dilute solution behavior, reduces to

$$F_2 = -L_{22}\frac{RT}{c_2}\frac{dc_2}{dy} \equiv -\mathcal{O}_2^i\frac{dc_2}{dy}, \qquad (2.81)$$

where $\mathcal{O}_2^i$ is the apparent salt permeability measured in an immersion experiment. This diffusion equation can be solved for our geometry and experimental method by standard techniques.[78]

It is obvious from a comparison of Eqs. 2.78 and 2.81 that the experimental salt permeation coefficients are equal only if there is no coupling of flows (and $\mathcal{O}_2^i$ is independent of c_2). More generally,

$$\mathcal{O}_2^d = \mathcal{O}_2^i - \frac{\alpha v_1 RT}{M_2}L_{12} \qquad (2.82)$$

and, since L_{12} is expected to be positive, a comparison of $\mathcal{O}_2^d$ and $\mathcal{O}_2^i$ is a useful test of the significance of the measurements of $\mathcal{O}_2^d$ and, incidentally, of $\mathcal{O}_1^d$. If $\mathcal{O}_2^d = \mathcal{O}_2^i$, there is no coupling. If $\mathcal{O}_2^d < \mathcal{O}_2^i$, there is coupling, and L_{12} can be evaluated. However $\mathcal{O}_2^d > \mathcal{O}_2^i$ is an almost certain indication of leakage paths through the membrane which do not communicate with the bulk of the membrane material. Such leakage paths must be separated from one another by a distance comparable to or greater than the sample thickness if they are not to participate in transport during the immersion experiments. They may therefore be better regarded as imperfections than as inherent characteristics of the membrane material.

Performance Objectives

In discussing desired membrane properties, it is important to realize that factors other than membrane permeability set a limit on the flux rates that can be achieved in practical systems. In Chapter 5 the problem of boundary-layer control will be discussed in detail; it is clear that boundary-layer effects place limits on practically useful flux rates in reverse-osmosis systems. For our present purposes, we will select 50 gpd/ft^2 (2.3×10^{-3} g/cm^2-sec) as a somewhat arbitrary estimate of what one might wish to achieve in a practical system. As mentioned in Chapter 3, flux rates of this order have been achieved in experiments with brackish water.

This limitation on useful membrane fluxes does not mean, of course, that high membrane permeabilities for water cannot be exploited. It only signifies that beyond some point higher permeabilities must be exploited by using lower system pressures rather than by increasing water fluxes.

The acceptable limits on salt permeation rate in a practical system depend on the salinity of the feed water and on the product salinity required. We shall concern ourselves here primarily with requirements for seawater desalination in a single-pass system, because this is perhaps the most difficult case encountered in practice, and because even in brackish water systems there will generally be a strong incentive to work with fairly concentrated solutions near the brine discharge. A salt-concentration reduction factor of 100 must be achieved if potable water of 500 ppm total solids content is to be prepared from seawater in a system in which the brine has an average concentration of 5 wt-%.

The effect of this requirement is best examined in terms of the separate membrane models already described, with the solution–diffusion membranes being a particularly important case. Economic studies like those discussed in Chapter 6 indicate that a reverse-osmosis seawater-conversion plant operating at pressures of about 100 atm may be economically attractive. Recognizing that the osmotic pressure of a 5 wt-% brine is about 37 atm, we can readily calculate from Eq. 2.17 that a concentration reduction factor of 100 is attainable at room temperature under these conditions for a permeability ratio $D_{1m}K_1/D_{2m}K_2 = 2100$. The desired flow rate of 2.3×10^{-3} g/cm^2-sec will be obtained (from Eq. 2.14) if the membrane permeation constant, $D_{1m}K_1v_1/RT\lambda$, is 3.7×10^{-5} g/cm^2-sec-atm. This is three to four times the membrane constant observed initially in typical high-selectivity cellulose acetate reverse-osmosis membranes (see Chapter 4). Permeation constants substantially higher than this are not useful at 100 atm, because of boundary-layer effects. They are desirable only if they are accompanied by an increased permeability ratio, which will then permit system operation at lower pressures. Figure 2–6 shows the maximum water- and salt-permeation constants desired on this basis for membranes intended to give a salt-concentration reduction factor of 100 at various pressures.

In membranes that behave according to the viscous-flow or charged-membrane models discussed earlier, water and salt flows within the membrane are strongly coupled, but the over-all behavior can still be satisfactory if the distribution coefficient for salt is sufficiently small compared with that for water, i.e., if the salt (or in the charged membrane case, one ion) is effectively excluded from the pore. In Eqs. 2.31

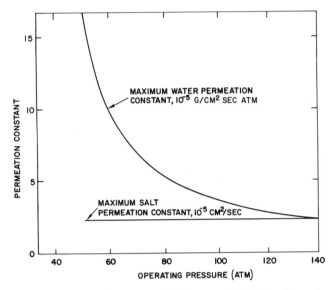

Fig. 2–6 Maximum acceptable water and salt permeabilities to achieve desalination in solution-diffusion membranes at various gross pressures. Fluxes are arbitrarily limited to 50 gpd/ft² to avoid boundary-layer salt buildup, and the values are calculated assuming a feed-water salt concentration of 5 wt-% and a desired concentration reduction factor of 100.

and 2.59 we have already seen the relationship between the maximum achievable salt-concentration reduction factors and the distribution coefficients.

Doubtless the longest-range forces available to us to produce this exclusion are the coulomb forces effective in the case of ion-exchange membranes. Dresner and Kraus[69] have discussed in some detail the difficulty of achieving good exclusion even in this case. It will suffice for our purposes to recall that the Debye length (a measure of the effective range of the coulomb force in an ionized medium) in seawater is only about 4 Å, and that therefore pore radii substantially smaller than this would be required to achieve good ion exclusion, even if quite high fixed-charge densities are attained in the membrane.

But again we must consider the limitations imposed by the boundary-layer problem. In the case of porous membranes as defined here we can restate the problem as follows: Diffusive processes within the membrane pores are governed by the same diffusion coefficients (or mobilities) that are operative in the boundary layer. Qualitatively, if the membrane pore length λt is less than the boundary-layer thickness, salt will diffuse away from the membrane-concentrated solution interface through the membrane pores (the diffusive term in Eq. 2.21, for example) more rapidly than it will diffuse back into the concentrated solution. The maximum concentration-reduction factor will therefore not be achieved.

The boundary-layer limitation is now conveniently stated as a practically achievable boundary-layer thickness. An estimate that an effective thickness of the order of 0.005 cm can be achieved at reasonable cost in practical systems is consistent with our earlier estimate of maximum permissible flow rate. The pore length must, then, be no less than this. From Eq. 2.18 the hydrodynamic permeation constant of a 50% porous membrane with pore radius 4 Å and pore length 0.005 cm is

$$\frac{H}{\lambda} = \frac{\epsilon r^2}{8\eta\lambda} = 2 \times 10^{-6} \text{ cm/atm-sec} \approx 2 \times 10^{-6} \text{ g/cm}^2\text{-sec-atm}, \qquad (2.83)$$

for a pore-fluid viscosity of one centipoise. This value is much less than the 1×10^{-5} g/cm^2-sec-atm already achieved in high-selectivity cellulose acetate, and the calculation indicates that even if the high fixed-charge densities and small pore radii which Dresner and Kraus[69] show to be essential in charged membranes with highly coupled salt and water flows can be achieved, higher-permeability seawater desalination membranes are not apt to be found in this direction. Where high salt concentrations are not at issue, of course, the permissible pore diameter increases, and, while pore lengths of the order of 0.005 cm must still be employed, the permeation constants of such membranes can be quite high.

In short, boundary-layer considerations set practical limits on the absolute membrane permeabilities that can be exploited practically in materials of given permeation properties; these limits should serve as valuable guides in our search for improved materials.

Real Membranes

In the foregoing paragraphs we have discussed membrane transport processes in terms of an over-all description (particularly in Section 2.2) and in terms of specific models (particularly in Section 2.3). It is perhaps appropriate to conclude this chapter by emphasizing that real membranes must yield results consistent with the general thermodynamic description but may or may not fall cleanly into any one of the model categories discussed here. In particular, we do not intend to imply that a membrane must be, for instance, either of the viscous-flow or of the solution-diffusion type. On the contrary, as Wilbrandt[79] suggested in 1935, real membranes will have characteristics spanning the range between these extremes. It is the purpose of models like that presented here for finely porous membranes to provide a physical picture of membranes of intermediate character.

As Kuhn[80] has already shown, the hydrodynamic permeability of a "porous" membrane in which the pore diameter is approximately one molecular diameter (and using bulk water viscosity) is the same as the hydrodynamic permeability of a "solution-diffusion" membrane having the same water content in which the diffusion coefficient for water is comparable to the self-diffusion coefficient for water in bulk water. Powell, Roseveare, and Eyring[81] have emphasized the fact that the basic molecular process determining diffusion coefficients and that determining viscosities is the same. It is the movement of one molecule past its neighbors into a new position. When clustering of water molecules occurs and essentially all of the neighbors of a typical water molecule are other water molecules, a viscous-flow situation exists, but when essentially all its neighbors are fixed in the membrane, a diffusive situation exists. No discontinuity is to be expected between these two extremes.

Symbol List

Symbols first appear in equation indicated, or in text shortly preceding or following this equation.

a_i	activity of component i	1.7
b	measure of membrane-solute interaction	2.39
c_i	concentration, mass per unit volume, of component i	2.4
$c_1 G_{11}$	clustering function	Section 2.3
c_{1m}^0	water concentration corresponding to monolayer coverage	2.67
C	constant in B-E-T equation	2.67
d	dielectric constant	2.73
D_i	diffusion coefficient for component i in laboratory system	2.16
D_{21}	diffusion coefficient for solute in center-of-mass system	2.20
E_a	heat of adsorption of monolayer	2.67
E_1	heat of liquefaction of adsorbed gas	2.67
f_{ij}	frictional coefficient for i interacting with j	2.38
F_i	total flux of component i	2.1
$\mathfrak{F}$	Faraday constant	2.4
H	hydrodynamic permeability	2.18
J_i	diffusive flux of component i in center-of-mass system	2.19
k	Boltzman constant	
K_i	distribution coefficient for component i	Section 2.1
L_{ij}	phenomenological coefficient	2.1
m_i	mobility of component i	2.13
M_i	molecular weight of component i	
n_i	molar concentration of component i	1.20
p	pressure	
$\mathcal{P}_i$	apparent permeability to component i	2.77

$\mathcal{P}_i^d$	apparent permeability to component i as measured in direct osmosis	2.78
r	equivalent cylindrical pore radius	2.18
R	gas constant	
t	tortuosity factor	2.18
T	absolute temperature	
u	center-of-mass velocity perpendicular to membrane surface	2.18
u^0	corrected value of u	2.25
u_2	velocity of solute perpendicular to membrane surface	2.38
v_i	partial molar volume of component i	1.6
X_i	thermodynamic force on component i	2.1
y	distance perpendicular to membrane surface	
Y_i	external force on component i	2.2
Z_i	mole fraction of component i	1.16
α	osmotic coefficient	2.8
$\gamma_\pm$	mean molar activity coefficient of salt	2.69
ϵ	fractional open area of porous membrane	2.18
η	viscosity of pore fluid	2.18
λ	membrane thickness	2.13
μ_i	chemical potential of component i	1.1
π	osmotic pressure	1.13
ρ_m	density of pore fluid	2.22
σ	surface tension	2.66
χ	molar concentration of fixed (positive) charge on membrane	2.52
ψ	electrostatic potential	2.50
ω	contact angle	2.66

Subscripts

1	solvent (water)
2	solute
3	membrane
$+$	cation
$-$	anion
m	within membrane

Superscripts

$'$	variable evaluated at interface between membrane and concentrated solution
$''$	variable evaluated at interface between membrane and dilute solution

References

1. Choo, C. Y., *Advan. Petrol. Chem. Refining* **6**, 73 (1962).
2. Li, N. N., R. B. Long, and E. J. Henley, *Ind. Eng. Chem.* **57**, 18 (1965).
3. Tuwiner, S. B., *Diffusion and Membrane Technology*, Reinhold Publishing Corp., New York, 1962.
4. Helfferich, F., *Ion Exchange*, McGraw-Hill Book Co., New York, 1962, pp. 339–420.
5. Schlögl, R., *Stofftransport durch Membranen*, Dr. Dietrich Steinkopf Verlag, Darmstadt, 1964.
6. Bergsma, F., and C. A. Kruissink, *Adv. Polymer Sci.* **2**, 307 (1961).
7. Rogers, C. E., in *Physics and Chemistry of the Organic Solid State*, D. Fox, M. M. Lubes, and A. Weissberger, editors, Interscience Publishers, New York, 1965, pp. 509–635.
8. Ferry, J. D., *Chem. Rev.* **18**, 373 (1936).
9. de Groot, S. R., *Thermodynamics of Irreversible Processes*, North-Holland Publishing Co., Amsterdam, 1959.
10. Ref. 5, p. 30.
11. Kedem, O., and A. Katchalsky, *J. Gen. Physiol.* **45**, 143 (1961).
12. Clark, W. E., *Science* **138**, 148 (1963).
13. Staverman, A. J., *Trans. Faraday Soc.* **48**, 176 (1952).
14. L'Hermite, *Ann. chim. phys.* [3] **43**, 420 (1855).
15. Laidler, K. J., and K. E. Schuler, *J. Chem. Phys.* **17**, 851 (1949).
16. Zwolinski, B. J., H. Eyring, and C. E. Reese, *J. Phys. Chem.* **53**, 1426 (1949).
17. Washburn, E. W. (editor), *International Critical Tables*, McGraw-Hill Book Co., New York, 1928, Vol. III, p. 297.
18. Shewmon, P. G., *Diffusion in Solids*, McGraw-Hill Book Co., New York, 1963, pp. 24, 124–125.
19. Jost, W., *Diffusion in Solids, Liquids, and Gases*, Academic Press, New York, 1952, p. 139.
20. Ref. 9, pp. 101–106.
21. Hartley, G. S., and J. Crank, *Trans. Faraday Soc.* **45**, 801 (1949). Also Crank, J., *Mathematics of Diffusion*, Oxford University Press, London, 1956, pp. 219–257.
22. Sourirajan, S., *Ind. Eng. Chem. Fundamentals Quarterly* **3**, 206 (1964).
23. Spiegler, K. S., *Trans. Faraday Soc.* **54**, 1408 (1958).
24. Faxen, H., *Ann. Physik* **68**, 89 (1922).
25. Lane, J. A., and J. W. Riggle, *Chem. Eng. Prog. Symposium Series*, A.I.Ch.E. **55**, No. 24, p. 127 (1959)
26. Ref. 4, p. 303.
27. Henderson, W. E., and C. M. Sliepcevich, *Chem. Eng. Prog. Symposium Series*, A.I.Ch.E. **55**, No. 24, p. 145 (1959).
28. Gosting, L. J., and M. S. Morris, *J. Am. Chem. Soc.* **71**, 1998 (1949).
29. Ref. 17, Vol. V, p. 23.
30. Sollner, K., *Z. Elektrochem.* **36**, 36 (1930).
31 Dresner, L., *J. Phys. Chem.* **67**, 1635 (1963).
32. Läuger, P., *Ber. der Bunsenges.* **68**, 352 (1964).
33. Teorell, T., *Trans. Faraday Soc.* **33**, 1053 (1937).
34. Teorell, T., *Z. Elektrochem.* **55**, 460 (1951).
35. Meyer, K. H., and J. F. Sievers, *Helv. Chim. Acta* **19**, 649 (1936).
36. Schmid, G., *Z. Elektrochem.* **56**, 181 (1952).
37. Läuger, P., and W. Kuhn, *Ber. der Bunsenges.* **68**, 4 (1964).
38. Schlögl, R., *Z. Physik. Chem.* **NF3**, 73 (1955).

39. Baldwin, W. H., D. L. Holcomb, and J. S. Johnson, *J. Polymer Sci.* **A3**, 833 (1965).
40. McKelvey, J. G., Jr., K. S. Spiegler, and M. R. J. Wylie, *Chem. Eng. Prog. Symposium Series*, A. I. Ch. E. **55**, No. 24, p. 199 (1959).
41. Myers, A. W., J. A. Meyer, C. E. Rogers, V. Stannett, and M. Szwarc, *Tappi* **44**, 58 (1961).
42. Yasuda, H., and V. Stannett, *J. Polymer Sci.* **57**, 907 (1962).
43. Flory, P. J., *J. Chem. Phys.* **10**, 51 (1942); *Principles of Polymer Chemistry*, Cornell University Press, Ithaca (1953), pp. 495–540.
44. Huggins, M. L., *Ann. N. Y. Acad. Sci.* **43**, 1 (1942).
45. Taylor, N. W., J. E. Cluskey, and F. R. Senti, *J. Phys. Chem.* **65**, 1810 (1961).
46. Glasstone, S., *Textbook of Physical Chemistry*, 2d ed., D. Van Nostrand Co., New York (1946), pp. 446 and 486.
47. Brunauer, S., P. H. Emmett, and E. Teller, *J. Am. Chem. Soc.* **60**, 309 (1938).
48. Langmuir, I., *ibid.* **40**, 1361 (1918).
49. Brunauer, S., L. S. Deming, W. E. Deming, and E. Teller, *ibid.* **62**, 1723 (1940).
50. Hill, T. L., *J. Chem. Phys.* **15**, 767 (1947).
51. Hendricks, S. B., R. A. Nelson, and L. T. Alexander, *J. Am. Chem. Soc.* **62**, 1457 (1940).
52. Shaw, T. M., *J. Chem. Phys.* **12**, 391 (1944).
53. Bull, H. B., *J. Am. Chem. Soc.* **66**, 1499 (1944).
54. Pauling, L., *ibid.* **67**, 555 (1945).
55. White, H. J., Jr., and H. Eyring, *Textile Res. J.* **17**, 523 (1947).
56. Dole, M., *J. Chem. Phys.* **16**, 25 (1948).
57. Hill, T. L., *ibid.* **14**, 263 (1946).
58. McLaren, A. D., and J. W. Rowen, *J. Polymer Sci.* **7**, 289 (1951).
59. Housman, J. A., in *Cellulose and Cellulose Derivatives*, E. Ott, H. M. Spurlin, and M. W. Grafflin, editors, Interscience Publishers, New York, 2d ed. (1954), Part I, p. 393.
60. Zimm, B. H., and J. L. Lundberg, *J. Phys. Chem.* **60**, 425 (1956).
61. Zimm, B. H., *Rev. Mod. Phys.* **31**, 123 (1959).
62. Starkweather, H. W., Jr., *J. Polymer Sci.* **B1**, No. 3, 133–138 (1963).
63. Lonsdale, H. K., U. Merten, and R. L. Riley, *J. Appl. Polymer Sci.* **9**, 1341 (1965).
64. Starkweather, H. W., *ibid.* **2**, 129 (1959).
65. Thompson, L. J., and F. A. Long, *J. Am. Chem. Soc.* **76**, 5886 (1954).
66. Gregor, H. P., *ibid.* **73**, 642 (1951).
67. Ref. 4, p. 145.
68. Robinson, R. A., and R. H. Stokes, *Electrolyte Solutions*, Butterworths, London, 1959, p. 78.
69. Dresner, L., and K. A. Kraus, *J. Phys. Chem.* **67**, 990 (1963).
70. Dresner, L., *ibid.* **67**, 2333 (1963).
71. Diamond, R. M., and D. G. Tuck, *Prog. Inorg. Chem.* **2**, 109 (1960).
72. Kraus, K. A., R. J. Raridon, and W. H. Baldwin, *J. Am. Chem. Soc.* **86**, 2571 (1964).
73. Merten, U., *Proc. First Intn'l. Desalination Symp.*, Paper SWD/44, Washington, D. C., Oct. 3–9, 1965.
74. Scatchard, G., *J. Phys. Chem.* **68**, 1056 (1964).
75. Åkerlöf, G., *J. Am. Chem. Soc.* **54**, 4125 (1932).
76. Ferry, J. D., *J. Gen. Physiol.* **20**, 95 (1936).
77. Glueckauf, E., *Proc. First Intn'l. Desalination Symp.*, Paper SWD/1, Washington, D. C., Oct. 3–9, 1965.

78. Barrer, R. M., *Diffusion in and through Solids*, Cambridge University Press, 1951, p. 437.
79. Wilbrandt, W., *J. Gen. Physiol.* **18**, 933 (1935).
80. Kuhn, W., *Z. Elektrochem.* **55**, 207 (1951).
81. Powell, R. E., W. E. Roseveare, and H. Eyring, *Ind. Eng. Chem.* **33**, 430 (1941).

3. Preparation and Performance of High-Flux Cellulose Acetate Desalination Membranes

S. Loeb

A suitable reverse-osmosis desalination membrane must meet three requirements: (1) It must desalinize a given feed water adequately. (2) It must have adequate desalinized water fluxes (flow rate per unit area of membrane) at reasonable pressures. (3) It must possess the above two characteristics for a reasonable length of time. The performance of a membrane must be judged in light of these conditions.

3.1 Early Work on Materials Semipermeable to Saline Solutions

In the past decade Reid and Breton[1] and, independently, Yuster, Sourirajan, and Bernstein[2] undertook screening programs to determine which film-forming materials would exhibit semipermeability to sea-water salts. Reid and Breton reported cellulose acetate to be almost uniquely qualified among materials considered. The second group also found cellulose acetate suitable and extended the list to cellulose acetate-butyrate and to cellophane treated with silicone emulsion. Later Loeb and Sourirajan[3] reported ethyl cellulose as having a high degree of semi-permeability. Baddour, Vieth, and Douglas[4] have tabulated the work of these early investigators.

Of all the semipermeable materials found, cellulose acetate appeared to have the most promise because its flux, although low, was much higher than that of the others. As discussed elsewhere, the flux capability of a reverse-osmosis membrane is most adequately characterized by the membrane constant A, which is determined by the membrane properties alone, at a given temperature. For a perfectly semipermeable membrane with brine-flow conditions such that the boundary layer is insignificant,

$$A = \frac{F_1}{\Delta p - \pi^0}, \qquad (3.1)$$

where A is the membrane constant, expressed here as g/cm^2-sec-atm, F_1 the flux in g/cm^2-sec, Δp the pressure drop across the membrane, and π^0 the osmotic pressure of the brine, both in atm.

In the discussion immediately following, A is calculated according to Eq. 3.1, even though the conditions specified for utilizing it were not met. However, further refinement in the calculation of A from the work of these early investigators is neither possible nor justified.

The desalination capacity of a membrane may be expressed in several ways: The simplest is a mere statement of the desalinized-water salt content, which can be compared with the U. S. Public Health Service standard of 500 ppm or less. However, this gives no idea of the desalination capacity unless accompanied by a statement of the feed-brine concentration. A commonly used term that does indicate desalination capacity is the percent salt rejected, defined as 100 times the difference between the feed- and product-water concentrations divided by the feed-water concentration.

To produce fresh water of 500 ppm salt content from seawater requires 98.6% salt rejected. Desalinized water having 1500 ppm of salt would be unacceptable, but if produced from seawater, the salt rejected would still be about 94.5%. Thus use of percent salt rejected tends to obscure important changes in membrane performance. A more sensitive term is the salt-reduction factor, defined as the feed-water concentration divided by the product-water concentration. The salt-reduction factor is the reciprocal of the relative permeability, as defined by Keilin.[5] Either term strongly reflects slight changes in membrane fabrication or other variables affecting desalination.

Reid and Breton,[1] Mahon,[6] and Loeb and Sourirajan,[3] all have done exploratory work with low-flux cellulose acetate membranes having rather good salt-reduction factors (Table 3–1). Reid and Breton prepared their membranes from a simple acetonic casting solution and attempted to maximize the membrane constant by making membranes only 6 μ thick. As seen in Table 3–1, they achieved a flux of only 0.33 $\times$ 10^{-4} g/cm^2-sec and a membrane constant of 0.82 $\times$ 10^{-6} g/cm^2-sec-atm.

Mahon attacked the low-flux problem indirectly by making very fine tubes of cellulose triacetate. Bundles of these tubes, 70–100 μ outer diameter, and with a 5–10-μ wall, would, according to his data, have about $\frac{1}{3}$ acre of surface per cubic foot. Based on his reported flux of 7 $\times$ 10^{-7} g/cm^2-sec, each cubic foot would produce 200 gallons per day

Table 3–1 Low-Flux Cellulose Acetate Membranes

| Investigators | Saline solution | | | Press. diff. (atm) | Flux F (10^{-4} g/ cm^2-sec) | Salt-red. factor* | Membrane constant A (10^{-6} g/ cm^2-sec-atm) | Membrane thickness microns | Membrane type |
	Type used	Molarity	Osmotic press. (atm)						
Reid and Breton[1]	NaCl	0.1 NaCl	4.9	40	0.33	25	0.82	6	Sheet, cast from simple acetonic solution
Mahon[6]	NaCl	0.17 NaCl	8.3	14	0.007	100 → 25	0.05	10	Fine tubes, cellulose triacetate
Loeb and Sourirajan[3]	Diluted sea- water	0.28 (sum of ionic species)	6.8	100	1.1	33	1.1	100	Sheet, ultra filtration membranes from Carl Schleicher & Schuell, heated

* Salt-reduction factor = 100/(100 − percent salt rejected).

(gpd), even though the membrane constant was only 5×10^{-8} g/cm²-sec-atm.

Loeb and Sourirajan attempted to increase the flux through the use of commercially available porous cellulose acetate membranes. Specifically, they tested ultrafiltration membranes "Ultrafein," made by Carl Schleicher & Schuell and allegedly having pores of 50 Å or less. These membranes were 100 μ thick and could be readily handled. They gave no desalination as received, but it was found possible to obtain appreciable desalination by the simple expedient of heating the membranes in hot water. In fact, the degree of desalination was a direct function and the flux an inverse function of the water temperature. Also it was observed that the membranes were side-sensitive: The "rough" side of the membrane had to be in contact with the feed brine to obtain good results.

Typical results obtained by Loeb and Sourirajan included a flux of 1.1×10^{-4} g/cm²-sec with a membrane constant of 1.1×10^{-6} g/cm²-sec-atm. The feed brine was seawater diluted to 1% dissolved salts. The membrane constant was about the same as that obtained by Reid and Breton, but a membrane 17 times thicker (Table 3-1) could be more readily handled. These encouraging results led Loeb and Sourirajan to experimentation with the production of cellulose acetate desalination membranes made to be porous, as will be discussed in the next section.

3.2 Preparation of High-Flux Membranes

It has been found possible to fabricate cellulose acetate desalination membranes such that the membrane constant is considerably increased over previous values without sacrifice of desalinizing properties. The performance of these membranes is sufficiently good that their commercial possibilities are being considered by a number of investigators.

There are several key steps required in the procedures developed for the fabrication of high-flux cellulose acetate desalination membranes. It is convenient to discuss these steps according to whether or not the membrane-casting solution contains electrolytes.

Fabrication from Casting Solutions Containing Electrolytes

As a result of experience gained with the Schleicher & Schuell membranes, Loeb and Sourirajan[3] embarked on the development of high-flux semipermeable membranes. In their search for an adequate means for making the membrane water-permeable, they encountered an article by Mlle. Dobry[7] in which she suggested the use of saturated aqueous magnesium perchlorate as a solvent for cellulose acetate in the preparation of ultrafiltration membranes. By incorporating acetone as a fourth component in the casting solution and by instituting a number of other changes from the original Dobry method, Loeb and Sourirajan found it possible to fabricate cellulose acetate membranes having greatly improved performance.

The fabrication technique developed may be described as follows:

1. The casting solution is a quaternary mixture of cellulose acetate–magnesium perchlorate–water–acetone in the proportions 22.2 — 1.1 — 10.0 — 66.7 wt-%. (Loeb and Manjikian[8] have reported improvements by the addition of small quantities of a fifth component, such as hydrochloric acid.)

2. The membrane is cast on a glass plate having 0.025-centimeter side runners to give this as-cast thickness to the membrane. The casting solution and all casting components are kept between $-5°$ and $-10°C$.

3. After an evaporation period of three minutes at this temperature, the membrane-plate assembly is immersed in ice water where it is kept for about one hour.

4. The membrane is removed from the plate and heated by immersion in water for 5 minutes at 65° to 85°C.

The performance obtained from membranes fabricated in this manner is shown in Fig. 3–1, the data for which were obtained in the cell system

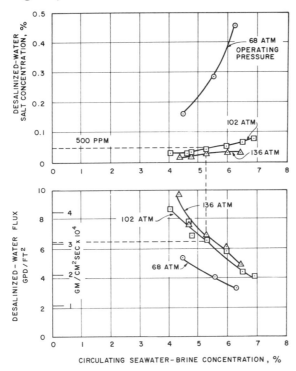

Fig. 3–1   Performance of high-flux membrane.

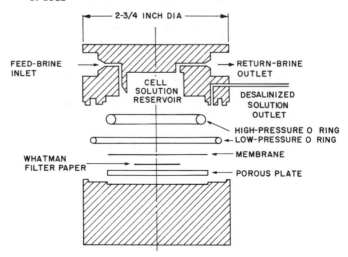

Fig. 3-2   Laboratory desalination cell.

of Figs. 3–2 and 3–3. Brine-circulation rates are thought to have been sufficiently high in this cell that performance was not appreciably diminished by excessive boundary-layer thicknesses.

The performance indicated in Fig. 3–1 is significantly better than the best shown in Table 3–1. For example, at 102 atm and at the maximum brine concentration, $5\frac{1}{4}\%$, fresh water of 500 ppm dissolved solids was provided. At this point, the flux was 3×10^{-4} g/cm²-sec, the salt-reduction factor was 105, and the membrane constant was 4.7×10^{-6} g/cm²-sec-atm.

The fabrication parameters cited were chosen largely on the basis of their influence on membrane performance. Each parameter is discussed below from this viewpoint.

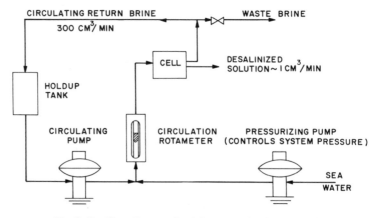

Fig. 3-3   Flow diagram for laboratory desalination cell.

Casting solution. It was found desirable to cast with both the casting solution and the necessary equipment at a temperature between −5° and −10°C. By this means the time between casting and immersion, to be discussed later, could be extended to a reasonable interval,[3] and the films so prepared had a better physical appearance than membranes cast at room temperature. Finally, membrane performance was found to be reproducible in this temperature range.

Generally, the acetone concentration was restricted to that necessary to provide a rather viscous casting solution. The effect of omitting either $Mg(ClO_4)_2$ or water is plotted in Fig. 3–4, which shows that the omission

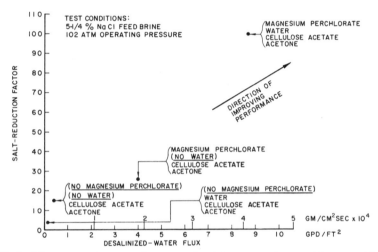

Fig. 3–4 Effect on membrane performance of omitting magnesium perchlorate and/or water from casting solution.

of magnesium perchlorate has a more serious deleterious effect than the omission of water. The use of ternary mixtures containing no water has been discussed by Baddour, Vieth, and Douglas.[4]

The influence on performance of any variation in cellulose acetate properties was determined mainly with the formamide-modified casting solutions to be discussed. However, the results would also be expected to apply to membranes fabricated from casting solutions containing aqueous electrolytes.

Tests made with special cellulose acetate samples* indicated that: (1) for cellulose acetate samples in the general composition range of Eastman E-398-3 powder, neither average cellulose acetate molecular weight nor molecular-weight distribution is a strong factor in determining membrane performance; (2) the acetyl content should be between 37.5 and 40.1%. The upper limit is determined by cellulose acetate-acetone solubility characteristics and the lower limit by membrane performance.

* Supplied by Mr. W. M. Gearhart, Eastman Chemical Products.

62   S. Loeb

Lonsdale, Merten, and Riley[9] have shown that the semipermeability of cellulose acetate should increase with acetyl content.

Other cellulose esters, in particular cellulose acetate-butyrate[10] and cellulose propionate[11] were used with some success in place of cellulose acetate, but both gave performances inferior to those obtained with the latter.

Ethyl cellulose could not be successfully substituted for cellulose acetate in quaternary mixtures containing aqueous magnesium perchlorate and acetone as other components. However, it has been used successfully in a ternary mixture of nonelectrolytes, as will be discussed later.

Loeb made a study of electrolytes suitable as additives in the casting solution. He concluded that the anion was responsible for the unique quality of a successful additive, and listed ClO_4^-, IO_4^-, MnO_4^-, ReO_4^-, BF_4^-, PF_6^-, NCS^-, tetraphenylboron, salicylate, HgI_4^{-2}, and $PtCl_6^{-2}$ as useful anions. He was able to obtain a numerical correlation between the utility of an additive anion and an experimentally obtained entropy change expressive of the residual ice-structure modification of the water by the anion.[12] Raridon and Kraus[13] have also emphasized the importance of the anion, based on their work with ternary mixtures of cellulose acetate model compounds, electrolytes, and water.

On the other hand, the work of Kesting[14] has led him to believe that the cation is determining. He concluded that cations, in particular those of high charge density, perform a solvating function between cellulose acetate and water by virtue of their hydration and by attachment to nucleophilic oxygen groups on cellulose acetate.

Magnesium perchlorate has been the most commonly used electrolyte in the casting solution. However, Keilin[5] has fabricated a number of membranes for bench-scale tests from solutions containing zinc chloride.

Solvents other than acetone have been used as partial or complete replacements for acetone. Methyl acetate, methyl ethyl ketone, methanol, and ethanol have been used but have been found to produce membranes giving indifferent performance,[15] as have formic acid and methyl formate.[16] Glacial acetic acid was found to be of some interest as a solvent. First of all, castings could be conducted at room temperature because of the low volatility of glacial acetic acid. Second, fairly good performance could be obtained without the necessity of including aqueous magnesium perchlorate in the casting solution. It was even possible to eliminate the heating phase by adjusting the time from film casting to immersion. The best performance obtained under these conditions was 3.4×10^{-4} g/cm²-sec and 0.24% salt from a $5\frac{1}{4}\%$ NaCl feed brine at 102 atm operating pressure. Unfortunately, the membrane made from the glacial acetic acid casting solution had poor physical properties. In particular it had poor tear strength.

Keilin[17] pointed out that p-dioxane can be substituted for acetone in the regular quaternary casting solution already discussed. As with glacial acetic acid solutions, membranes could be cast at room temperature. Presumably this was true because the volatility of p-dioxane is also much lower than that of acetone. Unfortunately, these membranes had rather poor reproducibility. He also showed that the water in the casting solution can be replaced by ethylene glycol.[5]

Membrane fabrication. The appropriate membrane thickness is obtained by the usual technique of obtaining relative motion between a casting surface and a spreader blade separated from it by an appropriate distance. The velocity of the spreader blade is not in itself critical in influencing membrane performance, since velocities have been varied between 75 and 500 cm/min without affecting performance significantly. However, spreader-blade velocity may affect membrane performance indirectly in batch-casting of long sheets. In this case blade velocity is an important variable, since the time between casting and immersion for the first part of the film may be appreciably different from that of the last part.

Total film thickness has an influence on membrane performance, but flux is by no means inversely proportional to thickness, as might be expected from application of Poisseuille's or Fick's law. The reason for this apparent anomaly is that the effective thickness of the film is only a small fraction of the total film thickness. The effective layer, which we will refer to as the osmotic skin, is at the membrane surface in contact with the spreader blade during casting. Riley, Gardner, and Merten[18] have stated that the osmotic-skin thickness is in the order of $0.25\,\mu$ (out of a total thickness of $100\,\mu$), based on electron-microscopic examination of the membrane edge. The evidence of Keilin,[17] obtained by dyeing experiments, is that the osmotic skin is on the order of $10\,\mu$ thick. This question will be discussed further in Chapter 4. The thickness of the membrane other than the osmotic skin consists of a relatively porous, spongy region, which offers much less resistance to flow than does the osmotic skin for the usually utilized total thickness of about $100\,\mu$. However, for thicker membranes this spongy region may offer an appreciable fraction of the total resistance.[11]

The chief requirement of the surface upon which the membrane is cast is that the surface be smooth and rigid. Membranes cast upon sandblasted brass or sandblasted glass have shown performance characteristics greatly below those cast on smooth brass or glass. This difference is probably due to the rough pattern induced on the membrane surface adjacent to the casting surface. When the membrane is ultimately used in desalination service, hydraulic compression causes a smoothing of this rough surface but at the expense of some roughening of the osmotic skin on the opposite surface. This roughening is effectively a stretching and would tend to damage the desirable structure set up in the osmotic skin during the heating phase. Successful casting has been accomplished on brass, glass, phenol formaldehyde, and paraffin (a nonpolar surface).

The membrane is immersed in ice water within a predetermined period after casting. The length of this evaporation period is important for membrane performance. As shown in Figure 3–5, performance of a

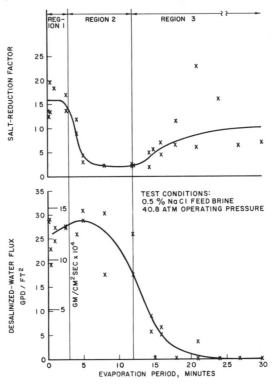

Fig. 3–5   Effect of evaporation period on membrane performance.

magnesium perchlorate-modified membrane is seriously deteriorated by allowing the evaporation period to extend too long. The permissible length of the evaporation period is a function of several variables, such as temperature of the casting solution and volatility of the solvent, as already discussed. The total membrane thickness also influences the allowable maximum evaporation period. Membranes having a total final thickness of only 0.005 cm might require an evaporation period not exceeding two minutes, whereas for membranes 0.01 cm thick a period of up to four minutes might be satisfactory. Keilin's[5] results with a zinc chloride-modified membrane indicated that ten minutes was excessive in that case.

The immersion liquid generally used is ice water. If the immersion water is at room temperature, membrane performance and physical properties become adversely affected. Casting-solution components such as magnesium perchlorate or acetone have been included in the immersion water, but membrane performance did not improve.[11,15] Other liquids have also been tried as substitutes for water. The minimum requirements for these liquids is that they be miscible with acetone, magnesium perchlorate, and water (in the casting solution) but immiscible with cellulose acetate. Methanol, ethanol, isopropanol, and

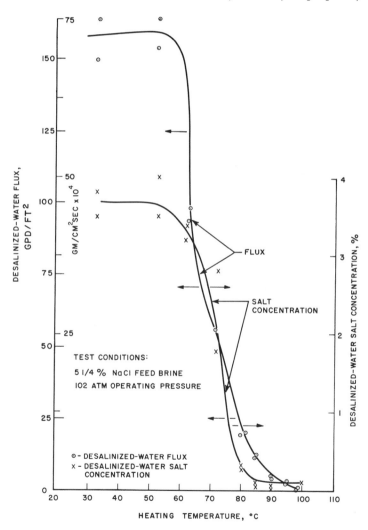

Fig. 3–6   Effect of heating temperature on membrane performance.

ethylene glycol met these requirements but were not found to be useful substitutes for water. The immersion period is usually on the order of one half to one hour, although virtually all the magnesium perchlorate is removed within a few minutes after immersion.[10]

Membrane heating. The last step in membrane fabrication is direct immersion in hot water for a period of 3 to 10 minutes. The membrane performance is not strongly responsive to time of heating once the time exceeds about two minutes. On the other hand, it is extremely sensitive to heating temperature, as illustrated in Fig. 3–6. The influence of heating starts between 55° and 60°C. Higher temperatures cause a decrease in flux of desalinized water and an improvement in desalination. Since the degree of desalination can be accurately adjusted by changing the heating temperature, this phase of the fabrication constitutes a step in which membrane properties can be matched to desalination requirements.

The advantage of being able to exert this type of control over the properties of the membrane is that for each desalination task the membrane properties can be adjusted to achieve a proper balance of energy and capital expenditures: energy in terms of pressure level of operation and fraction of feed brine recovered as potable water, and capital in terms of membrane surface required. Thus a membrane heat-treated at 80° to 83°C may be used to desalinate seawater and will produce a potable-water flux of 4 to 5 $\times$ 10^{-4} g/cm²-sec at an operating pressure of 100 atm. Similarly, a membrane heat-treated at 65° to 70°C may be used for many brackish waters and will typically produce 10 to 12 $\times$ 10^{-4} g/cm²-sec of potable water at an operating pressure of 40 atm. Use of the seawater membrane at this lower pressure would result in a product rate of only 2 to 3 $\times$ 10^{-4} g/cm²-sec but a water quality considerably better than that required to meet potability standards. The use of a lower heating temperature for the brackish-water desalination membrane enables energy and/or capital expenditures to be lower than those for a seawater desalination membrane used in brackish-water service.

Reproducibility of membrane performance. For large-scale uses, it is important to know the reproducibility obtainable in performance for a group of membranes.

Loeb[12] fabricated a number of flat sheet membranes measuring 20″ $\times$ 20″ by the techniques just described. These were made for use in a 500-gpd seawater desalination unit. A small disk was cut from each of these squares and tested in the laboratory desalination cell at 1500 psig and with a seawater feed brine. Results were as follows:

Mean flux	6.0 $\times$ 10^{-4} g/cm²-sec
Standard deviation in flux	7.5 $\times$ 10^{-5} g/cm²-sec
Mean salt-reduction factor	80.7
Standard deviation in salt-reduction factor	19.3

Fabrication from Casting Solutions Containing Only Nonelectrolytes

Manjikian, Loeb, and McCutchan[19] described a number of useful membrane casting solutions containing only nonelectrolytes. In these, the number of components may be four, three, or even two.

Of the compositions tested, the ternary mixture cellulose acetate–formamide–acetone, was found to be the most useful. Membranes made from this mixture are equal to or better than those fabricated from casting solutions containing electrolytes, and are simpler to produce. Casting can be reproducibly accomplished at room temperature, i.e., without cooling down the casting solution, the casting knife, plate, etc., to coldbox temperatures (although the immersion water should still be in the range 0° to 5°C).

Figure 3–7 shows the composition region for mixtures of cellulose acetate, formamide, and acetone from which membranes were successfully made. The boundaries of this region were limited by viscosity and homogeneity requirements of the casting solution, by the physical properties of the membrane obtained, and by membrane performance. Table 3–2 lists the performance of membranes cast at room temperature from

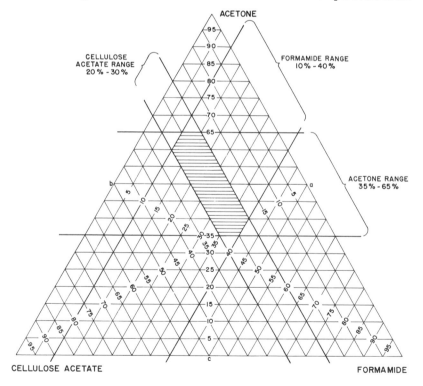

Fig. 3–7 Casting-solution region — cellulose acetate–formamide–acetone system.

Table 3-2   Performance of Membranes Cast at 23°C from Various Ternary Mixtures of Cellulose Acetate–Formamide–Acetone
Cell operating pressure: 41 atm; feed brine: 5000 ppm NaCl

Solution number	Casting-solution composition (wt-%)			Evaporation period, minutes	Heating temperature (°C)	Desalinized water	
	Cellulose acetate	Formamide	Acetone			Flux (10^{-4} g/ cm²-sec)	Salt content (ppm)
9	29.1	16.7	54.2	1	unheated	1.3	310
10	30	14.3	55.7	1	unheated	3.8	410
7	25	30	45	1	74.0	14	410
6	25	25	50	1	71.5	7.0	270
5	25	20	55	1	65.0	7.0	360

various formamide casting solutions. The composition consisting of cellulose acetate–formamide–acetone in the ratio 25:30:45 wt-% appeared to be optimum.

The maximum allowable room-temperature evaporation period was in the order of $1\frac{1}{2}$ minutes for the formamide mixture. The influence of heating temperature on membrane performance was similar to that of the magnesium perchlorate-modified membrane but the latter is heated a few degrees lower for the same performance.

Nonelectrolytic materials other than formamide have been described by Manjikian, Loeb, and McCutchan for use in casting solutions to produce cellulose acetate desalination membranes having promise. (They showed that the technique could also be applied to obtaining useful ethyl cellulose casting solutions.) The solution compositions are listed in Table 3–3.

The data of Table 3–3 indicate that urea, glyoxal, or hydrogen peroxide can effectively replace an electrolyte such as magnesium perchlorate in quaternary casting solutions. Hydrogen peroxide is of special interest as an additive. Since water itself is useless as an additive, it is quite surprising that partial replacement of the water by such a closely related compound would make so much difference in membrane performance. Since it has been shown that the utility of electrolytic additives is independent of their oxidizing capabilities, it is unlikely that the utility of hydrogen peroxide is due to this effect.

As for the ternary solutions, tetrahydrofurfuryl phosphate is an incomplete solvent for cellulose acetate, as is formamide. On the other hand, dimethyl sulfoxide, N-methyl-2-pyrrolidone, dimethyl formamide, triethyl phosphate, and acetic acid are complete solvents for cellulose acetate and the last three are useful in binary mixtures.

A number of organic compounds give clear homogeneous solutions in ternary mixtures with cellulose acetate and acetone but are not useful in producing good membranes. This group includes methyl formate, acrylic acid, oleic acid, phenol, propionic acid, diethanolamine, diethyl phthalate, tetrahydrofuran, diethylamine, acetonitrile, and pyrocatechol. Loeb[11] found polyethylene glycol to be inadequate in ternary mixtures of cellulose acetate–polyethylene glycol–acetone. Similarly, in binary mixtures acetone, p-dioxane, methyl ethyl ketone, and dimethyl sulfoxide are solvents for cellulose acetate, but useful casting solutions cannot be produced from their binary mixtures with cellulose acetate. Such solvents may be designated as "nonswelling" solvents, a term applied in connection with casting-solution membrane salts by Keilin.[17] In contrast, glacial acetic acid, previously discussed, is a "swelling" solvent.

Manjikian, Loeb, and McCutchan have stated the following necessary (but insufficient) conditions for components of cellulose acetate casting

Table 3-3   Nonelectrolytic Casting Solutions Giving Promising Membrane Performance

Cell operating pressure: 41 atm; feed brine: 5000 ppm NaCl

Type of solution	Additive compound	Casting-soln. composition wt-%		Casting temp. (°C)	Evap. period (min)	Heating temp. (°C)	Desalinized water	
							Flux $\left(10^{-4}\frac{g}{cm^2\text{-sec}}\right)$	Salt content (ppm)
	Urea	CA*	21.0					
		Urea	3.3	−10	6	Unhtd.	4.2	930
Quaternary		H₂O	13.2	−10	6	63.3	1.2	370
		Acet†	62.5					
(water		CA	21.5					
being	Glyoxal	Glyoxal	4.5	−10	17	70.3	8.9	370
fourth		H₂O	9.2					
component)		Acet	64.8					
		CA	22.0					
	Hydrogen	H₂O₂	2.6	−10	10	78.5	9.4	600
	peroxide	H₂O	10.4	−10	10	80.5	8.5	150
		Acet	65.0					
		CA	14.3	23	3½	Unhtd.	8.9	550
	Dimethyl	DMF	21.4	23	3½	60.0	2.5	300
	formamide	Acet	64.3					
		CA	25.0					
	Dimethyl	DMSO	37.5	23	3	62.0	2.3	750
	sulfoxide	Acet	37.5					
	Tetrahydro-	CA	20					
Ternary	furfuryl	THFP	20	−10	10	75.0	8.4	180
	phosphate	Acet	60					
		CA	25					
	Triethyl	TEP	25	−10	2	79.0	9.3	200
	phosphate	Acet	50					
		CA	22.5					
	Acetic acid	AA	9.1	−10	2	77.5	2.3	750
		Acet	68.4					
	N-methyl-	CA	22.0					
	2-pyrrol-	N-M-2-P	13.0	−10	16	75.0	2.7	250
	idone	Acet	65.0					
	Dimethyl	CA	25					
	formamide	DMF	75	23	8	93.0	5.1	140
Binary	Acetic acid	CA	20					
		AA	80	23	10	Unhtd.	2.9	650
	Triethyl	CA	20	−10	1.5	93.0	3.7	220
	phosphate	TEP	80	23	1.0	94.0	4.2	240

* CA — Cellulose Acetate
† Acet — Acetone

solutions other than cellulose acetate itself: (1) miscibility with water, since all components except cellulose acetate and water are removed upon immersion in water; (2) absence of chemical reactivity with other casting-solution components; (3) miscibility with other casting-solution components. Furthermore, in casting solutions containing nonswelling solvents, an appropriate additive must be included consisting of a single compound or an aqueous solution. It is desirable that, upon immersion in ice water, the additive be leached out after the nonswelling solvent.[4]

The development of successful binary and ternary mixtures demonstrates that neither water nor electrolytes are essential as components of casting solutions. As a corollary to this statement, it is clear that no ion-ion or ion-dipole interaction is required between casting components at any stage of fabrication. This latter statement applies also to casting solutions containing water, as evidenced by the utility of urea, glyoxal, or hydrogen peroxide in quaternary mixtures with cellulose acetate–water–acetone.

3.3 Performance Tests on Tubular Membranes

In the preceding section the influence of variables in membrane *preparation* on performance has been discussed. In this section, the influence of *operating conditions*, i.e., variables external to the membrane, is emphasized. The following operating variables will be considered: total pressure, or nominal driving pressure, the latter being defined as operating pressure minus osmotic pressure of feed brine; operating temperature; salt content of feed brine (the influence of salt type is left to a later section); and hydraulic parameters.

A number of investigators have examined the influence of the preceding variables on the performance of membranes produced by the techniques described. However, most of the investigations have been made with the membrane in the form of a flat sheet. Flat-sheet cells do not have a geometry readily amenable to relating membrane performance to hydraulic parameters, such as hydraulic radius and Reynolds number, because of discontinuities at the perimeter. These discontinuities include edges parallel and perpendicular to the flow direction, such as the entrance and exit of the cell. As pointed out by Merten,[20] the influence of such discontinuities may appreciably affect the flux of water and salt through the membrane.

A useful geometry for minimizing discontinuity effects is the long tube, i.e., a tube whose total length is much greater than its diameter. As previously discussed, Mahon[6] has studied very small tubes; and a group at Aerojet-General Corporation[21] has carried out exploratory tests in tube casting. Havens[22] has examined in some detail the commercial application of the techniques here described to the manufacture of a tubular membrane integral with an enclosing porous tube of Fiberglas reinforced plastic. The performance of this assembly was rather poor compared with that of the flat sheet.

It has now been found possible to make a tubular membrane assembly giving a performance closely approaching that of the flat sheet. Figure 3–8 shows the various components of such a tubular assembly. The membrane tube is fabricated by methods similar to those for produc-

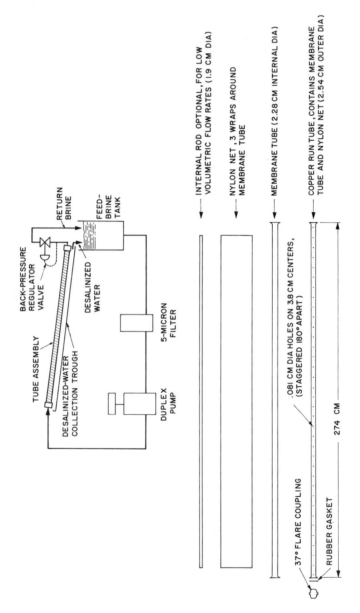

Fig. 3-8 Tubular-assembly components and flow diagram.

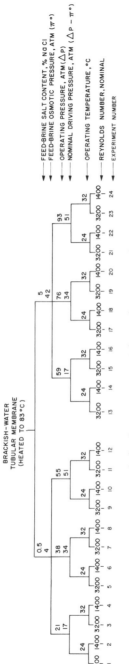

Fig. 3–9 Test program with brackish-water tubular membrane.

ing the flat sheet with the modifications necessary for the tubular geometry.[23] The formamide casting solution was used so that the membrane could be formed within a casting tube at room temperature. The membrane tube is wrapped in three layers of nylon cloth to provide a low resistance path to the holes in the run tube, within which the other components are retained concentrically. The geometry of the completed tube assembly is similar in a number of respects to that previously described by Van Oss.[24]

Membrane-tube assemblies of this type do not give optimum performance at the maximum volumetric brine flow rates of 72 cm³/sec available in these experiments. However, performance can be appreciably improved by inclusion of an internal rod to provide a narrow annulus. The relationship between hydraulic parameters and performance will be discussed quantitatively in Chapter 5.

Two groups of performance tests have been made with the tubular membrane having an internal rod, to determine membrane performance

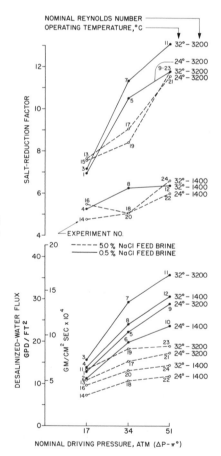

Fig. 3–10   Influence of nominal driving pressure on performance of brackish-water desalination membrane.

as a function of Reynolds number and the other parameters listed: tests with a high-flux, low-desalination "brackish-water" membrane, and with a low-flux, high-desalination "seawater" membrane. Figure 3–9 illustrates the program of 24 tests performed on the brackish-water membrane. An identical program was carried out with the seawater membrane. The outside diameter of the flow passage (the inside diameter of the membrane tube) was 2.28 cm and the inside diameter (the rod diameter) 1.90 cm; thus the hydraulic radius was 0.10 cm. The effective length of the tube was 266 cm, as determined by the length of the nylon wrap. This geometry is such that entrance and exit effects were believed to be minimized in modifying over-all performance results. A foot-by-foot desalination survey of the brackish-water membrane tube indicated no appreciable difference in desalination between the ends and the remainder of the tube.

The results of the tests with the brackish-water membrane tube are shown in Figs. 3–10, 3–11, 3–12, and 3–13. Figures 3–14, 3–15, 3–16, and

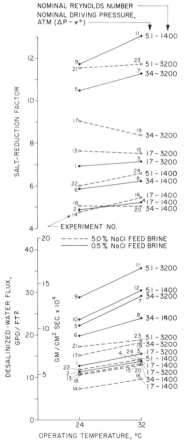

Fig. 3–11 Influence of operating temperature on performance of brackish-water desalination membrane.

3-17 show results with the seawater membrane. In these diagrams flux is given in g/cm²-sec or gpd/ft² and desalination as the salt-reduction factor, as previously discussed. The flux and salt-reduction factor are shown as dependent variables of four significant independent variables: Reynolds number, nominal driving pressure ($\Delta p - \pi^\circ$), operating temperature, and feed-brine salt content. Since only two or three points are shown on each curve, the true shape of the curve cannot be determined. However, the data should be useful for determining specific design points within the region shown and, more generally, for indicating the direction of the influence of the independent variables.

The brackish-water and seawater membranes behaved similarly in that:

1. Flux increased with increasing nominal driving pressure ($\Delta p - \pi^\circ$), operating temperature, and Reynolds number, but in the flow region studied, the Reynolds number was far less important than the other two

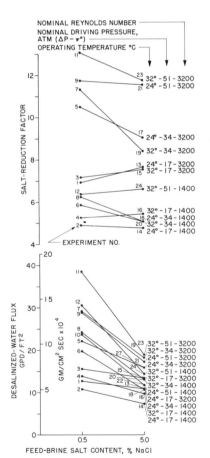

Fig. 3–12 Influence of feed-brine salt content on performance of brackish-water desalination membrane.

parameters. In particular, flux was rather insensitive to Reynolds number when 0.5% NaCl was used with the seawater membrane.

2. Flux decreased with increasing feed-water salt content at constant nominal driving pressure except for operation at low nominal driving pressures with the seawater membrane.

3. Salt-reduction factor increased with increasing Reynolds number and nominal driving pressure (discounting the curve that connects points 16, 20, and 24 in Fig. 3–10).

4. Salt-reduction factor was not a detectable function of operating temperature.

5. Salt-reduction factor was apparently not a function of feed-brine salt content for the brackish-water membrane but appeared to decrease with increasing feed-brine salt content with the seawater membrane.

The chief difference in the direction of the results with the two membranes was that the influence of total operating pressure on membrane constant was apparently much greater with the brackish-water mem-

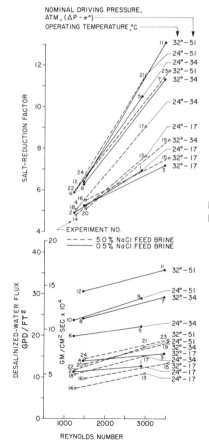

Fig. 3–13 Influence of Reynolds number on performance of brackish-water desalination membrane.

brane than with the seawater membrane. This is most clearly seen in Figs. 3–10 and 3–14. In both curves the flux lines for the 5% NaCl brine are lower than those for the 0.5% brine; this effect is due to the higher compaction at the higher (by 38 atm) actual operating pressure with the 5% brine. Furthermore, this difference in flux is more pronounced with the brackish-water membrane (Fig. 3–10) than with the seawater membrane (Fig. 3–14), because the former compacted more due to its more porous structure. This effect can be seen in a slightly different way by noting that the flux curves for the brackish-water membrane flatten with increased pressure more than the flux curves for the seawater membrane.

The phenomenon of membrane compaction sets a practical upper limit to operating pressure in cellulose acetate membranes. Because of this effect it has been found that, for a given membrane, steady-state flux may be lower at high pressure than at some lower pressure.

One other effect of operational variables on membrane performance should be mentioned here. Several investigators have found that minor

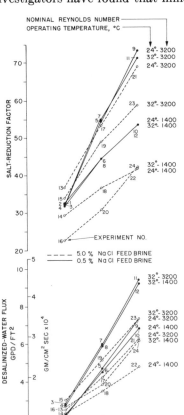

Fig. 3–14   Influence of nominal driving pressure on performance of seawater desalination membrane.

constituents in feed brine appear to have an appreciable influence on the desalination capacity of a membrane. Loeb[25] reported that trace quantities (10 to 20 ppm) of aluminum ion in the feed brine were effective in reducing the salinity of the desalinized water to 1000 ppm, whereas without aluminum ion the salinity would be 2000 ppm or higher (the feed brine being $5\frac{1}{4}\%$ NaCl). Later Loeb and Manjikian[26] found that Zephiran (a quaternary ammonium chloride, alkyl dimethylbenzyl ammonium chloride, where the alkyl chain consists of 8 to 18 carbon atoms) had a similar effect. With 40 ppm of Zephiran in a 5000-ppm NaCl feed brine, the salt content of the desalinized water was reduced to 200 ppm, while without Zephiran it is 400 ppm.

3.4 Membrane Life

As mentioned at the beginning of this chapter, a suitable reverse-osmosis membrane must retain good performance characteristics for an adequate period of time. Laboratory and field studies of membrane life

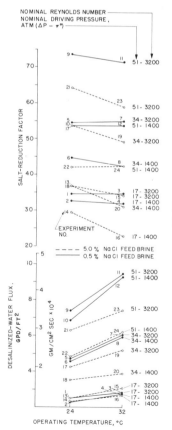

Fig. 3–15 Influence of operating temperature on performance of seawater desalination membrane.

have been conducted by a number of investigators with both seawater
and brackish-water feed brines.

Laboratory Tests

Reid and Breton[1] observed that cellulose acetate membranes failed
after a few weeks of continuous laboratory service. In their opinion this
failure was due to hydrolysis of the acetyl groups and the rate of hydrolysis was a direct function of the feed-brine salt content.

Keilin[5] attempted to verify this observation by storing membranes in
various solutions of sodium chloride up to 20% in concentration. He
found that, contrary to the results of Reid and Breton, membrane life
was increased with increasing concentration. His study indicated that
membrane deterioration might be due primarily to bacterial degradation; he therefore recommended storage of membranes in capped containers of deionized water.

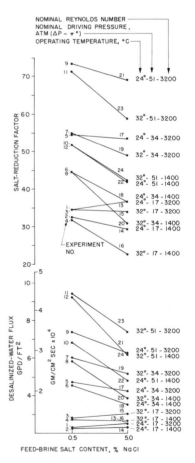

Fig. 3–16   Influence of feed-brine salt
content on performance of seawater
desalination membrane.

Lonsdale, et al.,[27] conducted a two-month laboratory life test with recycled synthetic seawater. During this period the salt-reduction factor dropped from 66 to 12 and the membrane constant decreased from about 8 to 4.5×10^{-6} g/cm^2-sec-atm. These workers also conducted a recycle life test with 10% sodium chloride and observed a large loss in the membrane's salt-rejection capacity within about one week.

In more recent experiments, Vos[28] found that membrane life is strongly dependent on feed-water pH and that the variability of results obtained in the past may therefore be attributable to differences in solution pH. One seawater membrane operated at 1500 psi in a 9 wt-% NaCl brine kept in the pH range between 5.0 and 6.5 was found to suffer a factor-of-two decrease in salt-reduction factor in an eight-month period, while another, operated in a 6.3 wt-% seawater brine, pH adjusted to 6.5 to 7.0, showed a factor-of-five decrease in the same period. A factor-of-ten decrease in salt-reduction factor was found to occur within two days at pH 10.

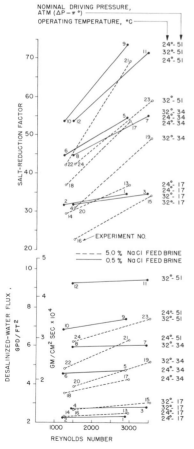

Fig. 3–17 Influence of Reynolds number on performance of seawater desalination membrane.

Field Tests

Since it is difficult to simulate field conditions in the laboratory, field tests are of special interest. In fact, with our present state of knowledge, life tests on location using the expected feed-water pretreatment and plant-operating conditions are probably desirable before a large plant is constructed.

Loeb and Manjikian[29] conducted a small-scale life test with seawater at the University of California Sea Water Laboratory at La Jolla. The cell was essentially that of Fig. 3–2, and the membrane was fabricated from an electrolyte-modified casting solution to produce potable water from seawater at 102 atm operating pressure. The seawater flow rate was 300 cm³/min on a once-through basis. The seawater was prefiltered through a sand filter, followed by a 10-μ polishing filter. Results of the test are shown in Fig. 3–18. The initial steady-state flux after reaching equilibrium in about a day was about 4×10^{-4} g/cm²-sec, and the salt content was about 500 ppm. In three months the flux dropped to about 2×10^{-4} g/cm²-sec, and the salt content increased to over 4000 ppm.

This deterioration in performance could have been caused by a combination of factors. Perhaps the most important was the accumulation of red-brown particulate matter on the surface of the membrane. This material evidently had an undesirable effect on membrane performance, since an appreciable improvement took place when the membrane surface was cleaned. This particulate matter got into the membrane even with the filtering system used. A finer filter may have been indicated. On the other hand it appeared possible that this particulate matter could have consisted of, or been deposited by, microorganisms, in which case filtration might not have been effective.

Another possible cause of membrane deterioration may have been the rather frequent down time (Fig. 3–18) due to pump unreliability. During the 96-day run the system was shut down for a total of 16 days for pump maintenance.

Loeb and Milstein[30] also made a three-week run on seawater with a 500-gpd plate-and-frame desalination unit. The test was conducted at Port Hueneme, California, on a once-through basis, at facilities provided by the U. S. Naval Civil Engineering Laboratory. At the end of the period, membrane performance decreased rather drastically. However, the decrease in performance appeared, as in the laboratory-scale life test previously discussed, to be due more to the accumulation of particulate matter on the surface of the membrane than to any deterioration of the membrane itself.

A six-month small-scale life test with brackish water was conducted by Loeb and Manjikian[31] at Coalinga, California, with a feed brine having the compositions shown in Table 3–4. The membrane was of the

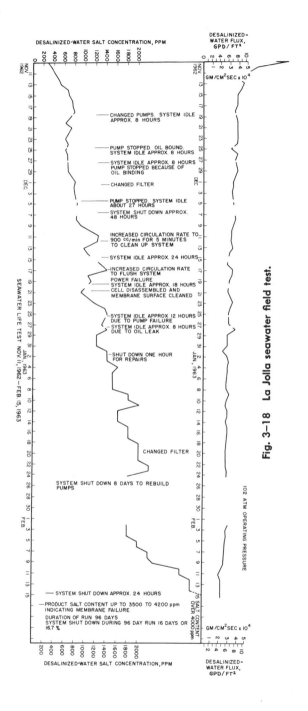

Fig. 3-18 La Jolla seawater field test.

Table 3-4   Coalinga Feed-Water Analyses

	Parts per million dissolved solids			
	4/15/63	6/8/63	8/30/63	10/5/63
Total dissolved solids	2520.0	2372	2442	2479.2
Alkalinity (bicarbonate)	—	170.8	170.8	167.8
Chlorides	262.4	297.9	248.2	265.9
Fluorides	—	0.14	—	—
Sulfates	1303.7	1199	1253.5	1260.5
Nitrates	5.2	0.7	0.8	4.0
Calcium	116.2	145.3	125.3	118.4
Magnesium	97.2	100.9	88.1	85.6
Sodium	529.0	468.0	524.1	541.0
Potassium	—	15.8	—	—
Iron	—	0.01	—	—
Manganese	—	0.11	—	—
Total hardness ($CaCO_3$)	—	—	659.4	655
pH	7.8	7.3	7.6	7.1

magnesium perchlorate-modified type heated to 65°C, in contrast to the seawater membrane, which was heated to 80.5°C. The lower heating temperature required for the brackish-water membrane was of course due to the difference in composition of the feed brine. Not only was the salt content much lower in the Coalinga water but the percentage of divalent ions, which are very readily removed, was higher. Because of the lower heating temperature the membrane had a high flux, even though only 41 atm operating pressure was used.

In this life test, down time was held to less than 1% by appropriate pump valving for instant use of the stand-by pump. Also a 5-μ filter, rather than a 10-μ one, as in the seawater run, was used.

The results are shown in Fig. 3-19. In the six-month period the flux of desalinized water dropped from 24×10^{-4} to 8×10^{-4} g/cm²-sec and the salt content increased from 150 to 300 ppm (with higher salt contents being encountered in between). Thus, at the predetermined conclusion of the run the membrane was still delivering potable water at a rather good flux.

Two thirds of the way through the run the cell was opened up, and the membrane found to be covered with an orange-brown precipitate similar to that found in the seawater life test. This material was removed manually, with the result that performance improved markedly. After conclusion of the run, the membrane was again found to be covered with this material, which upon analysis was found to be about 75% Fe_2O_3, with the bulk of the remainder having the empirical formula $(CH_2O)_x$.

These two life tests showed that the membrane was probably more immediately practical for long-term use in brackish-water than in sea-

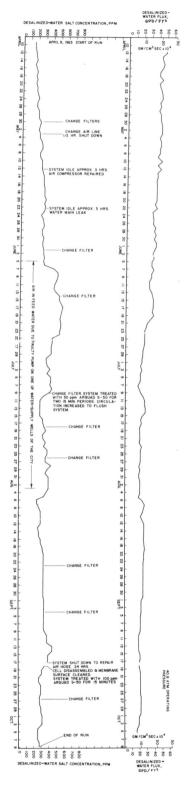

Fig. 3-19 Coalinga brackish feed-water field test.

water service. Furthermore it appears likely that the problem of particulate-matter deposition will have to be dealt with in any long-term field application of reverse-osmosis membranes.

Watson[32] reported as follows on a life test with brackish water in a unit producing desalinized water at the rate of 1000 gallons per day:

> A $5\frac{1}{2}$-month run with feed water containing nominally 5000 ppm total dissolved solids has been completed. The operating pressure was 750 psi. Membrane flux was in excess of 10 gallons per square foot per day throughout and the product water contained less than 500 ppm. The percentage recovery was 30% minimum, a condition in which the solubility of calcium sulfate was exceeded in the waste stream. Some minor amount of calcium sulfate scale was deposited on the membranes during this test. A second test run was conducted in which recovery was 60%.

3.5 Semipermeability of Cellulose Acetate to Various Solute Species

The semipermeability of cellulose acetate to sodium chloride and seawater salts has been stressed earlier in this chapter. However, it is worth while from both a theoretical and a practical viewpoint to consider more generally what species of solutes will pass through cellulose acetate and what species will be rejected.

Sourirajan conducted a large number of experiments to determine the semipermeability of cellulose acetate to various aqueous solutes.[33,34] His data on electrolytes indicate that the ability of cellulose acetate membranes to reject ions decreased with their order in the lyotropic series. For anions: citrate > tartrate = sulfate > acetate > chloride > bromide > nitrate > iodide > thiocyanate (where citrate is most highly rejected and thiocyanate the least). For cations: Mg, Ba, Sr, Ca > Li, Na, K, and Li > Na > K.

Rejection is a direct function of the valence of the ions, as can be seen from Sourirajan's orders of rejection. Loeb verified this in his Coalinga life test (Fig. 3–20). Similar effects of ionic valence were reported by Lonsdale.[27] The rejection order of the halides, as in the previous paragraph, was verified by Keilin[5] with sodium and potassium salts.

Glueckauf[35] explained the rejection orders on the basis of unhydrated radius, as well as valence, of an ion that finds itself in a medium, such as the osmotic skin of the membrane, of lower dielectric constant than the brine from which it came. In accordance with his development, order of rejection increases with increase in valence and decreases with increase in unhydrated radius of the ion.

Sourirajan also did some work with nonelectrolytic solutes. His data indicate that monohydroxy alcohols up to and including propyl alcohol passed rather readily, as did ethylene glycol, but glycerol was rather well rejected. Larger solutes, such as sucrose, dextrose, sorbitol, and pentaerythritol, were also well rejected. He stated[33] that the rejection of a solute at the solution-membrane interface is due to negative adsorption, in accordance with the Gibbs adsorption equation.

Hodges[36] attributed the difference in rejection between cations to a sieve effect. His hypothesis was that the hydrated cation for a well-rejected solute like Ca^{+2} would be larger than hydrated monovalent cations. Blunk[37] stated that if a solute species is larger than glucose,

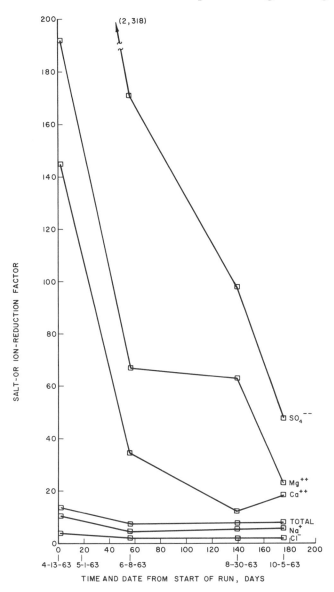

Fig. 3–20   Salt- or ion-reduction factor, Coalinga field test.

3.6 Å radius, it will be at least partially sieved by a cellulose acetate membrane fabricated for seawater desalination by the methods described herein. Thus he found (as did Sourirajan) that sucrose ($r = 4.4$ Å) was well rejected and predicted that other soluble nonelectrolytes of this size or larger would be rejected regardless of their chemical nature. Similarly, it can be expected that large electrolytic species such as tetrapropyl ammonium ion and larger quaternary ammonium cations would be rather strongly rejected. Keilin[5,17] also demonstrated a relationship between solute size and membrane selectivity, using various butanols and butylamines for this purpose.

Blunk's work was concerned largely with establishing criteria for the prediction of the semipermeability of cellulose acetate to small solutes. His technique consisted of testing the semipermeability to a variety of solutes, both electrolytes and nonelectrolytes. His data were examined in the light of Sourirajan's proposal and of the early findings of Reid and Breton that hydrogen-bonding* species such as hydronium, ammonium, and fluoride ions, and boric acid would tend to pass through the membrane.

In order to concentrate on the rejection characteristics of each of a series of similar ions, Blunk used a common counter-ion which tended to pass. His orders of rejection were as follows, progressing from strong to weak rejection:

$$HI > HBr > HCl > HF$$
$$NaClO_4 > NH_4ClO_4 > HClO_4$$
$$NaNO_3 > NH_4NO_3 > HNO_3$$

It will be noted that the order for the halogen acids is opposite to that obtained by Sourirajan and Keilin, who used halogen salts. Furthermore, the fact that perchloric acid and nitric acid are rejected less than perchlorate and nitrate salts is contrary to Glueckauf's findings by which a small cation such as a hydrogen ion should be rejected more than larger ions.

Blunk then confirmed that divalent and trivalent ions in compounds such as H_2SO_4, H_2SiF_6, and $(NH_4)_2CrO_4$ were strongly rejected regardless of hydrogen-bonding tendencies.

With regard to nonelectrolytes, all of these investigators found that small water-soluble solutes tend to pass. Among these are the following:

Hydrogen peroxide
Alcohols through n-butanol
Aldehydes through n-butyraldehyde

* Hydrogen bonding is defined as an electrostatic attraction (bridge) between an element having one or more unshared pairs of electrons and the positive nucleus of a hydrogen atom that has formed a covalent bond with a similar element. The elements in question are usually fluorine, oxygen, or nitrogen, i.e., strongly electronegative elements.

Acids through *n*-butyric acid
Amines through *n*-butylamine
Acetamide
Nitriles through *n*-butyronitrile
Urea

It should be noted that all these compounds contain hydrogen-bonding groups.

The experimental data obtained thus far on small solute species may be correlated qualitatively by the following criteria:

1. Electrolytes other than uni-univalent electrolytes will be strongly rejected regardless of hydrogen-bonding characteristics.

2. When hydrogen bonding cannot occur between the ionic species of a uni-univalent electrolyte, the rejections for a series of electrolytes having a common ion will decrease with increase in the size of the unhydrated counter-ion.

3. When hydrogen bonding can occur between the ionic species of a uni-univalent electrolyte, the rejections for a series of electrolytes having a common ion tends to decrease with increase in strength of the hydrogen bonds between the species. Caution must be exercised in the application of this last criterion. For example, the use of a small ion such as fluoride decreases rejection insofar as it exists in a strongly hydrogen-bonded complex (e.g., FHF^-), but increases rejection if it exists as a free ion, in which case size is decisive (criterion 2). Therefore, when hydrogen bonding is possible between species, it may be hazardous to attempt to predict the order of rejection from hydrogen-bonding considerations alone. As a case in point, HCl is rejected more than HF, indicating that the hydrogen-bonding criterion is indeed predominant, but NH_4F is rejected more than NH_4Cl, indicating that here ion size is more important.

4. Small water-soluble nonelectrolytes will tend to pass.

On the basis of these experimentally based criteria one may postulate the following mechanism for the passage or rejection of aqueous solutes by the membrane: Water is retained in the osmotic-skin part of the membrane in such a way that it still possesses the solubilizing properties attributable to its hydrogen-bonding capacity but has largely lost the solubilizing properties attributable to its high dielectric constant. Therefore, small species whose solubilities in water are due partially (hydrogen-bonding univalent ions) or wholly (nonelectrolytes) to their hydrogen-bonding capacities, tend to pass through the membrane. On the other hand, small species whose water solubilities are due primarily to the high dielectric constant of water tend to be rejected. These species include nonhydrogen-bonding univalent ions, and all ions of valence greater than unity regardless of hydrogen-bonding characteristics.

References

1. Reid, C. E., and E. J. Breton, *J. Appl. Polymer Sci.* **1,** 133 (1959).
2. Yuster, S. T., S. Sourirajan, and K. Bernstein, *Sea Water Demineralization by the Surface Skimming Process,* UCLA Department of Engineering Report 58–26 (1958).
3. Loeb, S., and S. Sourirajan, *Advan. Chem. Ser.* **38,** 117 (1962).
4. Baddour, R. F., W. R. Vieth, and A. S. Douglas, *Expanded Glassy Polymers as Reverse Osmosis Membranes,* Massachusetts Institute of Technology, Dept. of Chem. Engr., Desalination Research Lab. Report 316–1, DSR-9410 (Jan. 7, 1965).
5. Keilin, B., *The Mechanism of Desalination by Reverse Osmosis,* Office of Saline Water, Research and Development Progress Report No. 117, PB 166395 (Aug. 1964).
6. Mahon, H. I., *Hollow Fibers as Membranes for Reverse Osmosis,* Natl. Acad. of Sci., Natl. Res. Council. Publication No. 942, 345–354 (1961).
7. Dobry, A., *Bull. soc. chim. France, 5ᵉ Série,* **III,** 312 (1936).
8. Loeb, S., and S. Manjikian, *Brackish Water Desalination by an Osmotic Membrane,* UCLA Department of Engineering Report 63-22 (1963).
9. Lonsdale, H. K., U. Merten, and R. L. Riley, *J. Appl. Polymer Sci.* **9,** 1341 (1965).
10. Loeb, S., and F. Milstein, *Dechema Monographien* **47,** Verlag Chemie, Weinheim/Bergstrasse, 707 (1962).
11. Loeb, S., *Sea Water Demineralization by Means of a Semipermeable Membrane,* UCLA Department of Engineering Report 62-26 (1962).
12. Loeb, S., *Appropriate Electrolytic Additives in a Casting Solution Used for the Production of High Performance Cellulose Acetate Membranes Used in Reverse Osmosis Desalination,* Ph.D. thesis, UCLA Dept. of Engineering, University Microfilms, Inc., Ann Arbor (1965).
13. Raridon, R. J., and K. A. Kraus, *J. Colloid Sci.* **20,** 1000 (1965).
14. Kesting, R., *J. Appl. Polymer Sci.* **9,** 663 (1965).
15. Loeb, S., *Sea Water Demineralization by Means of a Semipermeable Membrane,* UCLA Department of Engineering Report 61-42 (1961).
16. Loeb, S., *Sea Water Demineralization by Means of a Semipermeable Membrane,* UCLA Department of Engineering Report 63-62 (1963).
17. Keilin, B., *The Mechanism of Desalination by Reverse Osmosis,* Office of Saline Water, Research and Development Progress Report No. 84, PB 181571 (Nov. 1963).
18. Riley, R. L., J. O. Gardner, and U. Merten, *Science* **143,** 801 (1964).
19. Manjikian, S., S. Loeb, and J. W. McCutchan, *Proc. First Intn'l. Desalination Symp.,* Paper SWD/12, Washington, D. C., Oct. 3–9, 1965.
20. Merten, U., *Ind. and Eng. Chem. Fundamentals* **3,** 210 (1964).
21. *Design and Construction of a Desalination Pilot Plant (A Reverse Osmosis Process),* Office of Saline Water, Research and Development Progress Report No. 86, PB 181574 (Jan. 1964).
22. *Sea Water Conversion,* Brochure of Havens Industries, San Diego, California, Spring, 1964.
23. Loeb, S., *Desalination* **1,** 35 (1966).
24. Van Oss, C. J., *L'Ultrafiltration dans le domaine de la chimie biologique,* Ph.D. Dissertation, Univ. of Paris, Faculty of Science, J. H. de Bussy, Amsterdam (1955).
25. Loeb, S., *Sea Water Demineralization by Means of a Semipermeable Membrane,* UCLA Department of Engineering Report 62-41 (1962).

26. Loeb, S., and S. Manjikian, *Brackish Water Desalination by an Osmotic Membrane*, UCLA Department of Engineering Report 63-37 (1963).
27. Lonsdale, H. K., U. Merten, R. L. Riley, K. D. Vos, and J. C. Westmoreland, *Reverse Osmosis for Water Desalination*, Office of Saline Water, Research and Development Progress Report No. 111, PB 181696 (April 15, 1964)
28. Vos, K. D., General Atomic Division of General Dynamics, San Diego, Calif., private communication, 1965.
29. Loeb, S., and S. Manjikian, *Field Tests on Osmotic Desalination Membranes*, UCLA Department of Engineering Report 64-34 (1964).
30. Loeb, S., and F. Milstein, *Design, Development, and Testing of a 500 Gallon Per Day Osmotic Sea Water Desalination Cell*, UCLA Department of Engineering Report 62-52 (1962).
31. Loeb, S., and S. Manjikian, *Ind. Eng. Chem. Process Design Development* **4**, 207 (1965).
32. Watson, E. R., *Engineering Developments in Reverse Osmosis*, 55th National Meeting, American Institute of Chemical Engineers, Houston (Feb. 8, 1965).
33. Sourirajan, S., *Ind. Eng. Chem. Fundamentals* **3**, 206 (1964).
34. Sourirajan, S., *ibid.* **2**, 51 (1963).
35. Glueckauf, E., *On the Mechanism of Osmotic Desalting with Porous Membranes*, *Proc. First Intn'l. Desalination Symp.*, Paper SWD/1, Washington, D. C., Oct. 3–9, 1965.
36. Hodges, R. M., Jr., *Polymer Films as Reverse Osmosis Membranes for Sea Water Desalination*, Ph.D. Thesis, Massachusetts Institute of Technology, Dept. of Chem. Eng., Cambridge, Mass. (July 1964).
37. Blunk, R. W., *A Study of Criteria for the Semipermeability of Cellulose Acetate Membranes to Aqueous Solutions*, UCLA Department of Engineering Report 64-28 (1964).

4. Properties of Cellulose Acetate Membranes

H. K. Lonsdale

It is generally recognized that the economics of reverse osmosis for desalination are largely determined by the properties of the membrane material, with high water flux and good selectivity both being important considerations. The fact that cellulose acetate membranes have a high water permeability has been known for some time.[1,2,3] In the course of surveying a number of polymers for use as reverse-osmosis membranes, Reid and several of his students at the University of Florida demonstrated that cellulose acetate membranes also exclude a number of inorganic salts quite effectively.[4,5] From the standpoint of high water permeability combined with good salt exclusion, cellulose acetate membranes were clearly the best material included in the early research of Reid and co-workers, and, in spite of several extensive searches for improved membrane materials in the intervening period, no suitable alternate has been found. It remained for Loeb and Sourirajan,[6] working at the University of California in Los Angeles, to prepare effectively very thin cellulose acetate membranes and thereby grossly increase the attainable water flux and simultaneously stimulate a widespread interest in reverse osmosis as an economic method for the desalination of sea and brackish waters. Thus, most of the reverse-osmosis studies carried out in the past few years in a number of laboratories have been made with cellulose acetate membranes. In Chapter 3, methods for preparing high-water-flux membranes were discussed and typical performance figures presented. In the present chapter, much of the published data on direct and reverse osmosis is reviewed and interpreted in terms of the equilibrium and transport properties of cellulose acetate membranes.

We begin with a brief survey of some of the relevant chemical and physical properties of cellulose acetate. The bulk of the chapter is then divided into a discussion of the properties of two kinds of cellulose acetate membranes: The first, which we shall call *normal* membranes, are available commercially or may be cast from solution in a suitable solvent. They are characterized by optical clarity and a density close to the literature value for the pure material. The second type to be discussed is that which has been modified in some way to give high water-flow rates. We shall refer to membranes of this general type as *modified* membranes. The only membrane of this type which has been studied in detail is that first developed by Loeb and Sourirajan[6] for specific use in reverse osmosis. The interpretation of reverse-osmosis studies carried out with membranes of this type from the point of view of transport properties has been somewhat difficult because of the complex physical structure of the membrane. However, structural studies have been quite illuminating, and it appears that the modified membranes can be treated as having the permeability properties of the normal membranes but possessing a grossly reduced effective thickness.

In addition to the normal and modified membranes, it appears that cellulose acetate membranes which are essentially of the "finely porous" type, as described in Chapter 2, can be prepared. Examples are to be found in the unannealed Loeb-Sourirajan membrane as well as in the relatively porous cellulose acetate membranes distributed by the Carl Schleicher & Schuell Company. The transport properties of these membranes can be reproducibly altered by heat treatment. The results of some of the studies carried out with these membranes will be discussed briefly.

Naturally, in a field as new and dynamic as this one, additional data are being produced at a significant rate, and some interpretations are subject to change. However, many of the properties of interest, particularly the equilibrium properties of solubility of water and salts in cellulose acetate and the nonequilibrium transport rates of these components in membranes, are now rather well established. In addition, one successful attempt to prepare very thin membranes, i.e., the Loeb and Sourirajan modified membrane, has been rather thoroughly studied, and a number of its features are understood. Among the several subjects not yet well in hand are the details of the formation of the modified membranes, their long-term characteristics in reverse-osmosis use, and the mechanism of salt flow in both normal and modified membranes. The current status of these and other problem areas is summarized in this chapter.

One additional note is in order here: References to temperature have been omitted from most of the discussion of the equilibrium and transport properties, except in the few cases where it was the parameter of interest. Unfortunately a good deal of the published data is reported without temperature assignment, and we have therefore uniformly omitted reference to temperature except as noted. It is assumed that most of the data were taken at approximately 25°C.

4.1 Properties of Cellulose Acetate

Cellulose acetate resins as prepared by the chemical industry are derived from wood pulp or cotton linters. The chemical processing is described elsewhere;[7] briefly, it consists of complete acetylation of the cellulose to the triacetate with acetic anhydride, acetic acid, and sulfuric acid, followed by the partial hydrolysis to a lower degree of substitution. The degree of polymerization of the commercially available products is typically in the range 100 to 300, and the molecular weight range is approximately 25,000 to 80,000. Molecular-weight determination from intrinsic viscosity measurements has been discussed by Moore and Tidswell[8] and more recently by Genung.[9]

All cellulose acetates contain some residual carboxyl groups, the importance of which apparently varies according to the application of the resin. Malm, Tanghe, and Smith[10] have observed that the viscosity of cellulose acetate solutions is increased if the resin has been washed in salt solutions. The effect is specific to the salts of divalent cations, it is greater in cellulose acetate derived from wood pulp than in that derived from cotton linters, and it is accentuated by high pH. Malm and coworkers have found a good correlation between this "salt effect" and the concentration of residual carboxyl groups on the cellulose acetate. The postulate is made that either an intermolecular crosslink is produced through the divalent cation or a salt of the acid is formed which increases the viscosity. Whatever the important species, it is not completely destroyed when water is added to an acetone solution of cellulose acetate. One of the cellulose acetates marketed by Eastman Chemical Products, E-398-3, a commonly used material for reverse-osmosis membranes, contains only 0.009 wt-% carboxyl groups,[11] much less than one carboxyl group per polymer molecule. Important effects on membrane properties are perhaps not to be expected from a substituent at this concentration, and in fact no direct correlation has been demonstrated. However, significant differences have been noted between the performance of modified membranes prepared from cellulose acetate resins from different producers; such differences may be attributable to the source of the cellulose in general and specifically to such variables as the concentration of carboxyl groups and the use of divalent cations in the manufacturing process.

Eastman markets cellulose acetate powders covering the range of composition from 37.3% to 43.2% acetyl. The diacetate, 2.5-acetate, and triacetate have the respective compositions 35.0, 40.2, and 44.8% acetyl, and the materials with the best film-forming properties are in the general range of the 2.5-acetate. While Eastman, for example, markets cellulose acetate powders with a precisely defined average degree of substitution, the range of the degree of substitution in a given sample is not as well known. In addition, the distribution of acetyl groups along a given cellulose backbone is not well defined. In view of the dependence of a number of the properties, particularly the transport properties, of cellulose acetate on the average degree of substitution, it is possible that the distribution of acetyl groups could result in differences between otherwise identical materials.

Cellulose acetates are dispersed by a number of common solvents, depending on the degree of substitution. Some solubility data are presented in Table 4–1. Cellulose acetates are also soluble in a variety of

Table 4–1   Solvents for Cellulose Acetate

Solvent	Approximate cellulose acetate solubility range (% acetyl)
Acetone	38–42
Dioxane	<34–42
Pyridine	<34–42
Dimethyl formamide	<34–42
Tetrachloroethane	40–43

concentrated aqueous solutions of perchlorate salts.[12,13] Not all perchlorates are of equal solvating power; magnesium and beryllium perchlorates are among the best, while the sodium and potassium salts are ineffective.

It has been noted that cellulose acetate resins are not completely dispersed by organic solvents and that incompletely dissolved, highly swollen fragments frequently remain in the solution.[14] These particles are believed to be the result of an incomplete dispersion of the cellulose during the manufacture of the acetate, which leaves small aggregates inaccessible to acetylation. These aggregates are considered to be regions highly crosslinked with hydrogen bonds. The turbidity of solutions of cellulose acetate in organic solvents has been attributed to the presence of fiber fragments or unswollen particles that have a higher density and a higher refractive index than the true solution. However, even those highly swollen particles which are invisible under microscopic examination because of a refractive index equal to that of the solution can apparently clog fritted-glass filters. The incompletely dissolved fragments are believed to have a significant influence on the solubility of cellulosics in general; the fact that cellulose acetate solutions spread incompletely on water and do not form continuous monomolecular films has been attributed to their presence.[15] Hydrogen-bond-breaking agents such as guanidine and urea markedly improve the ability of cellulose acetate to form complete films when cast on a water surface. Variables in the manufacturing process can produce wide variations in the solubility and viscosity of cellulose acetates, presumably because of the presence of these fragments, with the material derived from wood pulp considerably inferior to the cotton-linter material as a film former. The implications of these several observations to the preparation and performance of cellulose acetate reverse-osmosis membranes are not well defined. The rheology and colloidal properties of the solutions from which membranes are cast have not been explored to any appreciable extent. The variations exhibited in water-transport rate and salt exclusion of modified cellulose acetate membranes in reverse-osmosis applications and the imperfections often found in these membranes indicate that this research area requires further investigation.

A good deal of speculation has been offered concerning the role of polymer crystallinity in determining the transport properties of membranes, including cellulose acetate membranes. X-ray diffraction studies have shown that cellulose triacetate is moderately crystalline but the 2.5-acetate, with which most of the reverse-osmosis membranes are prepared, is amorphous; in fact, cellulose acetate has been described as unique among the cellulosics for its low degree of crystallinity.[4,16,17] X-ray measurements on this material give only a broad double peak, representative of weak, uncoordinated interferences. The state of aggregation is likely to be dependent on the method of preparation, and the presence of localized highly ordered regions in some membranes cannot be ruled out. However, they have not been detected, and the preparation of normal membranes via a wide range of preparative procedures that would be expected to affect crystallinity does not appear to alter the transport properties extensively.

Typical of the behavior of amorphous polymers, cellulose acetate undergoes second-order or "glass" transitions, observed as abrupt changes in the temperature derivative of any extensive thermodynamic property, such as specific volume or heat content. A second-order transition is considered to be a manifestation of a new rotational degree of freedom in the polymer, consisting of the articulated movement of polymer segments in which as many as forty carbon atoms participate.[18] There have been several studies of second-order transitions in cellulose acetate, and a number of transition temperatures have been reported. Perhaps the most extensive of these studies is that of Daane and

Barker.[19] Using a dilatometric technique, they have found minor transitions in unplasticized 2.5-acetyl cellulose acetate at 15°, 50°, 90°, and 114°C. Apparently no major "glass-to-rubber" transition, which occurs in a number of amorphous high polymers, takes place in cellulose acetate below 114°C. It is clear from the results of a number of investigations that the glass-transition temperatures are a strong function of the degree of substitution of the cellulose acetate. It has been observed in other polymer systems that these transition temperatures vary with molecular weight, external pressure or tension on the sample, plasticizer content, the speed of the test with which it is observed, and other variables.[18,20,21] Furthermore, discrepancies as large as 20°C have been observed in transition temperatures on similar polymer samples.[18] No observations of second-order transitions in modified cellulose acetate membranes have been reported. In view of the several variables cited and the fact that water serves as an excellent plasticizer for cellulose acetate and no doubt alters the transition behavior, it is difficult to draw any conclusions about the occurrence or importance of such transitions in modified membranes.

A number of other properties of cellulose acetate resins are presented in an Eastman publication.[7]

4.2 Normal Cellulose Acetate Membranes

Normal cellulose acetate membranes have been examined in some detail with respect to their permeability to water and various salts. The membranes used have limited applicability to practical water desalination because they were too thick to yield interesting water-throughput rates. Very thin membranes can of course be prepared, and their preparation is discussed in the next section. However, using membranes strong enough to be convenient to work with, i.e., several microns thick, several investigators have measured some of the equilibrium and transport properties of cellulose acetate. These properties are expected to be directly applicable to the modified membranes discussed in Section 4.3 or to other very thin membranes. The applicability is not a foregone conclusion, however, in view of the expected dependence of transport properties on the details of the state of aggregation. In the few instances in which a meaningful comparison can be made, the results obtained on normal membranes apply to modified membranes rather well when the effective thickness of the two types of membrane is taken in account.

Transport Properties — Direct-Osmosis and
Reverse-Osmosis Experiments

The treatment of the transport through solution-diffusion membranes has been given in a number of places, including papers by Laidler and

Shuler[22] and by Lonsdale, Merten, and Riley,[23] and in Chapter 2 of this book. Working relationships for the flow of both solvent (water) and solute (salt) can be obtained either from the tenets of irreversible thermodynamics, as is done in Chapter 2, or by assuming that Fick's law is obeyed and that the two flows are uncoupled. The two approaches arrive at the same result provided the proper form is selected for the phenomenological coefficients. These treatments will not be reproduced here in detail, but the important assumptions will be restated for purposes of completeness and continuity:

1. It is assumed that the flux is a monotonic function of the gradient in the chemical potential of each species across the membrane and that the flows of the several species are uncoupled.

2. It is assumed that the activity of the solvent is proportional to its concentration at all points, i.e., that Henry's law is obeyed.*

3. The chemical potential of each species is assumed to be continuous across the membrane-solution interfaces.

4. The permeabilities and the effective membrane thickness are assumed independent of pressure.†

Under these conditions, the water flux can be shown to be given by a relation of the type

$$F_1 = -\frac{D_{1m}c_{1m}v_1}{RT}\frac{(\Delta p - \Delta \pi)}{\lambda}, \tag{4.1}$$

where D_{1m} and c_{1m} are the diffusion coefficient of water and the water concentration (in g/cm^3) in the membrane, respectively; Δp and $\Delta \pi$ are the differences in applied pressure and osmotic pressure across the membrane; λ is the effective membrane thickness across which Δp and $\Delta \pi$ are exerted; v_1 is the partial molar volume of water in the membrane; and R and T are the gas constant and absolute temperature, respectively.

The salt flux is similarly described by the equation

$$F_2 = -D_{2m}K\frac{\Delta c_2}{\lambda}, \tag{4.2}$$

* The assumption that the activity of water in the membrane is proportional to its concentration is clearly inexact, as an examination of the sorption isotherm shows. However, the deviation from Henry's law is not great, and the added complexity required to improve the mathematical statements is probably not justified at this time.

† There is an exception to this statement as well. As Michaels, Bixler, and Hodges have pointed out,[24] the concentration of dissolved water in the membrane is not strictly independent of pressure, because an applied hydrostatic pressure of 100 atm increases the vapor pressure of water (i.e., the relative humidity) by approximately 5% and Eq. 4.1 should be modified accordingly. However, the presence of dissolved salts lowers the relative humidity by an approximately equal amount in the case of seawater, for example, and rather than modify Eq. 4.1 for these contributions we shall use it as it stands, recognizing that it is not strictly correct.

where D_{2m} and K are the diffusion coefficient and distribution coefficient, respectively, for the solute species, and Δc_2 is the difference in concentration of solute in the two solutions separated by the membrane. The quantity Kc_2 is then just c_{2m}, the salt concentration within the membrane. In deriving Eq. 4.2 it is necessary to make the assumption that K is essentially independent of c_2.

Equations 4.1 and 4.2 constitute working relations for the transport of water and solute through a solution-diffusion membrane. From a number of measurements carried out with normal cellulose acetate membranes, these membranes appear to be basically of the solution-diffusion type, although salt flow in many experiments is not adequately described by Eq. 4.2.

The quantities $D_{1m}c_{1m}$ and $D_{2m}K$ are typical permeation coefficients, and the flow of water and the degree of salt exclusion expected for given conditions of salt concentration and pressure can be derived from these coefficients. The salt rejection in reverse osmosis is given by

$$S \equiv \frac{c_2' - c_2''}{c_2'} = 1 - \frac{c_2''}{c_2'},$$

where the superscripts prime and double prime refer to the solutions on the high-pressure and low-pressure side of the membrane, respectively. Now, in reverse osmosis,

$$c_2'' = \frac{F_2}{F_1} c_1'',$$

where c_1'' is the concentration of water (g/cm^3) in the solution on the low-pressure side of the membrane. Substituting from Eqs. 4.1 and 4.2,

$$S = 1 - \frac{F_2 c_1''}{F_1 c_2'} = \left[1 + \frac{D_{2m}KRTc_1''}{D_{1m}c_{1m}v_1(\Delta p - \Delta \pi)} \right]^{-1}. \tag{4.3}$$

It is interesting to note that the salt rejection is independent of the thickness of the membrane. Another significant corollary to Eq. 4.3 is that for membranes that are not completely salt-excluding, salt rejection will occur at pressures below the osmotic pressure. Thus, in a reverse-osmosis application, even if p is less than π on the high-pressure side of the membrane, Δp may exceed $\Delta \pi$ because of finite salt flow.

Equation 4.3 predicts that salt rejection improves with increasing pressure; this fact is a consequence of the nature of the driving forces in reverse osmosis, as pointed out by Clark[25] as well as in Chapter 2. Thus, the rate of transport of water and salt is proportional to the chemical potential gradient of each species across the membrane. For both species this gradient is governed by the differences in both pressure and concentration in the two solutions. For water the relative magnitude of these two contributions is expressed by Δp and $\Delta \pi$, and in most practical applications Δp is made to exceed $\Delta \pi$ substantially. In the case of good salt exclusion, however, the ratio of salt concentrations is very large, and the contribution of the concentration term to the chemical potential gradient for salt dominates the pressure term completely. Thus, increasing the pressure increases the water flow while leaving the salt flow nearly unchanged.

In Eqs. 4.1 to 4.3 we have expressions for the flow of water and salt and for the salt rejection in terms of experimental variables and the permeability coefficients for the two components. Obviously, these expressions will be obeyed only if the assumptions made in deriving them are correct. There are now sufficient data in the literature to check most of these assumptions.

The earliest transport property data on cellulose acetate membranes were obtained by Reid and Breton.[4,5] They carried out reverse-osmosis experiments in a simple high-pressure cell in which brine circulation in the high-pressure chamber was provided for by means of a convective loop. The flow of water through a cellulose acetate membrane was demonstrated to be approximately inversely proportional to its thickness, in accordance with Fick's law. The results are given in Table 4–2

Table 4–2 Effect of Membrane Thickness on Flow Rate and Salt Rejection
(Plasticized cellulose acetate membranes)
Reverse-osmosis data of Reid and Breton.[5]

Thickness (μ)	Water flux (μl/cm^2-hr)	Salt rejection (%)
22	19.1	99
15	33.4	95
11	53.1	98
5.6	117.8	96
3.7	116.5	96

and plotted in Fig. 4–1. The measurements were carried out at 40.8 atm applied pressure with a brine of 0.1 M NaCl. The results are not completely applicable to cellulose acetate because the membrane contained about 20% by weight of a mixture of placticizers. By extrapolating the results it appears that the flow vanishes at a finite membrane thickness; this may be a manifestation of a boundary-layer limitation at the highest flow rates (see Chapter 5), evidence for which is seen in the fact that the salt rejection decreases as the membrane thickness decreases or as the water flow increases. Substituting the water-flow data into Eq. 4.1, one can calculate a water permeability coefficient, $P_1 \equiv D_{1m}c_{1m}$, of 7.8×10^{-7} g/cm-sec. With this value and Eq. 4.3, one can calculate a salt permeability coefficient, $P_2 \equiv D_{2m}K$, of 2 to 8×10^{-10} cm^2/sec. These coefficients are to be compared with those observed in unplasticized cellulose acetate membranes which will be discussed later.

Breton gives data on water flow and salt rejection as a function of the

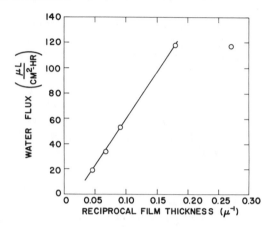

Fig. 4–1   Water flux versus reciprocal film thickness. Feed = 0.1 M NaCl, pressure = 40.8 atm. Data of Reid and Breton[5] on plasticized membranes.

applied pressure (Fig. 4–2); the salt rejection is seen to improve with increasing applied pressure, in agreement with Eq. 4.3. Figure 4–2 also shows the predicted curve from Eq. 4.3 using an arbitrarily chosen ratio P_1/P_2 of 600 g/cm³. Over-all, the fit is fairly good.

Reid and Breton[5] studied water flow and salt rejection at a constant applied pressure as a function of the acetyl content of unplasticized cellulose acetate membranes (Fig. 4–3). From the results obtained one can calculate both the water and salt permeability as a function of acetyl content; a summary of the permeabilities is contained in Table 4–3. It is

Table 4–3   Water and Salt Permeability Coefficients in Normal Cellulose Acetate
Membranes as a Function of Acetyl Content
(40.8 atm applied pressure, 0.1 M NaCl[26])
Reverse-osmosis data of Reid and Breton.[5]

Acetyl content (wt-%)	Water flux per unit applied pressure (μl/hr-cm²-atm)	NaCl rejection (%)	Water permeability P_1 (g/cm-sec)	Salt permeability P_2 (cm²/sec)
35.5	2.2	85.2	5.0×10^{-7}	4.5×10^{-9}
37.2	1.7	90.1	3.9×10^{-7}	2.2×10^{-9}
38.6	1.3	94.1	3.0×10^{-7}	9.5×10^{-10}
39.4	1.2	97.1	2.7×10^{-7}	4.2×10^{-10}
40.4	0.8	99.2	1.8×10^{-7}	7.6×10^{-11}
42.6	0.6, 0.3*	—	$1.4, 0.7 \times 10^{-7}$	—

* Duplicate values reported.

clear that both permeability coefficients decrease as the degree of acetylation increases and that the salt permeability is much more sensitive to changes in acetylation than is the water permeability. This of course

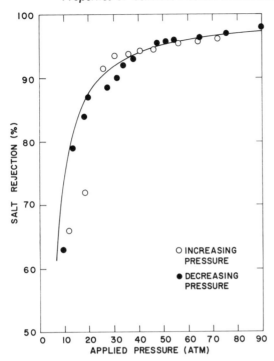

Fig. 4-2   Effect of pressure on semipermeability to sodium chloride. 40%-acetyl cellulose acetate membrane. 0.1 M NaCl feed. (Data of Breton.[4])

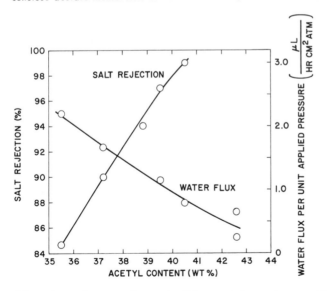

Fig. 4-3   Effect of acetyl content of normal cellulose acetate membranes of the water flux and the semipermeability to sodium chloride. Applied pressure = 40.8 atm, feed = 0.1 M NaCl. (Data of Reid and Breton.[5])

is simply a restatement of the fact that salt rejection increases and water flux decreases as the degree of acetylation is increased.

Reid and Breton also examined the semipermeability of commercial cellulose acetate membranes to salts other than sodium chloride.[5] The results are reproduced in Table 4-4 in which we have also calculated the

Table 4-4   Semipermeability of Normal Cellulose Acetate Membranes (Du Pont CA-48) to Aqueous Solutions of Various Solutes
Reverse-osmosis data of Reid and Breton.[5]

Solute	Concentration	Applied pressure (atm)	Solute rejection (%)	P_1/P_2 (g/cm³)
NaCl	0.11 M	58	96	610
MgCl₂	0.031 M	49	99	2900
CaCl₂	0.0054 M	54	98	1200
Na₂SO₄	0.018 M	34	97	1300
NaBr	0.0012 M	58	93	310
NaF	0.0011 M	57	86	150
H₃BO₃	0.04 M	54	46	21
NH₃*	0.17 M	54	30	11
Ocean water	4%	54	96	1200

* This membrane was apparently chemically attacked during the test; the rejection of NaCl at 56 atm was only 90% after the NH₃ test.

ratio P_1/P_2 using Eq. 4.3 and estimating osmotic pressures, when necessary, from literature values of the osmotic coefficients of the various species. The cellulose acetate membranes used in these tests were Du Pont products, identified as CA-48; the degree of acetylation of this material has not been divulged by the manufacturer. At least two trends are apparent from these results: The semipermeability to divalent ions is considerably greater than that for monovalent ions; and species that are at least partially undissociated in aqueous solution, i.e., H₃BO₃ and NH₃, are poorly rejected. It appears that the latter is at least not entirely the result of chemical attack on the membrane.

Some additional data on the performance of commercial cellulose acetate membranes at high pressures were given by Reid and Spencer[27] and are listed in Table 4-5 along with values of P_1 and P_2 calculated from Eqs. 4.1 and 4.3. The feed brine was 0.1 M NaCl and the membrane thickness 22 μ. The membranes were designated Du Pont CA-43; the acetyl content was not specified, and the membranes were presumably plasticized. Over the pressure range studied, the permeability to water and salt was approximately constant, indicating that these permeability parameters are not strongly pressure-dependent and that the flow of both constituents through these membranes is primarily diffusive and

Table 4–5   Water-Flux and Salt-Rejection Characteristics of Normal Cellulose Acetate
Membranes (Du Pont CA-43) at High Pressures
Reverse-osmosis data of Reid and Spencer.[27]

Applied pressure (atm)	Water flux (μl/cm²-hr)	NaCl rejection (%)	Water permeability P_1 (g/cm-sec)	Salt permeability P_2 (cm²/sec)
270	17	99	5.4×10^{-8}	1.1×10^{-10}
205	14	99	5.8×10^{-8}	0.9×10^{-10}
135	7	97	4.5×10^{-8}	1.3×10^{-10}

not viscous in nature. In these experiments an induction period of 2 to 3
days was evident in the permeabilities, with salt rejection increasing
and water flux decreasing during this period. The performance characteristics of these membranes were probably considerably affected by the
presence of plasticizer.

The transport properties of unplasticized normal cellulose acetate
membranes have also been measured by Lonsdale, Merten, and Riley[23]
in direct-osmosis experiments. Laboratory-cast membranes of cellulose
acetates of several degrees of acetylation were used to separate cham-
bers of pure water and 5 wt-% NaCl solution. From the rate of transport
of water and salt, the permeabilities were calculated according to Eqs.
4.1 and 4.2. The results, taken at approximately 25°C, are presented in
Table 4–6. These authors refer to their permeability results as "apparent

Table 4–6   Permeabilities of Normal Cellulose Acetate Membranes
(Direct osmosis with 5.0 wt-% NaCl)
Data of Lonsdale, Merten, and Riley.[23]

Acetyl content (wt-%)	Membrane thickness (μ)	Water flux (g/cm²-sec)	Apparent permeability to H_2O, P_1 (g/cm²-sec)[1]	NaCl flux (g/cm²-sec)	Apparent permeability to NaCl, P_2 (cm²/sec)
33.6	28	1.9×10^{-5}	1.8×10^{-6}	8.0×10^{-7}	4.5×10^{-8}
	23	1.9×10^{-5}	1.4×10^{-6}	7.9×10^{-7}	3.6×10^{-8}
37.6	19	9.0×10^{-6}	5.7×10^{-7}	4.4×10^{-8}	1.7×10^{-9}
	19	9.1×10^{-6}	5.7×10^{-7}	3.1×10^{-8}	1.2×10^{-9}
39.5	20	3.3×10^{-6}	2.2×10^{-7}	4.4×10^{-8}	1.7×10^{-9}
	13	6.3×10^{-6}	2.8×10^{-7}	1.7×10^{-8}	4.5×10^{-10}
	15	5.4×10^{-6}	2.8×10^{-7}	7.4×10^{-8}	2.3×10^{-9}
39.8	28	2.7×10^{-6}	2.6×10^{-7}	5.3×10^{-9}	3.0×10^{-10}
	29	2.5×10^{-6}	2.5×10^{-7}	1.2×10^{-8}	6.7×10^{-10}
	51	1.1×10^{-6}	2.0×10^{-7}	1.8×10^{-8}	1.8×10^{-9}
	28	3.4×10^{-6}	3.2×10^{-7}	4.6×10^{-9}	2.6×10^{-10}
43.2	14	3.2×10^{-6}	1.5×10^{-7}	7.9×10^{-9}	2.2×10^{-10}

permeabilities" because of the possibility that some transport may have occurred through imperfections in the membrane. This reservation also applies to much of the permeability data reported in this chapter, and it is particularly relevant to the salt-permeability results. Because of the high intrinsic semipermeability of cellulose acetate membranes, the salt flow through imperfections can be a substantial contribution to the total salt flow, even though the excess water flow is trivial relative to the diffusive flow through the membrane. It is clear from Table 4–6 that both water and salt permeabilities decrease as the acetyl content of the membrane increases, in agreement with the work of Reid and Breton reported in Table 4–3. The water-permeability results in both tables are summarized in Fig. 4–4, and the salt-permeability data in Fig. 4–5. The results obtained by Reid and co-workers with commercial membranes have been omitted from this comparison because of uncertainties concerning plasticizer effects. The agreement in the water-permeability results is quite good and, in general, the scatter is small. This agreement between the results obtained in reverse-osmosis experiments and in direct-osmosis experiments is an indication that Eq. 4.1 is a good phenomenological description and that the driving forces are correctly stated.

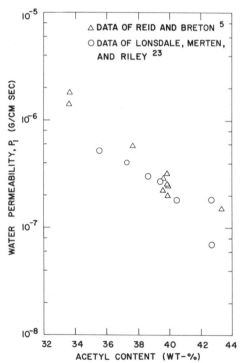

Fig. 4–4   Water permeability as a function of acetyl content of normal cellulose acetate membranes.

The salt-permeability results from these two studies also agree fairly well although the scatter is somewhat worse. It is again tempting to conclude, since these two sets of results were obtained in direct- and in reverse-osmosis experiments, that the agreement supports the developments leading to Eqs. 4.2 and 4.3. However, some salt flow may well occur through leakage paths in both types of experiment, and the agreement may be to some extent fortuitous. For example, microscopic pores could exist in these membranes, which would allow the same amount of salt flow via diffusion in an experiment with no applied pressure as they do via diffusion or viscous flow in a reverse-osmosis experiment. To complicate the matter further, the size and shape of these pores might well be a function of pressure. If a portion of the salt flow is viscous in nature, one would expect it to increase with increasing pressure. The data on the salt flow as a function of pressure in normal membranes are quite limited. However, from results such as those presented in Fig. 4–2, one can calculate the ratio of water to salt permeability, P_1/P_2, and without knowing the water permeability *per se* one can rest for a pressure dependence of the salt flow. In Table 4–7 the results of such a calculation, based on the data of Reid and Breton,[5] are presented. Although there

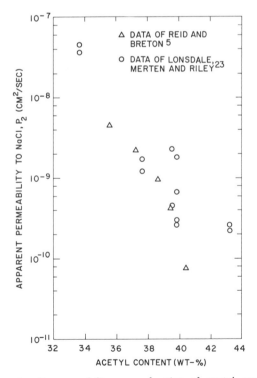

Fig. 4–5 Apparent salt permeability as a function of acetyl content of normal cellulose acetate membranes.

Table 4–7   Ratio of Water to Salt Permeability in Normal-
Cellulose Acetate Membranes versus Pressure
(40%-acetyl cellulose acetate; 0.1 M NaCl)
Reverse-osmosis data of Reid and Breton.[5]

Applied pressure (atm)	Salt rejection (%)	P_1/P_2 (g/cm³)
5.5	59	750
12	88	1350
23	90	650
35	93	590
68	93	310
68	94	330
102	97	450

is some scatter, the permeability ratio clearly decreases with increasing applied pressure, indicating that the salt flow increases with pressure. This conclusion is based on the assumption that the water permeability is not a decreasing function of pressure.

The dependence of water permeability on pressure has not been thoroughly studied, and the limited investigations in this area are not in good agreement. For example, data indicating that water permeability in normal membranes is not a function of pressure are available in the work of Vos and Hatcher.[28] In a reverse-osmosis test they found a water permeability for a 39.8%-acetyl membrane of 2.1×10^{-7} g/cm-sec at applied pressures of 34, 68, and 102 atm with 0.8% NaCl brine. This value remained invariant with pressure and with time over an eighteen-day period. It is in good agreement with the results of direct-osmosis experiments carried out at 1 atm (Table 4–6). The results obtained by Reid and Spencer[27] on Du Pont films at high pressures also indicate that water permeability is pressure-independent, although the lack of information on the history of these specimens leaves the data somewhat less useful.

On the other hand, Reid and Kuppers[29] report that the water permeability is a decreasing function of pressure particularly during initial pressurization. In one experiment the permeability dropped from $> 8 \times 10^{-7}$ to about 2×10^{-7} g/cm-sec as pressure was increased from about 6 to 68 atm. The permeability then remained constant as pressure was reduced. The steady-state value agrees well with the data in Table 4–6. The membrane used in this experiment was cast from an acetone solution of 40%-acetyl cellulose acetate. In other tests, even those membranes that had been initially subjected to high pressures showed subsequent pressure-dependent permeability, although the effect was not great (see Table 4–9).

Additional data on the permeability of normal cellulose acetate membranes are available in the work of Birkhimer and Harriott,[30] who measured water-flux and salt rejection in a reverse-osmosis apparatus and analyzed the water-flux data essentially in accordance with Eq. 4.1, except that they assumed parallel flows of pure water and undiluted brine through the membrane. They report a possible dependence of water permeability on the surface on which the membranes were cast. The results, expressed in the units used here, were $P_1 = 1.4$, 2.3, and 3.3×10^{-7} g/cm-sec, respectively, for membranes cast on a mercury surface, cast on polished stainless steel, and for a commercial, plasticized membrane. All membranes were prepared from 39.7%-acetyl material. Considering that these results were moderately scattered, the agreement with the data of Reid and Breton[5] and of Lonsdale, Merten, and Riley[23] is acceptable.

The effect of several membrane preparative variables on the permeability of normal membranes has also been studied.[23] Some of the variables introduced were a postcast annealing of the membranes, the nature of the casting solvent, and the addition of water to the casting solution. The results of these experiments are summarized in Table 4-8. A comparison of these results with those of Table 4-6 indicates that the data are usually consistent to within a factor of two. The scatter is quite large, however, and small effects of annealing treatment or of solvent on the permeabilities cannot be discounted.

Based on these several studies, it is concluded that unplasticized, acetone-cast membranes containing about 40% acetyl have a water permeability at room temperature of $2.6 \pm 1.0 \times 10^{-7}$ g/cm-sec. A small dependence on pressure is possible although not well established, and it is clear that variables in membrane preparation can be important. More definitive studies along these lines are warranted.

The temperature dependence of water permeability has been established as a result of the reverse-osmosis experiments of Reid and Kuppers,[29] carried out with acetone-cast membranes; their results are summarized in Table 4-9. The water-permeability values decrease somewhat with increasing pressure, but the activation energy is insensitive to pressure, and the mean value is about 5 kcal/mole. It should be pointed out that this is the activation energy for permeation and not for diffusion. Since the enthalpy of solution of water in cellulose acetate is negative, the activation energy for diffusion is actually greater than 5 kcal/mole. The enthalpy of solution has been reported to be -1.3 kcal/mole,[31] making the activation energy for diffusion slightly greater than 6 kcal/mole. This is a reasonable value. Barrer[1] has compiled values of the activation energy for the permeation of water in several types of membrane, although cellulose acetate is not included in the tabulation. His values range from 3 to 8 kcal/mole with the value

Table 4-8   Effect of Some Variables on Water and Salt Permeability of Normal Cellulose Acetate Membranes
(Direct osmosis with 5.0 wt-% NaCl)
Data of Lonsdale, Merten, and Riley.[23]

Acetyl content (wt-%)	Solvent/treatment	Membrane thickness (μ)	Water flux (g/cm²-sec)	Permeability to H₂O, P_1 (g/cm-sec)	Salt flux (g/cm²-sec)	Apparent permeability to NaCl, P_2 (cm²/sec)
39.5	Acetone/membrane heated to 80°C	22	2.2×10^{-6}	1.7×10^{-7}	2.4×10^{-8}	1.1×10^{-9}
39.8	Acetone/membrane heated to 80°C	18	2.7×10^{-6}	1.6×10^{-7}	1.4×10^{-9}	4.8×10^{-11}
	Acetone/membrane heated to 80°C	32	1.2×10^{-6}	1.3×10^{-7}	1.1×10^{-8}	7.1×10^{-10}
	Acetone/membrane heated to 100°C	18	4.0×10^{-6}	2.4×10^{-7}	3.3×10^{-8}	1.2×10^{-9}
	Acetone/membrane heated to 100°C	35	7.8×10^{-7}	9.1×10^{-8}	1.3×10^{-9}	9.0×10^{-11}
	Acetone/membrane heated to 160°C	26	2.5×10^{-6}	2.2×10^{-7}	1.2×10^{-8}	6.0×10^{-10}
33.6	Pyridine	42	1.3×10^{-5}	1.8×10^{-6}	5.2×10^{-7}	4.4×10^{-8}
	Pyridine-H₂O (6.6:1)	40	7.5×10^{-6}	1.0×10^{-6}	2.9×10^{-7}	2.3×10^{-8}
39.8	P-dioxane	35	6.2×10^{-6}	7.2×10^{-7}	4.3×10^{-8}	3.0×10^{-9}
	P-dioxane-H₂O (6.6:1)	35	1.4×10^{-6}	1.7×10^{-7}	9.7×10^{-10}	6.8×10^{-11}
	Pyridine	31	2.6×10^{-6}	2.7×10^{-7}	3.9×10^{-9}	2.4×10^{-10}
	Pyridine-H₂O (6.6:1)	32	2.3×10^{-6}	2.5×10^{-7}	3.8×10^{-9}	2.4×10^{-10}
43.2	Pyridine	32	2.9×10^{-6}	3.1×10^{-7}	6.1×10^{-9}	3.9×10^{-10}

Table 4–9   Activation Energy for the Permeation of Water Through Cellulose Acetate Membranes (40% Acetyl)
Reverse-osmosis data of Reid and Kuppers.[29]

Membrane thickness (μ)	Applied pressure (atm)	Water permeability, P_1 (g/cm-sec), at 30°C	Activation energy (kcal/mole)
8.4	17	1.5×10^{-7}	5.2
	34	1.0×10^{-7}	5.0
	51	0.88×10^{-7}	5.0
	58	0.95×10^{-7}	5.0
17	17	1.3×10^{-7}	7.7
	34	1.2×10^{-7}	4.8
	51	1.0×10^{-7}	4.9
	68	0.92×10^{-7}	6.1

reported for cellulose nitrate 4.7 kcal/mole, compared with Reid and Kuppers' value of about 5 kcal/mole.

There have been a number of other measurements of the permeability of cellulose acetate membranes to water, but all of them were carried out with water in the vapor phase.[32–38] Reviewing these data indicates that there is a rather wide spread in results from different laboratories on apparently similar materials and, moreover, that all of these results are lower by a factor of two to five than those here reported for liquid-water permeation. In the water-vapor permeation experiments, at least one side of the membrane was maintained at less than 100% relative humidity; the discrepancy may be the result of a strong dependence of the diffusion coefficient on concentration or of a non-Henry's law sorption behavior of water, both of which have been reported.[32,38] However, a direct-osmosis experiment has been performed[23] in which concentrated NaCl solutions were used on both sides of the membrane in order to lower the relative humidity to an average of about 80%. The diffusion coefficient for water was reduced by about a factor of two, not enough to bring all of the liquid-water and water-vapor permeation results into agreement. The difference between the permeation coefficients is thus not resolved; other cases of discrepancies between permeabilities in polymer systems as determined in experiments carried out in the vapor phase as opposed to the liquid phase have been reported.[39–41]

Sorption of Water and Salts

The solubility of water and various salts in cellulose acetates of varying acetyl content has been measured. The water content of several cellulose acetates at 95% relative humidity has been reported in a compilation by Eastman Chemical Products, Inc.,[7] and some additional data obtained at 100% relative humidity[23] are in good agreement if the Eastman data are increased by a factor of 1.05 to approximate the 100% relative-humidity condition. The results of these two sets of measurements are presented in Fig. 4–6. (The observed data have been converted

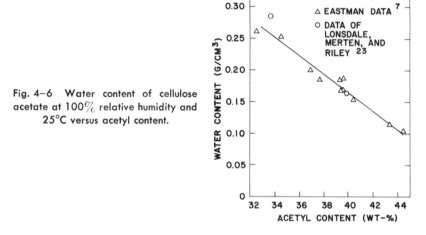

Fig. 4–6 Water content of cellulose acetate at 100% relative humidity and 25°C versus acetyl content.

from units of wt-% to g/cm³ by using the density; the density of cellulose acetate is 1.3 g/cc,[7] and that of the cellulose acetate–water solution was calculated by assuming the volumes to be additive.) These water-content data are consistent with the results of Newsome and Sheppard[42] who found a water content at 30°C of 12.3 wt-% at 100% relative humidity with 39%-acetyl material. From their results on heats of sorption, one can convert this to a water-content of about 0.17 g/cm³ at 25°C, in good agreement with the data in Fig. 4–6. These water-content data are also consistent with the value reported by Tankard[43] who found that the nonsolvent water, i.e., water unavailable to act as a solvent for ionic materials and therefore to be regarded as dissolved in the membrane, is 14.1 wt-% or 0.205 g/cm³ in 36.9%-acetyl cellulose acetate.

These water-content values have been combined with the water-permeability data of Fig. 4–4 to calculate a diffusion coefficient for water in cellulose acetates of several acetyl contents,[23] and the results are summarized in Fig. 4–7. Clearly, water permeability, water content, and the diffusion coefficient all decrease as the acetylation increases. The diffusion coefficients are surprisingly large, not much smaller than the self-diffusion coefficient for liquid water, reported by Wang[44] as 2×10^{-5} cm²/sec at 25°C; they are also in the range of diffusion coefficients of water in various organic liquids near room temperature.[45]

The sorption of a number of salts from aqueous solution by cellulose

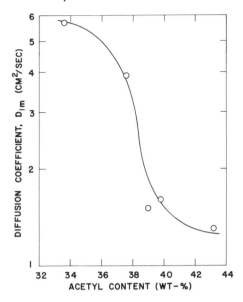

Fig. 4-7 Diffusion coefficient of water in cellulose acetate membranes versus acetyl content. (Data of Lonsdale, Merten, and Riley.[23])

acetate membranes has been studied by Thomas and Barker[37] as well as by Lonsdale, Merten, and Riley.[23] In the first of these studies, Eastman 4650 cellulose acetate membranes containing 40.0% acetyl and with a viscosity-average molecular weight of 53,000 were immersed in solutions of various uni-univalent salts. After a 24-to-48-hour period, the 267-μ-thick films were removed and analyzed for salt content. The results for the alkali chlorides and potassium halides are presented in Table 4-10.

Table 4-10 Distribution Coefficient of Several Salts in 40%-Acetyl Cellulose Acetate Membranes
Data of Thomas and Barker.[37]

Salt	Solution concentration (mg/g)	Net membrane concentration (μg/g)	Distribution coefficient K $\left(\dfrac{\text{g/cc membrane}}{\text{g/cc solution}}\right)$
LiCl	4.2	81	.025
NaCl	5.9	140	.031
KCl	7.5	42	.0073
RbCl	12.1	710	.077
CsCl	16.8	590	.046
KF	5.8	47	.010
KCl	7.5	45	.008
KBr	11.9	160	.017
KI	16.6	710	.056

The potassium halide concentrations in the membrane have been corrected for a high potassium "blank," which probably makes these data of lower quality than those for alkali chlorides. The reproducibility of the results was stated to be ±20%. The results are expressed as a distribution coefficient defined as the salt content per unit volume of membrane divided by the salt concentration in the solution. The salt concentration in the membrane on a weight basis was multiplied by the density of cellulose acetate to effect this conversion of units. It was also found that the distribution coefficient for KCl was independent of the KCl concentration in solution within the accuracy of the measurements over the concentration range 0.1 to 1.0 M.

Salt-sorption measurements have also been carried out in combination with measurements of the salt-diffusion coefficient.[23] Here the rate of approach to equilibrium was followed when membranes approximately 100μ in thickness were immersed in 5% NaCl solution. From the applicable diffusion equation, the diffusion coefficient for salt could be obtained from the time-dependent concentrations, and the distribution coefficient was obtained from the salt concentration at essentially infinite time. The time-dependent data were found to obey Fick's law. A summary of the results of these "immersion" experiments is presented in Table 4–11, and plots of both D_{2m} and K as a function of the

Table 4–11   Distribution and Diffusion Coefficients for NaCl from Immersion Measurements
Data of Lonsdale, Merten, and Riley.[23]

Acetyl content (wt-%)	Distribution coefficient, K $\left(\dfrac{\text{g/cc membrane}}{\text{g/cc solution}}\right)$	Diffusion coefficient, D_{2m} (cm²/sec)
33.6	0.17, 0.17	$2.9 \pm 0.6 \times 10^{-8}$
37.6	0.060*	$4.3 \pm 2.0 \times 10^{-9}$
39.8	0.035	$9.4 \pm 1.1 \times 10^{-10}$
43.2	0.014, 0.016	$3.9 \pm 1.3 \times 10^{-11}$

* Recently redetermined.

acetyl content of the membranes are presented in Fig. 4–8. The effect of heating 39.8%-acetyl membranes to 80°C in a water bath prior to the diffusion measurements has also been examined; the values obtained were $D_{2m} = 8.6 \pm 2.0 \times 10^{-10}$ cm²/sec and $K = 0.029 \pm .02$, or very nearly the same as the results on unheated samples. The distribution coefficient was found to be essentially independent of concentration in the range 1.6 to 10.6% NaCl, in good agreement with the results of Thomas and Barker for KCl.[37] The diffusion coefficient for sodium chloride has also been found to be relatively independent of salt concen-

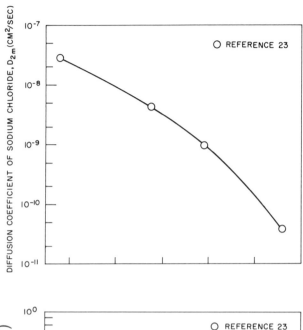

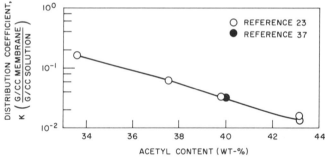

Fig. 4–8 Diffusion coefficient and distribution coefficient of NaCl in cellulose acetate membranes versus acetyl content. (Data of Lonsdale, Merten, and Riley[23] and of Thomas and Barker.[37])

tration, with a value of $D_{2m} = 1.3 \pm 0.4 \times 10^{-9}$ cm²/sec being obtained with 0.5% NaCl.[23]

The data of Thomas and Barker[37] are compared with those of Lonsdale, Merten, and Riley[23] for NaCl in Fig. 4–8, with clearly good agreement. Knowing the diffusion coefficient for NaCl, it is possible to calculate the time necessary to saturate completely the relatively thick samples used by Thomas and Barker. This time is about 2 to 3 days, or about the duration of their experiment. However, the time necessary to saturate their samples with the more slowly diffusing salts is even longer; it is probable that some of the samples were never saturated with respect to salt. Some of the data of Table 4–10 therefore probably represent lower limits.

The salt-permeability coefficient $D_{2m}K$ for NaCl as a function of acetyl content can be calculated from Tables 4–10 and 4–11 and Fig. 4–8. If these permeabilities are compared with those observed in reverse-osmosis and direct-osmosis experiments summarized in Fig. 4–5, it is clear that the immersion values are uniformly and considerably smaller. The immersion values are to be preferred because they are not subject to the problem of film perfection. The very small volume of imperfections necessary to invalidate direct-osmosis and reverse-osmosis experiments would accommodate too little salt solution to affect the immersion measurements. It appears, then, that a large fraction of salt transport occurs through imperfections in these normal membranes and that these imperfections are of such a character as to lead to about the same values of apparent salt-permeability coefficient in direct-osmosis as in reverse-osmosis experiments. Such imperfections may be actual holes or they may be microscopic regions having grossly higher permeability to salt ions. Although there appears to be no published research on these imperfections in normal cellulose acetate membranes (Michaels, Bixler, and Hodges[24] have made a study of them in modified membranes, as will be discussed in Section 4.3), we can make estimates of their size, if they are indeed micropores, with some of the data already available. For example, one can demonstrate from the reverse-osmosis results of Breton[4] that even a few pores one micron in diameter would have permitted more salt transport by simple viscous flow than was observed. Thus, the pores must be not more than a few thousand angstroms in diameter. From the results of Lonsdale, et al., we can also conclude that most of the pores must be farther apart than the thickness of their membranes, i.e., about 100 μ. Pores closer together than this would have led to short-circuit diffusion paths into the interior of their membranes. Pores this widely spaced obviously cannot be very numerous; therefore they cannot be extremely small—i.e., they must be more than a few angstroms in diameter. To gain further insight into the source and nature of these imperfections will require further research.

One can use the measured water permeability from the direct-osmosis experiments, the salt permeability from the immersion experiments, and the transport phenomenology summarized by Eqs. 4.1 to 4.3 to calculate the water and salt flux through a normal membrane of a given thickness as a function of the driving force. The results of a calculation of this type for a 1-μ-thick, 40%-acetyl membrane are presented in Fig. 4–9. A 0.1 M NaCl brine has been assumed. It has been further assumed that the water permeability is independent of pressure and that there are no significant boundary-layer effects. The plot of salt rejection versus pressure is based on the salt-permeability coefficient taken from Fig. 4–8. Shown for comparison are the experimental results of Breton[4] taken under the same conditions. (The membrane thickness does not affect the

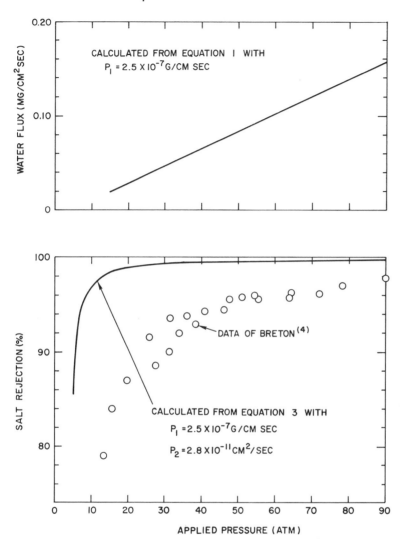

Fig. 4–9   Water flux and salt rejection vs. pressure for a 40%-acetyl cellulose acetate membrane. Conditions: 0.1 M NaCl, 1-μ-thick membrane.

salt rejection.) The importance of a better understanding of the nature of salt flow is apparent from a comparison of the calculated and observed salt-rejection curves.

Physical Properties

Data on the physical strength of cellulose acetate membranes have application to their use in reverse-osmosis equipment at high pressures. Strength data are of direct value, for example, in the calculation of the maximum permissible size of pores in the supports for the very thin membranes of practical interest in economic reverse-osmosis systems. Creep data are also of interest since membranes in practical devices are exposed to high pressures for many months and the extent of plastic flow might be expected to have an important bearing on the long-term performance of the membranes. Life tests of modified membranes, referred to briefly here and discussed in greater detail in Chapters 3 and 7, indicate that membrane performance is time-dependent; this is probably due, in part, to a slow change in membrane structure.

Unfortunately there seem to be few of these physical-property data available. The Handbook of Plastics[46] lists mechanical-property values for "cellulose acetate" and "high-acetyl transparent cellulose acetate." Neither the acetyl content nor the molecular weight of the resins is specified, and the materials may have contained plasticizer. Some of the data are reproduced in Table 4–12, even though they may have only

Table 4–12   Some Mechanical Properties of Cellulose Acetate[46]

	Cellulose acetate	High-acetyl transparent cellulose acetate
Tensile strength (psi)	3100–8000	4500–8000
Elongation (%)	12–50	5–35
Modulus of elasticity (10^5 psi)	1.0–4.4	2.0–3.6
Compressive strength (psi)	13,000–36,000	—

qualitative value. Some indication of the fact that these materials are not typical of the acetates of greatest interest here is derived from the moisture sorption data listed, i.e., 1 to 3 wt-%. We expect that the samples contained plasticizer and therefore that the two strength values and the elastic modulus in the table are probably less (and the elongation is greater) than the corresponding values appropriate to the pure material. In a list comparing these parameters with those of more than twenty other plastics, cellulose acetate is ranked about in the middle.

Reid and Kuppers[29] have carried out measurements of the compressive strength of 40%-acetyl cellulose acetate membranes. From the compression results on three layers of 17-μ-thick dry films one can calculate a compressive modulus of 4000 to 8000 psi, a very low range of values. During measurements on wet films, the samples appeared to swell with time, indicating perhaps that they were not completely equilibrated initially with water. The final series of measurements of this study were reproducible, and from them one can calculate a compressive modulus of 66,000 psi for wet films.

Tensile-strength measurements on wet films have also been reported,[47] with the results presented in Table 4-13. The samples designated 398-3,

Table 4-13   Tensile Strength Measurements on Normal Cellulose Acetate Membranes
Data of Lonsdale, Merten, Riley, and Vos.[47]

Cellulose acetate type (Eastman designation)	Thickness (mils)	Ultimate strength (psi)	Modulus of elasticity (10^3 psi)	Elongation at failure (%)
398-3	0.6	2600	116	6
	0.9	3100	199	7
	1.5	3100	145	6
	1.6	3000	160	6
	1.9	2700	143	5
398-6	0.9	2900	185	15
398-10	1.2	3500	156	25

-6, and -10 represent increasingly higher molecular weight 39.8%-acetyl materials. There was no significant trend in strength or modulus of elasticity with increasing molecular weight, but the elongation-to-failure increased markedly. The results are qualitatively consistent with the compilation in Table 4-12.

In summary, while no correlation has been attempted between physical-strength parameters and long-term behavior of membranes at high compressive loads in reverse osmosis, one can show from these results that at typical operating pressures the membranes will have to be provided with a support whose pore size is of the same order of magnitude as the membrane thickness. For the very thin membranes necessary for economic desalination, very fine, porous supports will be required. From the elastic modulus one would expect a reduction in thickness of dense cellulose acetate on the order of 1% at the highest pressures normally considered practical in reverse osmosis, and it seems improbable that such a small change could effect a gross change in transport properties. It is worthy of note that membranes cast from the higher molecular weight resin appear to have more favorable physical properties.

4.3   Modified Cellulose Acetate Membranes

In spite of the excellent intrinsic permeability properties of cellulose acetate membranes, the water flux one can achieve with normal membranes thick enough to have sufficient strength for survival at high pressures is uninterestingly low. For example, the highest water flux observed by Reid and co-workers with their thinnest membranes (4 to

5 μ) was not more than 3×10^{-5} g/cm²-sec, somewhat less than a gallon per square foot of membrane per day* at a net pressure of about 40 atm. It is generally agreed that in order to make the reverse-osmosis process economically interesting, it is necessary to work with membranes with higher water-permeation rates.

In Chapter 3 the preparation of highly selective cellulose acetate membranes with a water flux more than an order of magnitude higher than the best attained by Reid and co-workers was discussed. It is our purpose in this section to present the results of a number of experiments performed with these high-flux membranes, which to date appear to represent the most significant improvement in the preparation of cellulose acetate membranes and which, therefore, have received most of the attention of the several laboratories engaged in research in this field. This section is divided into a discussion of porous membranes, the structure of the Loeb-Sourirajan membrane, some theories concerning the mechanism of formation of this modified membrane, diagnostic reverse-osmosis experiments, the compaction of modified membranes at high pressure, and the lifetime and hydrolysis rate of cellulose acetate membranes.

The Preparation of Porous Membranes

To gain insight into the structure of the modified membranes it is worth while to review the literature on the preparation of porous membranes. This literature is quite extensive, although a review by Ferry[48] conveniently summarizes research in this field through the mid 1930's. Only a few of the more pertinent studies will be considered here.

Elford has studied the preparation of porous nitrocellulose membranes in some detail.[49-51] He found that porous membranes can be prepared by one of several methods: (1) casting a membrane from an ether-ethyl alcohol solution (i.e., collodion) and immersing it in water at the point of incipient gelation; (2) impregnating a filter paper with an acetic acid solution of nitrocellulose and gelling by water immersion; and (3) casting a membrane from a collodion solution containing acetone and amyl alcohol as additives and allowing it to dry in air. Using method 1 the time between casting the membrane and immersing it in water was varied. On increasing the air-dry time the following products were obtained: a precipitate of nitrocellulose in water; a coarse, opaque membrane possessing a "microgel" structure and consisting mainly of aggregates of microscopic size; an opalescent membrane having only a slight granularity resolvable under the ultramicroscope and therefore described as an "ultragel"; and a strong, transparent, apparently dense film. With method 2, it was noted that the flow of water through the

* Multiply water flux in g/cm²-sec by 2.1×10^4 to convert to units of gpd/ft².

membranes was not inversely proportional to their thickness, indicating a nonhomogeneous membrane. Using method 3, highly porous membranes were prepared, their pores covering a size range from less than 100 Å to several microns within narrowly defined limits. Elford proposed that the membranes cast from a mixture of four solvents spontaneously gel into a porous structure when the acetone and amyl alcohol are concentrated by the evaporation of ether and ethyl alcohol to the point where they exhibit "mutual antagonism in solvent action toward nitrocellulose." Additives to collodion that are good solvents for nitrocellulose favor dispersion and thus result in less porous membranes, whereas poor solvents or nonsolvents, such as water, increase the tendency toward aggregation, resulting in increased porosity.

Grabar[52] prepared membranes similar to those of Elford by the addition of certain agents, called "gellifying liquids," to a nitrocellulose solution. He noted that the concentration and rate of evaporation of the additive affects the water content and thickness of the resulting membrane. Furthermore, if the evaporation of solvent is stopped by water immersion before the gel is well formed, the water precipitates the nitrocellulose in the interior of the gel and the membrane becomes nonhomogeneous.

Vaughan[53] used Elford's method to prepare porous cellulose acetate membranes. His procedure was to cast membranes from acetone solutions containing n-amyl alcohol as "precipitant," allow the solvents to evaporate until the membranes were nearly dry, and then to pour ethanol over them. The resulting membranes were partly clear and partly opaque; the opaque regions were effective as ultrafilters, the clear regions being relatively impermeable. Membranes cut from the opaque, presumably porous, regions were semipermeable with respect to a solution of sucrose octaacetate in benzene or water. The rise of solution in a conventional osmometer was about 50% of the theoretical value, indicating that the membranes were selective in spite of their high porosity. The fact that the clear regions were relatively impermeable suggests that in the opaque regions the effective membrane thickness is much less than the gross thickness.

The Schleicher & Schuell membranes used by Sourirajan in his extensive reverse-osmosis studies are probably of the general type prepared by Vaughan. Although the method of their preparation is not available to us, we know that they possess a very high water permeability, especially in the unannealed state, and yet are somewhat selective to simple salts. Sourirajan found that increased thermal annealing of these membranes shrinks them physically, at the same time improving selectivity and decreasing water permeability. When compared with the modified membranes of Loeb and Sourirajan to be discussed in the next section, the most highly annealed of the Schleicher & Schuell membranes has both a lower water flow and poorer selectivity under the same experimental conditions.

All of these procedures and the resulting membranes bear some similarity to those of Loeb and Sourirajan; i.e., the membranes are largely porous but nevertheless selective to relatively low-molecular-weight solutes. The amount of correspondence in detail and in the mechanism of membrane formation may become clearer following some consideration of the structure of the Loeb-Sourirajan membrane.

Structure of the Loeb-Sourirajan Membrane

The structure of Loeb-Sourirajan membranes has been examined in some detail by Riley, Gardner, and Merten.[54] Using conventional light-microscopy techniques, they found the membranes to be devoid of structure at magnifications up to 500X. However, in the electron microscope at a magnification of about 8000X the membrane proved to consist of a fine-pored matrix with a very thin, dense layer of cellulose acetate on the surface identifiable as the air-dried surface. The structure of the as-cast membrane appears to have been fairly well preserved in the samples by impregnation with an epoxy resin. The dense surface layer was estimated from the electron micrographs to be about 0.25 μ thick when the total membrane thickness was 100 μ; the porous substructure was estimated to have a pore size on the order of 0.1 μ. Electron photomicrographs of cross sections of both a modified and a normal membrane (cast from acetone and allowed to dry completely in air) are presented in Figs. 4–10 and 4–11, respectively.

In a subsequent publication,[55] Riley, Merten, and Gardner showed that greater resolution could be obtained by freeze-drying the membrane and replicating with palladium and carbon for the electron microscope. Electron photomicrographs of the top, or air-dried, surface, the bottom surface, and a cross section are reproduced in Figs. 4–12 to 4–14. The contrast between the top and bottom surfaces is clear, and there was no evidence of porosity on the air-dried surface down to about the 100-Å level. In cross section, the membrane is better defined in Fig. 4–14 than in Fig. 4–10, and the pore size appears somewhat greater (estimated to be 0.4 μ), perhaps because of differences in the technique of preparation.

It seems clear from these results that the modified membrane is actually a composite membrane consisting of a very thin, dense layer on the air-dried surface and a porous substructure; a similar model was first suggested by Loeb and Sourirajan.[6] Since these membranes have been shown to exhibit semipermeability to salts about equal to that of the normal membranes,[5,23] one concludes that they are basically diffusion-type barriers, so that Eqs. 4.1 to 4.3 should apply. The dense surface layer is clearly the only portion of the membrane which is sufficiently

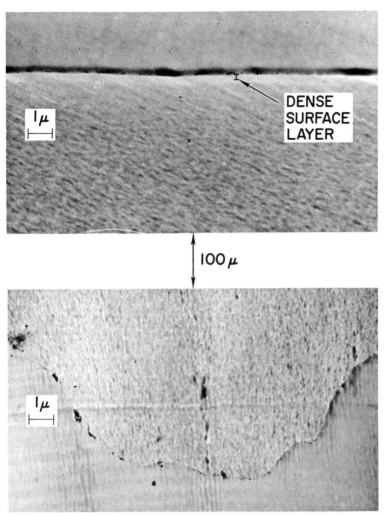

Fig. 4–10   Composite of two electron photomicrographs of cross sections of modified cellulose acetate membranes. (From Riley, Gardner, and Merten.[54])

physically continuous to act as this barrier, and it would appear that the very high fluxes observed with these modified membranes are the result of their effective thinness.

Using Eq. 4.1 one can calculate the effective thickness of a modified membrane of the Loeb-Sourirajan type from its water flux. The permeability properties of the dense surface layer must be assumed equal to those of the normal membranes, as summarized in Tables 4–3 and 4–6. There is obviously no *a priori* assurance that this is the case, but the consistencies that result from this assumption suggest that the assump-

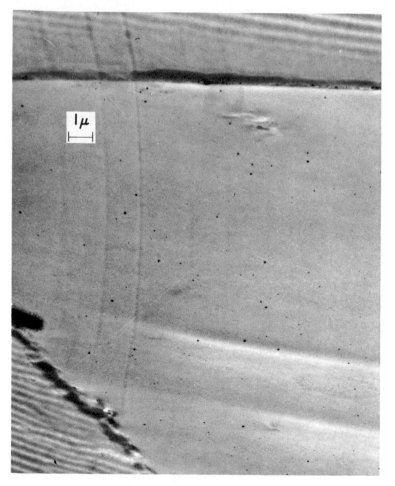

Fig. 4–11   Electron photomicrograph of the cross section of a normal cellulose acetate
membrane. (From Riley, Gardner, and Merten.[54])

tion is valid. Some typical results observed with modified 39.8%-acetyl
cellulose acetate membranes are a flux of 5.1×10^{-4} g/cm²-sec in a
direct-osmosis experiment with 5.0% NaCl brine ($\Delta p = 0$, $\Delta \pi = 41$
atm), and a flux per unit pressure of 0.9 to 1.2×10^{-5} g/cm²-sec-atm in
reverse-osmosis experiments with sodium chloride brines.[23] The effective
membrane thicknesses calculated from these data and a water permeability of 2.6×10^{-7} g/cm-sec are 0.15 and 0.16 to 0.21 μ, respectively,
consistent with the estimate made by Riley, Gardner, and Merten from
electron micrographs. Furthermore, the agreement between the results
obtained at zero applied pressure with those obtained at high pressure
supports the assumption that the water permeability is not strongly

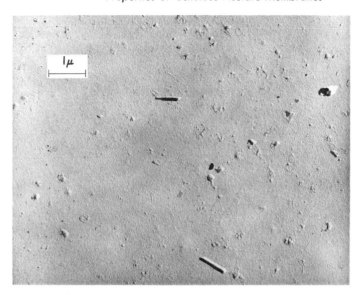

Fig. 4–12 Electron photomicrograph of a preshadowed carbon replica of the air-dried surface of a modified cellulose acetate membrane. The membrane was dehydrated by freeze-drying. (From Riley, Merten, and Gardner.[55])

Fig. 4–13 Electron photomicrograph of a preshadowed carbon replica of the bottom surface of a modified cellulose acetate membrane. The membrane was dehydrated by freeze-drying. (From Riley, Merten, and Gardner.[55])

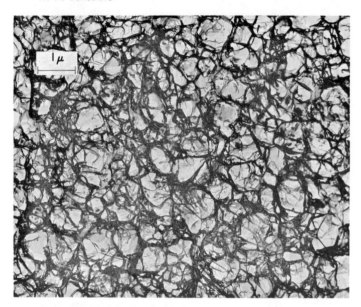

Fig. 4–14   Electron photomicrograph of a preshadowed carbon replica of the cross section of a modified cellulose acetate membrane. The membrane was dehydrated by freeze-drying. (From Riley, Merten, and Gardner.[55])

pressure dependent. Thus it is clear that most of the resistance to flow of water and salt is in the dense surface layer and that, with an uncertainty of perhaps ±25%, the thickness of this layer is 0.2 μ when prepared according to the original formulation of Loeb and Sourirajan.[6]

There is additional qualitative evidence that the dense layer provides essentially all the resistance to the flow of both water and salt. Thus, the membranes are known to be directional, and it has been found, for example, that scratching the air-dried surface with a fine wire screen increases the water flow and virtually eliminates the selectivity to sodium chloride.[56]

The effective thickness of these modified membranes can be varied over a wide range. Membranes that are thinner in their gross dimension were reported to give higher water flux under the same reverse-osmosis conditions.[57] This can be reconciled in at least two ways: The thickness of the dense surface layer may vary with the gross thickness of the membrane, a not unreasonable circumstance; or there may be some resistance to the flow of water in the porous substructure. It has also been found[58,59] that, by means of assorted modifications in the membrane-preparation procedure, membranes can be prepared which yield a higher water flux with concomitant lower selectivity under the same experimental conditions. Such membranes have found use in desalinating brackish waters where very high selectivity is not required. In keeping with the previous

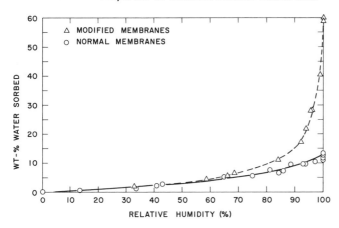

Fig. 4–15   Water sorption versus relative humidity for normal and modified membranes. (Data of Lonsdale, Merten, and Riley.[23])

description of these modified membranes, one might conclude that the dense layer has been made so thin that the number of imperfections has increased; however, from the fact that the salt rejection of these "high-flux" membranes is reduced, a more reasonable conclusion is that the nominally dense surface layer appears to be somewhat porous. However, at this point the simple diffusion model of water and salt flow, which is not entirely adequate for the basic Loeb-Sourirajan membranes, breaks down completely and one must resort to more complex membrane models, such as the finely porous model of Chapter 2, to describe the transport behavior in these very high flux membranes.

Further insight into the nature of the porous substructure of the modified membranes may be obtained from the water sorption measurements of Lonsdale, et al.[23] Sorption isotherms for both a normal and a modified membrane are reproduced in Fig. 4–15. The excess water in the modified membrane is held by capillary action in the pores, and by subtracting the amount of water in solution in the normal membrane from that observed in the modified membrane the authors were able to calculate the water sorbed in capillaries as a function of relative humidity. By assuming spherical pores, the distribution in pore size has been calculated from the relationship between vapor pressure, surface tension, and radius of curvature (Fig. 4–16). Most of the water is held in pores in the 0.01-to-0.3-μ range, a conclusion in general agreement with electron-microscopy studies.[54,55]

Mechanism of Formation of the Loeb-Sourirajan Membrane

A good deal of effort has gone into detailed studies of the mechanism of formation of this modified membrane.[60–64] As a result, even though

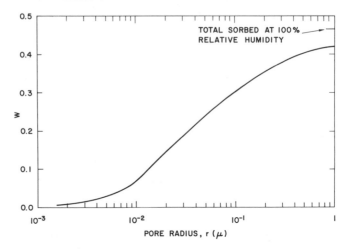

Fig. 4–16   Volume of water sorbed in capillaries in a modified membrane (w = cubic centimeters of water per gram of membrane held in pores of radius less than r). (Data of Lonsdale, Merten, and Riley.[23])

our understanding is not complete and a few points are still being debated, much of this mechanism has been qualitatively explained.

To summarize the steps in the Loeb-Sourirajan procedure briefly, a membrane is cast from a solution of cellulose acetate and other ingredients in a suitable solvent; it is allowed to dry in air, usually below 0°C, although successful membranes have been cast at higher temperatures if the air-dry time is suitably shortened; the membrane is then immersed in cold water and finally, to improve semipermeability, heated in water at temperatures up to 90°C.

Several investigators seem to agree on what is happening during some of these steps. During the air-dry period, acetone is lost from the membrane surface and the dense surface layer apparently forms.[64] When the partially formed membrane is then immersed in water, the water diffuses rapidly into its interior and the water concentration soon exceeds the limit of solubility of cellulose acetate; gelation then occurs by coagulation. From the fact that the bulk of the membrane is subsequently very permeable to water one can conclude that this porous substructure is a precipitate of cellulose acetate in water, with both the water phase and the resin phase being physically continuous. The largely amorphous character of the membranes has been demonstrated by X-ray-diffraction studies.[60]

The annealing step was first used by Loeb and Sourirajan[6] with Schleicher & Schuell membranes to improve selectivity. As noted in Chapter 3, these membranes are directional after heat treatment, indicating that they possess an incipient surface layer which is consolidated during annealing. In the case of the Loeb-Sourirajan membrane, a similar phenomenon occurs during the heat-treatment step: the membrane shrinks and loses some of its capillary water[63,64] and the porosity of the surface layer decreases, as evidenced by a marked improvement in selectivity. Even unannealed membranes were found quite selective to the dye Biebrich Scarlet which, in its water-soluble sodium sulfonate form, has a molecular weight of about 500. From this observation it has been estimated that the diameter of the pores in the surface layer before heat treatment is about 10 Å.[64] Although it may not be the correct interpretation, one may consider that these pores close up by simple surface-tension forces at the annealing temperature. No good correlation has been established between the annealing temperature and the reported second-order transition temperatures in cellulose acetate.

The role of the extra ingredients in the casting solution has been given close attention. In the modified membranes first described by Loeb and Sourirajan,[6] these ingredients were magnesium perchlorate and water, the use of perchlorates having been suggested by the work of Dobry[12] and Biget.[13] Since that time a large number of other additives has been studied and the effect of many of these on both the water flux and salt rejection of the membranes has been observed.[60,65] The factors determining the effectiveness of various "membrane salts" have been discussed at length and will not be repeated here. While a number of other effective salts have been found, magnesium perchlorate is still at least as effective as any.

It is well established[13,61,66] that the membrane salt is completely washed out of the membrane before it is actually used; the only interaction thus occurs as the membrane is being formed. Kesting,[61] using infrared techniques, has found that the membrane salt has no chemical effect on the cellulose acetate. The role of this salt in the formation of the membrane remains somewhat obscure. Kesting proposes that the cations in the membrane salt are associated with hydroxyl groups and that this association leads to swelling. Banks and Sharples,[64] however, have prepared a membrane of cellulose triacetate (which contains no hydroxyl groups) and found that the use of membrane salts and the procedure of Loeb and Sourirajan gave membranes with good selectivity and with much higher water flux than that obtained with normal cellulose triacetate membranes. The importance of the association of membrane salt with the cellulose acetate is thus a moot point.

A somewhat pragmatic point about the use of membrane salts is that without them the water flux through the membrane is much lower,[6,59,62] even with the Loeb-Sourirajan procedure. Furthermore, membranes so prepared swell with capillary water after preparation. It would appear, then, that these salts are effective in producing a water-continuous porous substructure.

Manjikian[67] reports that modified membranes can be prepared with the use of a variety of non-ionic additives. Membranes cast from acetone-formamide solutions are said to have water-permeation rates and semi-permeability equal to those of the very high flux or brackish-water membranes described by Loeb and Manjikian.[58] Further, highly selective membranes can also be prepared from these solutions. Manjikian also reports that the water flux is not time dependent with these membranes, in contrast to the Loeb-Sourirajan modified membranes. Furthermore, using this new solvent system, modified membranes with fairly high selectivity can be prepared without heat treatment. Even more significant, perhaps, is the report that modified membranes can be successfully prepared from a single solvent, i.e., with either dimethyl formamide, acetic acid, or triethyl phosphate. Additional successful variations on the method of preparing modified membranes of the Loeb-Sourirajan type have been published.[64]

The various solvents, additional ingredients, and procedures used in preparing modified membranes are thus quite reminiscent of the methods of Elford, Vaughan, and others, and the membranes resulting from the later studies seem to emulate their predecessors in many ways. For example, the formamide used by Manjikian[67] to prepare modified membranes is not a good solvent for cellulose acetate and might be likened to the precipitating or "gellifying" agents proposed by Vaughan[53] and Grabar.[52] The Schleicher & Schuell cellulose acetate membranes may also be said to be of this general type. They exhibit some selectivity to salts and also permit water fluxes which, while lower than those achieved with the Loeb-Sourirajan membrane, are still much higher than one would expect for a fully dense membrane. The analogy between the modified membranes as described here and those prepared by Elford, Vaughan, and others is instructive but certainly not complete. For example, neither the Elford membranes nor the Vaughan membranes showed high selectivity to low-molecular-weight constituents. Moreover, neither of these early workers reported that the membranes were directional when used in ultrafiltration or dialysis experiments, so that the presence of a surface layer cannot be established. However, membrane directionality might explain the lack of reproducibility in their experiments, noted particularly by Vaughan.

Diagnostic Reverse-Osmosis Experiments

A vast number of reverse-osmosis experiments has been carried out in the past several years, many of them with modified membranes of the Loeb-Sourirajan type.[6,23,24,56−60,64−66,68−73] It is not our purpose to refer to all of these experiments, a large portion of which were reviewed in the preceding chapter, but rather to consider only those that add to our understanding of the properties of such membranes.

It is important to note at this point that not only the acetyl content but also the source of the cellulose acetate resin from which membranes are cast has proved significant. In some of his early studies[68] Loeb varied the source of the cellulose acetate from his standard Eastman material to a Celanese product. With a Celanese 36.8%-acetyl cellulose acetate membrane Loeb found that the water flow was about one third of that observed with a membrane prepared in the same way with Eastman 39.8%-acetyl cellulose acetate under equal salt-rejection conditions. A similar observation is reported by Banks and Sharples,[64] who, using British Celanese cellulose acetate of 41.1% acetyl content, found that the membranes were much stronger and gave water flows about one tenth those of membranes of comparable salt rejection prepared from Eastman cellulose acetate. The high strength and low flow have been reconciled with the postulate that the dense surface layer is much thicker in the membrane made from the Celanese material. However, normal (i.e., fully dense) cellulose acetate membranes have only about two to three times the strength of modified membranes, so that a tenfold increase in thickness of the dense layer would change the strength of the membrane only slightly. Nevertheless, it is clear that not all cellulose acetates are alike even when their degrees of substitution and of polymerization are equal; some of the possible reasons for this were discussed in Section 4.1.

Unless otherwise indicated, the results and discussion that follow refer to Eastman 39.8%-acetyl cellulose acetate.

Membrane directionality. It has been noted several times that the modified membrane is asymmetric; i.e., it is effective in desalination only if the air-dried surface is juxtaposed with the brine. There are two reasons for this: First, if the membrane is used in the inverted position, salt accumulates in the porous substructure because of water removal and cannot be adequately removed by simple circulation of the brine. As a result, salt flow increases while water flow decreases. A second reason is that the membrane apparently cannot support high "negative" pressures. This is very nicely demonstrated in the experiments of Banks and Sharples.[64] Both water-flow rate and salt rejection were measured as a function of pressure where first the dense side and then the porous side of a membrane were subjected to a pressure cycle. The high-pressure solution was dilute NaCl (1000 ppm), so that osmotic pressure corrections should have been small. However, the boundary-layer effect for salt flow could have been substantial when "negative" pressures were used. The tests were performed with a modified membrane prepared from Celanese cellulose acetate; the experimental results are reproduced in Fig. 4–17. The flow and salt-rejection results were taken on the same membrane in the alphabetical order indicated. The portion of the experiment A–B is typical of the results normally obtained with these

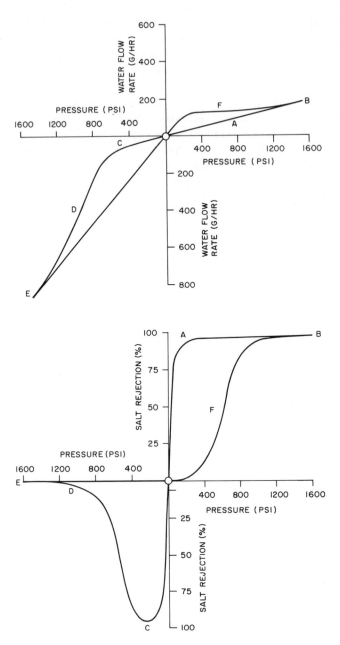

Fig. 4–17   Water flow and salt rejection as a function of positive and negative pressure. A Celanese cellulose acetate modified membrane. (Results of Banks and Sharples.[64])

membranes, and the relation between salt rejection and pressure is in accord with Eq. 4.3. On decreasing the pressure through zero the membrane was initially still highly semipermeable and performed as it had in the "normal" direction. However, at an applied pressure of about -300 psi the water flow began to increase more rapidly than it had in the "normal" orientation, and the salt rejection decreased sharply (Region C–D–E). On returning to positive pressures (E–F) the membrane did not regain its original performance until the highest pressures had again been reached. These results are conveniently understood in terms of a model of pores that can be opened at moderate negative pressures and reclosed at high positive pressures. It has been speculated that those pores that open up in the surface layer are present in the unannealed membrane; the behavior observed at high negative pressures is consistent with this assumption.

Water flow. That water flow is diffusive in nature and can be described by a relation of the form of Eq. 4.1 seems to be fairly generally agreed upon.[23,24,64] Two observations have been made of the temperature dependence of water flow from reverse-osmosis measurements. One is that due to Lonsdale, Merten, and Riley[23] who report an activation energy of 4.2 kcal/mole; this value is to be compared with the value of 5 kcal/mole reported by Reid and Kuppers[29] for flow through normal membranes. Michaels, Bixler, and Hodges[24] obtained an activation energy for water permeation of 5.9 kcal/mole. All of these values include the negative heat of sorption of water of 1.3 kcal/mole; we may thus conclude that the activation energy for diffusion of water is in the range of 5 to 7 kcal/mole. Furthermore, salt rejection has been found to be relatively independent of temperature,[23] indicating that the activation energies for both water and salt transport are similar.

Michaels, et al., have devised a useful test of Eq. 4.1 which avoids the problem of changes within the membrane. Water flow was observed as a function of net pressure (i.e., applied less osmotic pressure) by varying the applied pressure with fixed brine concentration and also the brine concentration at a fixed applied pressure. It was found that at a fixed applied pressure Eq. 4.1 was obeyed quite satisfactorily.

Rejection of various solutes. The semipermeability of modified membranes to a number of solutes other than sodium chloride has been studied in reverse-osmosis experiments, the most extensive investigations being those of Sourirajan[74–76] with Schleicher & Schuell membranes and those of Blunk[69] with the modified membrane. The results of Sourirajan are not of immediate application to desalination problems because of the relatively small uni-univalent ion selectivity, but they nevertheless establish some clear trends that are apparently applicable to the more selective modified membrane. The trends in semipermeability, as observed by Blunk, were noted in Chapter 3. Some of Blunk's data are

Table 4-14 Selectivity of Modified Cellulose Acetate Membranes to Several Solutes
Pressure 102 atm. Data of Blunk.[69]

Solute	Concentration (moles/liter)	Water flux (g/cm^2-sec)	Rejection (%)	Apparent water permeability P_1 (g/cm-sec)	Apparent solute permeability P_2 (cm^2/sec)
NaCl	0.90	7.2×10^{-4}	98.1	2.6×10^{-7}	2.0×10^{-10}
NaBr	0.51	6.9×10^{-4}	98.0	1.9×10^{-7}	3.1×10^{-10}
KCl	0.71	7.4×10^{-4}	95.8	2.2×10^{-7}	5.3×10^{-10}
NaNO$_3$	0.029	1.2×10^{-3}	90.1	2.6×10^{-7}	1.9×10^{-9}
NaClO$_4$	0.43	1.1×10^{-3}	86.3	2.3×10^{-7}	2.9×10^{-7}
NH$_4$ClO$_4$	0.45	8.5×10^{-4}	77.4	2.1×10^{-7}	5.0×10^{-9}
NH$_4$NO$_3$	0.031	1.3×10^{-3}	80.3	2.8×10^{-7}	4.7×10^{-9}
CaCl$_2$	0.47	6.7×10^{-4}	99.1	2.1×10^{-7}	5.3×10^{-10}
Na$_2$SO$_4$	0.37	6.2×10^{-4}	99.3	1.6×10^{-7}	1.0×10^{-10}
HNO$_3$*	0.040	1.3×10^{-3}	51.3	2.7×10^{-7}	1.8×10^{-8}
NH$_4$OH*	0.050	1.4×10^{-3}	6.2	2.9×10^{-7}	3.0×10^{-7}
Sodium lauryl sulfate	0.0043	1.8×10^{-3}	98.2	3.8×10^{-7}	1.1×10^{-10}
Sucrose	0.15	1.5×10^{-3}	99.7	3.4×10^{-7}	5.0×10^{-11}
Tetramethyl ammonium chloride	0.48	8.9×10^{-4}	99.6	2.5×10^{-7}	5.0×10^{-11}
Tetraethyl ammonium chloride	0.32	1.1×10^{-3}	99.4	2.7×10^{-7}	1.0×10^{-10}

* This test was conducted at approximately 0°C to reduce chemical attack. Nevertheless, some loss in selectivity to NaCl occurred during the test.

reproduced here in Table 4–14 for purposes of a more quantitative comparison. In order to test against possible chemical or other deterioration in the membranes, their permeability to sodium chloride was checked both before and after each experiment with a new salt. Except as noted, these tests were negative; i.e., the sodium chloride permeability did not change significantly during the test. All of these measurements were carried out at an applied pressure of 102 atm. In addition to giving the water and salt flux, we have calculated the apparent permeability coefficients P_1 and P_2 by assuming the effective thickness of the membrane to be 0.16 μ, a value selected to give $P_1 = 2.6 \times 10^{-7}$ g/cm-sec for the sodium chloride experiment. This is the value of the water-permeability coefficient observed on normal cellulose acetate membranes of the same acetyl content, 39.8%, as the modified membranes used by Blunk. Literature values[77] of osmotic coefficients were used to calculate the osmotic pressure difference.

The absolute values of the permeability coefficients are somewhat uncertain because of the unknown effective thickness of the membranes, but they are relatively correct and have the additional virtue of being corrected for variations in brine concentration. It is clear that the water permeability is quite constant in most of these experiments, while the salt permeabilities cover a range of several orders of magnitude. The compounds most effectively excluded are salts of divalent ions (this has been observed in a number of laboratories), sucrose, and the tetralkyl ammonium salts. Several simple inorganic salts, notably the perchlorates and nitrates, are not highly rejected, while ammonia is highly permeable. At the concentration used in Blunk's experiments, nearly all the ammonia is in the NH_3 form, the ratio of the concentration of NH_3 to that of NH_4^+ being about 50, and even though there was some chemical attack during this experiment the water-flux data indicate the membrane remained essentially intact. It is perhaps noteworthy that the water permeability with sodium lauryl sulfate brines was somewhat higher than the norm. One rationalization of this observation is that sodium lauryl sulfate dissolved in the cellulose acetate and the water permeability of the resulting membrane is greater than that of pure cellulose acetate. From the excellent exclusion observed, one can conclude that the diffusion coefficient of sodium lauryl sulfate is exceedingly small.

The semipermeability of modified membranes to the sodium and potassium halides has also been measured,[59] with the results presented in Table 4–15. The membranes were prepared with $ZnCl_2$ rather than with $Mg(ClO_4)_2$ as the membrane salt; the reverse-osmosis measurements were all conducted at 102 atm applied pressure with 0.6 M salts as feed. The water flux through the membrane was 1.4×10^{-3} g/cm²-sec before the salts were added to the system, and 0.90×10^{-3}

Table 4–15 Semipermeability of Modified Membranes at 102 atm to 0.6 Molar Solutions of Some Simple Salts
Data of Keilin.[59]

Salt	Salt rejection (%)	Apparent salt permeability P_2 (cm²/sec)
NaF	99.5	7.0×10^{-11}
NaCl	98.4	2.3×10^{-10}
NaBr	95.5	6.5×10^{-10}
NaI	93.6	9.2×10^{-10}
KF	99.0	1.4×10^{-10}
KCl	97.2	4.0×10^{-10}
KBr	95.1	7.0×10^{-10}
KI	89.1	1.6×10^{-9}

g/cm^2-sec with salts present. This drop in water flux is much more than can be accounted for on the basis of osmotic pressure, and it apparently represents either a change in the effective thickness of the membrane or a boundary-layer effect. From the salt-rejection data of Table 4–15 we have calculated a salt-permeability coefficient for the several species by assuming $P_1 = 2.6 \times 10^{-7}$ g/cm-sec. The clear trend in salt permeability in these two series is I > Br > Cl > F and K > Na. Reid and Breton's work[5] with normal membranes, reported in Table 4–4, gives the order of salt permeability of the sodium halides as F > Br > Cl. The distribution-coefficient data of Thomas and Barker,[37] listed in Table 4–10, show that K varies in the order I > Br > F > Cl, and Rb > Cs > Na > Li. If one assumes a correspondence between D_{2m} and K, one can conclude that these several measurements generally support the contention that as one goes down the periodic chart the permeability of the membrane to the alkali and halide ions increases.

Some data have also been reported[60] on the semipermeability of modified membranes to acetamide, N-(n-butyl) acetamide, and sucrose. At an applied pressure of 102 atm and with a negligible osmotic pressure gradient across the membrane, the observed rejection of these species was 60, 88, and > 99.9%, respectively. These results illustrate the rather well-established fact that a number of low-molecular-weight organic species are not highly excluded; this is not surprising in view of the expected high solubility of these species in the membrane.

The foregoing results show that the selectivity of the modified membrane, and therefore presumably of all cellulose acetate membranes, varies widely with the nature of the solute and that this is true for both inorganic and organic solutes. From the trends already established reasonable estimates can be made about the semipermeability with respect to an arbitrary compound. It is not entirely clear, however, to what extent the measured semipermeability values represent the intrinsic properties of cellulose acetate and to what extent they reflect the degree of perfection of the membrane.

Salt flow and membrane imperfections. The matter of salt transport through these modified membranes has received wide attention. It has been observed in several laboratories that the salt rejection is quite variable from membrane to membrane even under identical experimental conditions and with nominally identical membranes. This variability led to the conclusion that the membranes contain imperfections whose size and local number density vary significantly, even from place to place in a single membrane. As discussed in Section 4.2, imperfections in the general sense are postulated to exist even in normal membranes many microns thick; thus it is not surprising that they also exist in the 0.2-μ-thick dense surface layer of the modified membrane. One can calculate that the rejection of sodium chloride by 39.8%-acetyl membranes at a net pressure (i.e., $\Delta p - \Delta \pi$) of 60 atm should be 99.7%, based on its permeability to water and salt. The best rejections observed to date with modified membranes are about 99.3%,[78] and typically the salt rejection under these conditions is 97 to 99%.

Some of the early evidence as to the nature of the excess salt flow was obtained by Loeb,[66] who noted that rejection of salts was better when the brine was prepared from Los Angeles tap water rather than from distilled water. It was postulated that this was due to the presence of a small amount of colloidal aluminum salts which served to plug pores in the membrane. Pursuing this idea further, Loeb and Manjikian[70] subsequently added Zephiran, a tetralkyl ammonium chloride, to the brine at concentrations on the order of 100 ppm and noted improved salt rejection. It has also been found that when 1-μ-diam polystyrene spheres were added to the feed solution some of them passed through the membrane.[66]

One can calculate the flow of salt through 1-μ holes and compare it with observed salt flows. From Poiseuille's law of viscous flow,

$$F = \frac{\epsilon r^2}{8\eta} \frac{\Delta p}{t\lambda}, \tag{4.4}$$

where F is the flow of solution per unit area of membrane per unit time, expressed in g/cm²-sec, ϵ the fractional area of the membrane represented by pores, r the radius of the pore, η the viscosity of the fluid, t the tortuosity of the pore, and the other symbols have been defined. Let us assume one hole 1 μ in diameter is present in a 20-cm² membrane, a tortuosity of 2, and an applied pressure of 100 atm. The viscosity of the solution is taken as that of water, i.e., 1 cp, and the thickness as that of the effective layer, taken to be 0.2 μ. The value of ϵ is then 3.8 $\times$ 10^{-10}, and F is 3.0 $\times$ 10^{-5} g/cm²-sec. The diffusive flux of water through the membrane under these conditions is calculated to be 9.5 $\times$ 10^{-4} g/cm²-sec; thus, the flux of undiluted brine represents 3.1% of the total water flow, meaning that with no additional salt flow by other mechanisms (e.g., diffusion through the membrane) the salt rejection would be no better than 96.9%. Salt rejections are generally somewhat better than this, and one can conclude that the maximum possible pore size in typical membranes is on the order of 1 μ and that if pores this large are present they must be widely separated. Actually, one can assume that there is a gradation in pore size within a given membrane and, because of the strong dependence of viscous flow on pore size ($F \alpha r^4$), pores smaller than 100 Å, for example, could be very numerous. We tentatively conclude, therefore, that pores less than one micron in diameter can exist in modified membranes and the bulk of the salt flow must occur through these.

While a few pores as large as 1 μ may be admissible, it is also clear from selectivity results that much of the excess salt flow must occur through pores that are effectively much smaller than 1 μ. Thus, it is well established that membranes that give greater than 99% rejection of divalent ions such as sulfate and other solutes such as sucrose and quaternary ammonium compounds are capable of rejecting only 98% of the sodium chloride (cf., for example, the data in Table 4–14). If, as appears to be the case from permeability results obtained in the immersion measurements, much of the sodium chloride flow is through small pores, we must conclude that at least some of the pores that admit sodium chloride are capable of excluding other species that are not much larger. Even assuming that the forces that exclude these species are long range, such as Coulomb forces, we find that some of the pores must be smaller than a few tens of angstroms in diameter.

The use of a number of additives to the feed solution has been studied in several laboratories, and it appears that certain agents are effective in improving salt rejection. Keilin has reported the most promising results[59] with polyvinylmethyl ether (PVM), small additions of which to the feed have significantly improved salt rejection while slightly reducing water flux. The effect of the PVM decayed over a period of about a day after it was flushed from the system. Data have also been presented for another additive, Dowfax (a commercial product, apparently similar to polyethylene oxide), which indicate a reduction in product salt concentration by perhaps as much as a factor of 2. It is tempting to ascribe this reduction in salt flow to the elimination of salt leakage paths. However, water flux is also reduced somewhat when the additive is present in the brine (more than could be accounted for by elimination of undiluted brine flow through the membrane), so that a surface phenomenon or significant solubility of the additive in cellulose acetate may be the important cause. It has been suggested that the additive may form a "quasi membrane" with excellent salt exclusion.

Further experiments on the "salt leakage" problem are reported by Banks and Sharples.[64] A number of polymers were added to the feed solution in an attempt to improve selectivity. None of the additives, including PVM, significantly improved the salt rejection of highly semi-permeable, i.e., heat-treated, membranes. In membranes that had not been heat-treated and therefore exhibited high water flows with poor salt exclusion, PVM and other additives did improve salt rejection and also reduced the water flux. In fact, the data on relative water and salt fluxes with the more permeable membranes are roughly in keeping with the pore-plugging concept. However, other polymers of the same size range are ineffective, and it is suggested that the additive partakes in some specific interaction with the unheated membranes.

An independent study of the effects of PVM addition to the feed solution was made by Michaels, et al.[24] They found that at a concentration of ~100 ppm PVM was effective in decreasing the salt permeability by about 20 to 25% (cf. Fig. 4–18), with essentially no change in water permeability. These measurements were carried out with highly selective membranes and at least qualitatively confirm the findings of Keilin.

A possible reason for the varying results observed with PVM addition is derived from the fact that PVM is soluble in cold but not in hot water.[79] Above 33°C PVM precipitates from dilute aqueous solutions; the temperature at which this occurs is quite sharply defined. The state of aggregation in solution below this temperature is not known, however, and it is entirely possible that the size of micelles is temperature depend-

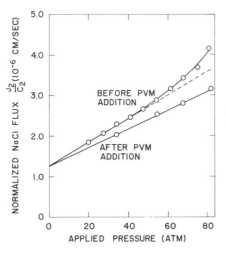

Fig. 4–18 Normalized NaCl flux versus pressure at 25°C before and after treatment with polyvinylmethyl ether. Feed = 0.025 M NaCl. (Data of Michaels, Bixler, and Hodges.[24])

ent; this would determine either the performance of this additive as a hole-plugging agent or the extent of its chemical interaction with cellulose acetate.

If there are micropores in the membranes, one would expect to see a viscous flow of essentially undiluted brine through these pores and thus a pressure-dependent salt flow. Several measurements have been made of the pressure dependence of the flow of several salts in reverse-osmosis experiments.[23,24,67] The first of these are apparently those of Lonsdale, et al.[23] Using 100 ppm NaCl as feed, they measured salt rejection as a function of pressure; their results with two nominally identical membranes are presented in Fig. 4–19. The two lines represent the expected

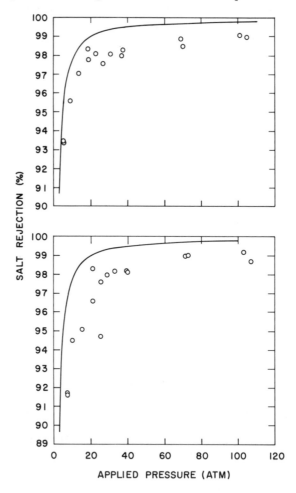

Fig. 4–19 Salt rejection versus pressure for two modified membranes. Feed is 1000 ppm NaCl. (Data of Lonsdale, Merten, and Riley.[23]) The solid lines were calculated from Eq. 4.3 with $P_1 = 2.6 \times 10^{-7}$ g/cm-sec and $P_2 = 3.2 \times 10^{-11}$ cm^2/sec.

salt rejection based on Eq. 4.3, the water-permeability coefficient given in Table 4–6, and the salt permeability as calculated from the immersion data of Table 4–11. Clearly the observed salt rejections are below the "theoretical" value, as was observed in Section 4.2 to be true in the work of Breton[4] on normal membranes. Lonsdale, et al., also measured the flux of salt from a mixed $CaSO_4$-$NaCl$ brine as a function of pressure and assumed, on the basis of the observed high impermeability of cellulose acetate membranes to $CaSO_4$, that all $CaSO_4$ flow had to be through membrane imperfections. The chloride and calcium ion fluxes observed in their experiments are presented in Figs. 4–20 and 4–21, respectively. The brine used was 500 ppm Cl^- as $NaCl$ and 90 ppm Ca^{++} as $CaSO_4$.

The Ca^{++} flux was quite different through two nominally identical membranes, supporting the hypothesis that the flow occurred through random imperfections. The Ca^{++} flux at zero pressure should then be the diffusive flux through these imperfections and through the bulk of the membrane. It was then assumed that the pores that permit the flow of Ca^{++} would also leak $NaCl$, and the authors calculated the total expected flow of Cl^- from the viscous flow contribution (as determined from the Ca^{++} data and the relative concentrations of $NaCl$ and $CaSO_4$ in the brine) and the diffusive contribution, i.e., the pressure-independent, "calculated" curve in Fig. 4–20. The agreement between the predictions and the observations is sufficiently good to conclude that most of the excess Cl^- flow can be accounted for in this way.

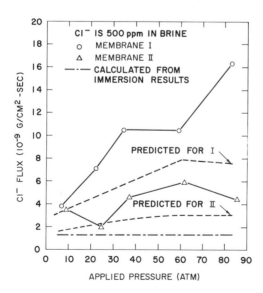

Fig. 4–20   Chloride ion flux across a modified membrane versus pressure. (Data of Lonsdale, Merten, and Riley.[23])

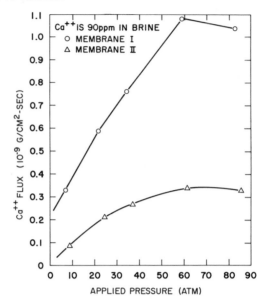

Fig. 4–21   Calcium ion flux across a modified membrane versus pressure. (Data of Lonsdale, Merten, and Riley.[23])

More detailed observations of the pressure dependence of salt flow have been made by Michaels, et al.[24] By varying the membrane-casting technique, these investigators prepared a modified membrane with an unusually large effective thickness, in order to reduce the water flux so that boundary-layer phenomena would not be important. At the same time the effect of the presence of micropores may have been magnified. All of the measurements were made with a single piece of membrane so that the problem of variations between membrane samples was eliminated. For a better interpretation of the results, the thickness of the dense surface layer of the membrane was measured, using a light-microscopy technique involving focusing on the top and bottom surfaces of this layer. The thickness thus measured in a number of places across the membrane surface yielded an average value of 3.5 μ with a standard deviation of 1.6 μ; a rounded value of 4 μ was used. From the data on water flux as a function of pressure, and the water permeability of cellulose acetate as measured in the direct osmosis experiments,[23] we estimate an effective thickness of about half their reported value, i.e., 1.8 μ. Some of the results on the pressure dependence of sodium chloride flow are presented in Fig. 4–18. The salt-flux data have been normalized for the salt-concentration gradient so that the ordinate represents a property of the membrane only. The effect of PVM is apparent; however, it does not reduce the flow to the zero-pressure intercept value. This intercept should represent the diffusive contribution to salt flow, most of which occurs presumably through the membrane and not through pores. Using an effective membrane thickness of 4.0 μ, one can calculate a salt permeability of 5.0×10^{-11} cm²/sec, a value still somewhat greater than that derived from Table 4–11; for an effective thickness of 1.8 μ the disagreement is, of course, greater.

Further data on the pressure-dependent flow of sodium chloride and other salts are presented in Fig. 4–22. The additive PVM was present in the feed solution during these measurements except as noted. Michaels, et al., observed that all their data could be fit by the general equation $J_2 = a + b\Delta P$ and that three types of flow mechanisms would lead to such a relationship. These three flow models are different combinations of three distinguishable kinds of flow behavior: diffusive flow of salt in the pores, diffusion in the bulk of the membrane, and viscous flow of undiluted brine through pores. Two of these combinations can be ruled out from the data on the grounds that pores small enough to restrict viscous flow at high pressures so as to achieve the observed semipermeability will not admit enough salt flow at zero pressure gradient to match the observations; in other words, in the plot of salt flux versus pressure the slope is too small relative to the intercept. These investigators assumed a tortuosity factor of 2.5 for the pore, giving it an effective length of 10 μ. The calculation of viscous flows was made by assuming Poiseuille's law, but the validity of this law for very small channels is not well established. The model that does not lead to inconsistencies depicts a significant fraction of the salt flow as occurring diffusively through the membrane itself, whereas the remainder occurs as viscous flow of undiluted brine through pores. The slope of the plots in Figs. 4–18 and 4–22 should therefore be $\epsilon r^2/8\eta t\lambda$ and the intercept should be $D_{2m}K/\lambda$. By a somewhat arbitrary selection of the velocity of pore fluid they have estimated that the fractional pore

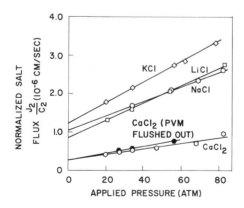

Fig. 4–22   Normalized fluxes of some chloride salts at 25°C. (Data of Michaels, Bixler, and Hodges.[24])

area ϵ is less than 1.6×10^{-5} and that r is therefore greater than 40 Å. In support of their conclusions, Michaels, et al., measured the variation of pressure-dependent salt flow with temperature in order to calculate activation energies. From the zero-pressure intercept values of the salt flow an activation energy of 5.7 kcal/mole was calculated for the pressure-independent permeation process which, as they note, is significantly greater than the activation energy for the viscous flow of water, 4.2 kcal/mole.[80] The fact that PVM reduces the pressure-dependent salt flow is consistent with a mixed-diffusion plus viscous-flow model.

However, two important inconsistencies remain in the model of Michaels, et al., as they themselves note: First, the activation energy for the pressure-dependent portion of the salt flow was found to be 7.2 kcal/mole or almost twice that expected for simple viscous flow; and second, the slope of the salt-flux-versus-pressure lines varies with salt type; this is also not expected for nondiscriminating viscous flow. They conclude that the pressure-dependent portion of the salt flow is a "stress-biased, thermally-activated transport," which is in itself a kind of mixed diffusion-viscous flow model.

Additional data on salt flow as a function of pressure have come from Manjikian.[67] Using modified membranes cast from the acetone-formamide solvent system he found that the salt flow in highly selective membranes was relatively insensitive to pressure up to 100 atm, contrary to the results here reported. It may well be that these relatively unexplored membranes are devoid of pores, but the observed salt rejections do not appear to be any better than those noted here under similar conditions.

From this survey of the "salt-leakage" problem we can perhaps conclude the following: Salts are known to diffuse through the bulk of cellulose acetate membranes, and for sodium chloride at least the true diffusion and distribution coefficients have been measured. Salt flux through all membranes reported on to date, both normal and modified membranes, appears to exceed the expected value based on a simple diffusion model. From the variability in duplicate measurements and from the pressure dependence of salt flux it appears that some salt, in almost all cases the bulk of the salt, is flowing through imperfections and, in spite of many detailed studies, the number and size distribution of these pores have not been established. A possible accommodation of these results is that the flows of salt and water are strongly coupled in the irreversible thermodynamics sense by a mechanism other than simple viscous flow of undiluted brine. Two factors appear to rule out coupled flows of this type as the reason for "salt leakage." As Kraus, Raridon, and Baldwin[81] pointed out, in the limit of strong coupling one expects salt rejection not greater than the value $1 - K/c_{1m}$, or about 70%, but much higher values are normally obtained. Second, in direct-osmosis experiments, coupled flows should lead to salt fluxes that are too small, because salt and water flows are in opposite directions. However, as we have seen,[23] the salt flow is too high in these experiments as well.

A clearer understanding of the "salt-leakage" problem requires further research.

Membrane Compaction

It is well established that modified membranes show decreasing water-permeation rates with time at a fixed pressure, and it is also known that as the brine is pressurized the water flux is not exactly linear in the net pressure, particularly at high pressures. We shall refer to these two effects collectively as "compaction" effects. The first of these phenomena is clearly demonstrated in the results of Sourirajan and Govindan,[82] given in Fig. 4–23. Perhaps the most dramatic observation of time-dependent flux was that encountered by Loeb and Manjikian[71] in a six-month field test with a brackish-water source at Coalinga, California. At an applied pressure of about 40 atm, the water flux through the membrane dropped from 2.4×10^{-3} to 0.85×10^{-3} g/cm²-sec; however, at least part of this decrease in flux was probably the result of a deposit formed on the membrane surface. The earliest reference to the second of these compaction effects appears in some of the original research reported by Loeb and Sourirajan[6] in which it was found that the water

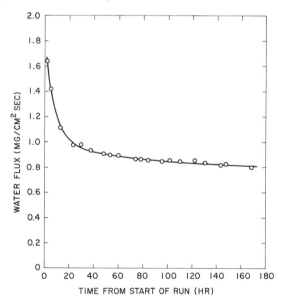

Fig. 4–23 Variation of water flux with time in a continuous run with seawater at 102 atm. (Data of Sourirajan and Govindan.[82])

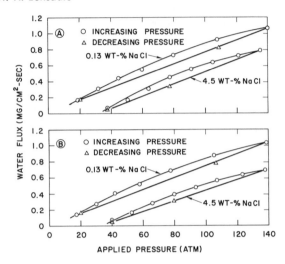

Fig. 4–24   Water flux versus applied pressure for four modified membranes. (Data of Lonsdale, Merten, and Riley.[23])

flux at 136 atm pressure was only slightly greater than that at 102 atm. Further data on this effect can be seen in a typical plot of water flux versus net pressure for two nominally identical membranes, as reproduced from the data of Lonsdale, et al.[23] in Fig. 4–24. The circled data points were taken as the pressure was increasing, the triangles during periods of decreasing pressure. It appears from this figure that the membranes are not completely restored to their original permeation characteristics as the system is depressurized, at least in short-time tests.

Additional evidence of membrane compaction can be derived from the results of Michaels, et al.[24] When water flux was measured as a function of net pressure by maintaining a fixed osmotic pressure while varying the applied pressure, the apparent water permeability decreased by perhaps 20% as the applied pressure was increased from 25 to 80 atm.

There has been only one report of a modified membrane that apparently showed no compaction effects. Using distilled water as feed, Banks and Sharples[64] found that water flux was quite linear in the applied pressure over the range 0 to 100 atm, with a flux per unit applied pressure of 5×10^{-6} g/cm^2-sec-atm. This suggests that compaction effects depend strongly on the method of membrane preparation. It has been generally observed that once pressurized to 100 atm or more modified membranes suffer a largely nonrecoverable reduction in water flux per unit net pressure but that subsequent pressure cycling below the maximum applied pressure does not lead to a substantial additional compaction effect, at least not in short tests. Thus, the order in which water-flux data are obtained is important; perhaps the membrane described above was initially exposed to high pressures.

The only obvious macroscopic change occurring in the membrane during pressurization is a reduction in gross thickness. A nonrecoverable decrease in thickness of from one third to one half has been generally observed after use at 100 atm. It has also been noted that the amount of capillary water sorbed after pressurization is much less than that sorbed by the as-cast membrane.[64]

Three possible explanations of the changes in membrane properties associated with compaction are possible: First, the water permeability may be time- or pressure-dependent. However, as has been noted, the limit on the possible pressure dependence appears to be well within the observable compaction effects, in which a reduction in flow of a factor of two or more is not uncommon. In addition it has been found that at a constant applied pressure of 41 atm the water permeability of a normal, 37%-acetyl membrane was invariant with time over a nine-month period.[4] Second, it is possible that viscous resistance to flow in the porous substructure increases with time or pressure to the point where it is a substantial fraction of the total resistance to flow in the membrane. Third, it is conceivable that the salt-rejecting surface layer of the membrane grows in thickness due to plastic flow or creep. A simple test to select between the latter two mechanisms is available: If the effective thickness of the membrane increases, the flux of both water and salt should decrease and salt rejection should remain invariant. However, increased resistance to viscous flow in the substructure should reduce the net driving force across the salt-rejecting layer for water only, and salt rejection should decrease while salt flow remains invariant.

Unfortunately, there are relatively few data with which to make this test and some of these data are conflicting. Most of the long-term tests in which both water flux and salt rejection are reported have been made with the very high flux, "brackish-water" membranes for which the simple diffusion model is inadequate for both water and salt flow. A second reason for the paucity of test data is that hydrolysis of the cellulose acetate membranes, which tends to increase both water and salt flow, is a complicating factor in tests which are of sufficient duration to be interesting. Recognizing these limitations, we have calculated the water and salt flux from experiments of Loeb and Manjikian,[58,71] with the results presented in Tables 4–16 and 4–17. Table 4–16 refers to a short-term experiment with high-flux membranes known to be particularly susceptible to compaction. The water flux is presented in the form of a membrane constant A, which represents the water flux per unit net pressure difference; i.e., $A \equiv F_1/(\Delta p - \Delta \pi)$. The salt permeation results are similarly expressed in terms of flow per unit concentration difference, a parameter to which we shall refer as the salt-permeation constant and designate B; i.e., $B \equiv F_2/\Delta c_2$. The parameters A and B are membrane-performance parameters that combine both the permeability and the

Table 4-16   Water and Salt Flow in "High-Flux" Membranes versus Pressure
(Feed brine is 0.5% NaCl)
Data of Loeb and Manjikian.[58]

Applied pressure (atm)	Water flux (10^{-3} g/cm²-sec)	Salt rejection (%)	Membrane constant A (10^{-5} g/cm²-sec-atm)	Salt-permeation constant B (10^{-5} cm/sec)
27	0.90	91.2	3.8	8.7
41	1.28	94.0	3.5	8.2
68	1.94	95.6	3.0	8.9
102	2.46	96.4	2.5	9.2

effective membrane thickness. Thus, in terms of quantities already defined,

$$A = \frac{D_{1m}c_{1m}v_1}{RT\lambda} \quad \text{and} \quad B = \frac{D_{2m}K}{\lambda}.$$

The data in Table 4-17 are taken from the results of the Coalinga field test. The reasons for some of the scatter in the field-test results were discussed by Loeb and Manjikian. It appears from these results on high-flux membranes that the membrane constant decreases with increasing pressure or with time at constant pressure, whereas the salt-permeation constant does not. These findings are not consistent with an increase in effective membrane thickness. The same may be said for the results of Michaels, et al.,[24] who found that salt flux increased linearly with pressure in their experiments with a modified membrane, while the water

Table 4-17   Water and Salt Flux in a Six-Month Field Test
(41 atm applied pressure. Feed brine is 2500 ppm total dissolved solids)
Data of Loeb and Manjikian.[71,83]

Date	Water flux (10^{-3} g/cm²-sec)	Salt rejection (%)	Salt flux (10^{-7} g/cm²-sec)
April 9	2.4	94.0	3.6
April 13	2.1	93.6	3.4
May 9	1.9	90.0	4.7
June 6	1.6	88.0	4.7
June 9	1.5	80.0	7.6
June 24	1.7	80.0	8.3
June 25	1.2	83.2	5.0
July 9	0.95	84.0	3.8
July 15	1.1	88.0	3.3
August 9	1.0	88.0	3.1
September 9	1.0	86.0	3.7
October 5	0.85	88.8	2.4

flux increased less rapidly than predicted by Eq. 4.1. Banks and Sharples also found that salt rejection decreased with time at pressure.[64] There are, however, a number of contradictory observations — for example those reported by Sourirajan and Govindan,[82] to the effect that salt rejection is invariant as the water flux decreases. Such results are consistent with an increased effective membrane thickness. It is difficult, in view of these divergent results, to define the nature of membrane compaction categorically. Additional, well-controlled experiments are desirable in this area. All of the observations concerning the time dependence of salt rejection must be tempered with the fact that cellulose acetate membranes are known to hydrolyze, and hydrolysis also leads to loss in salt rejection.

Some data are indirectly applicable to the compaction effect.[47] These are some tensile-strength measurements similar to those reported in Table 4–13 for normal membranes. The results of tests on modified membranes are contained in Table 4–18. With one exception, all of

Table 4–18   Tensile-Strength Measurements on Modified Cellulose Acetate
Membranes
Data of Lonsdale, Merten, Riley, and Vos.[47]

Cellulose acetate type (Eastman designation)	Thickness (mils)	Ultimate strength (psi)	Modulus of elasticity (10^3 psi)	Percent elongation at failure
398-3	2.0	1000	51	8
	2.8	1100	74	11
	3.7	1000	63	8
	4.0	900	50	13
	4.4	1000	60	15
398-3, unannealed	3.6	800	54	17
398-6	4.3	1100	60	11–20
398-10	4.7	1300	51	42

these membranes were annealed after casting, essentially in conformity with the Loeb-Sourirajan procedure. The strength of the modified membranes is noted to be about 40% of that of the normal membranes, consistent with the observation that they contain about 60 volume-% water. The implication is that the porous substructure contributes to the strength of the membrane even though it is highly permeable to water.

The long-term creep behavior of modified cellulose acetate membranes does not appear to be known, but from the tensile-strength measurements and from the assumption that the strengths in tension and in compression are not too dissimilar, the compaction of membranes at pressures well below 100 atm is not surprising and, in fact, to be expected. This is a somewhat undesirable feature of these modified membranes which otherwise combine two important advantages: effective thinness and sufficient strength to support pressures of 100 atm or more without rupturing. The relatively large variations observed in the magnitude of the compaction effect suggest that subtle changes in membrane-preparation procedures are important; however, no systematic study of the interdependence of details of membrane preparation and compaction effects has been reported.

Kinetics of Membrane Hydrolysis and Membrane Life

In the early work of Breton[4] it was observed that normal cellulose acetate membranes exhibited a decrease in semipermeability with an associated increase in water-flow rate after a period of use of a few days. The membranes deteriorated in about this time period in the presence of sodium chloride feed brines, but their durability with magnesium chloride or dextrose feed solutions was greatly lengthened and no change in water-flow rate was observed after nine months of continuous use in distilled water at 41 atm. Among the other findings of Breton were that the failure was pH dependent, being somewhat more rapid at pH 5.5 than at pH 4.0 in the presence of about 0.5 wt-% NaCl, and that a cellulose acetate membrane of 43%-acetyl content far exceeded the durability of a 37%-acetyl membrane in terms of length of time of high semipermeability. X-ray diffraction, birefringence, and infrared-spectroscopy studies demonstrated that failure was accompanied by increased molecular orientation and increased hydroxyl content, indicating that it was associated with the hydrolysis of the cellulose acetate. Chemically speaking, this material is an ester, and esters are well known for their instability to water, reacting to form an alcohol and an acid (in this case, less highly substituted cellulose acetate and acetic acid), and the reaction is usually highly base- and acid-catalyzed.

There are many references in the literature to studies of the acid- and base-catalyzed hydrolysis of cellulose acetate, but these are under either very basic or very acid conditions, and the extrapolation to the more neutral conditions expected in reverse osmosis applications is tenuous at best. However, a systematic study of the kinetics of hydrolysis of modified cellulose acetate membranes has been made by Vos, Burris, and Riley.[84] These investigators, using modified membranes because of their high porosity, have shown that the reaction rates in these membranes are not diffusion limited. The hydrolysis rate has been measured as a function of both pH and temperature. The reaction is catalyzed by acid and even more strongly by base, and there is an observable uncatalyzed reaction as well.

Some of the results of the work of Vos, et al., are presented in Fig.

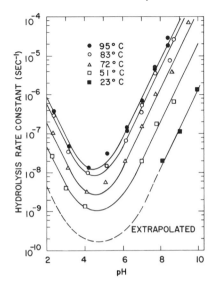

Fig. 4–25 Hydrolysis rate constant versus pH at several temperatures. (Data of Vos, Burris, and Riley.[84])

4–25. The hydrolysis rate constant K is a typical first-order reaction rate constant. The pH at which the reaction rate is a minimum is in the range 4.5 to 5.0. These results were applied to the calculation of membrane lifetime as a function of pH. This is possible with the aid of the data on salt and water permeability as a function of acetyl content presented in Tables 4–6 and 4–11. The permeabilities of both constituents increase as the cellulose acetate is deacetylated, but the salt permeability increases much more rapidly, resulting in a sharp decrease in salt rejection with deacetylation, consistent with the work of Breton.[4]

By developing empirical relationships between the permeabilities and the acetyl content and using the first-order rate equation, the following empirical relationships have been found between membrane performance parameters and time:

$$\ln A = 10.7 \, Kt + \text{constant}, \qquad (4.5)$$

and

$$\ln B = 29.6 \, Kt + \text{constant}, \qquad (4.6)$$

where A and B are the membrane constant and salt-permeation constant, respectively, as previously defined. The application of the hydrolysis-kinetics data to lifetime calculations is made somewhat difficult by the fact that the feed solution and the product water are generally not of the same pH, presumably because of the relative rates of transport of those species that determine the pH, i.e., H^+, OH^-, HCO_3^-, and $CO_3^=$. With feed waters containing a significant amount of bicarbonate, the product water is usually more acidic than the feed by 0.5 to 1 pH unit. Thus, the membrane is not uniformly deacetylated. Nevertheless Vos, et al., have shown, for example, that salt rejection should decrease markedly in the first few weeks of operation at a pH in the range 8 to 9, which is the pH of a number of natural water sources, and that a useful membrane lifetime of a few years is to be expected in pH-adjusted brines. A number of good correlations have been found between the observed increase in salt flux with time in tests up to a year in duration using Eq. 4.6.[85] Similar correlations based on water flux are more difficult because of membrane compaction.

These results explain the varied durability observed by Breton[4] and others. Breton's observation concerning the effect of NaCl brines may be rationalized in terms of possible pH changes accompanying corrosion in the reverse-osmosis equipment. Vos, Hatcher, and Merten[85] have demonstrated that the presence of sodium chloride does not in itself affect membrane durability. Other observations by Banks and Sharples on the loss in membrane semipermeability at high brine pH[64] are at least qualitatively consistent with the hydrolysis-kinetics results. They also demonstrated rather conclusively that membrane failure is not the result of bacterial effects, as has been suggested on occasion.

An additional enlightening note on the hydrolysis of modified membranes can be found in the electron-microscopy research of Riley, et al.[55] In attempting to obtain replicas of the surface of membranes that had slowly lost their semipermeability in reverse-osmosis tests, it was noted that the cellulose acetate could not be completely dissolved away from the replica. An electron photomicrograph of a replica of a partially

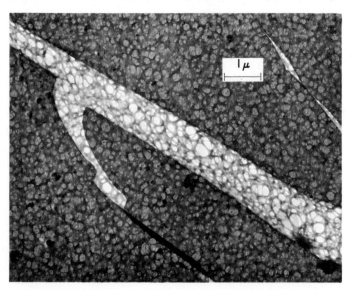

Fig. 4–26   Electron photomicrograph of a preshadowed carbon replica of the air-dried surface of a hydrolyzed modified cellulose acetate membrane. The membrane was dehydrated by freeze-drying. (Results of Riley, Merten, and Gardner.[55])

failed membrane is shown in Fig. 4-26. The network visible both through the replica and in a crack in the replica constitutes some of the membrane surface that did not dissolve in acetone. The acetone solubility of cellulose acetates was shown in Table 4-1 to be a function of the degree of acetylation. The surface exposed to the brine was partially insoluble in acetone, and presumably the bulk of the membrane had not hydrolyzed sufficiently to become acetone insoluble.

Other Studies of High-Flux Membranes

We include here the results of some studies on cellulose acetate membranes not of the conventional Loeb-Sourirajan type. Some of these are merely the result of modifications of the Loeb-Sourirajan methods, but the membrane performance is generally so different that Eqs. 4.1 to 4.3 are probably no longer valid.

Both Loeb and Manjikian[58,71] and Keilin[59,60] have prepared membranes suitable for the desalination of brackish waters, where high selectivity is not required. These membranes give water fluxes several times those originally reported by Loeb and Sourirajan[6] (typically 3 to 4 $\times$ 10^{-5} g/cm²-sec-atm at fairly low pressures); they are prepared by variations in the relative concentrations in the membrane-casting solution or by reduced heat treatment of the membrane. They are presumably diffusive-viscous flow barriers whose properties are perhaps describable in terms of the finely porous model of Chapter 2, but no detailed attempt has yet been made to fit a model of this type to the results obtained. However, the application of any model to account for the properties of these very useful membranes will be complex because of the apparent pressure sensitivity of the pore dimensions, as is true in the case of cellophane, for example.[86] Some indication of this complexity is evident from the salt-flux results of Manjikian,[67] who observed that the salt flux is essentially independent of pressure in membranes cast from a formamide-acetone solvent when the membranes are annealed at 81°C. As the temperature or time of heat-treating is decreased, the salt flux becomes more pressure dependent and the flux at the zero-pressure intercept also increases as the annealing conditions are reduced as though the membrane were becoming more porous. The salt flux at the zero-pressure intercept increases more rapidly with decreasing annealing temperature than does water flux, suggesting that a significant fraction of the water flow is also becoming viscous. Unfortunately there does not appear to be a wealth of diagnostic measurements on these membranes. We have here noted some of their compaction properties, and other properties are reported in Chapter 3.

Skiens and Mahon[73] have apparently succeeded in preparing modified membranes of cellulose triacetate. Based on the permeability properties of the triacetate reported in Tables 4–3, 4–6, and 4–11, one would expect that these membranes will exhibit excellent salt exclusion and somewhat lower water permeability than that found in cellulose 2.5-acetate membranes. The membranes were cast from solution (the composition of which was not stated), and the approximate Loeb-Sourirajan technique was used, except that the membranes were not heat-treated. Results of reverse-osmosis tests with these membranes are summarized in Table 4–19. The constancy in the parameters A and B shows that the

Table 4–19   Reverse-Osmosis Experiment with Cellulose Triacetate Membrane
(Conditions: membrane area, 46 cm²; feed brine, 1.0% NaCl; membrane Thickness, 58 μ[87])
Data of Skiens and Mahon.[73]

Applied pressure (atm)	Water flux (10⁻⁵ g/cm²-sec)	Salt rejection (%)	Membrane constant A (10⁻⁶ g/cm²-sec-atm)	Salt permeation constant B (10⁻⁶ cm/sec)
14.6	1.4	67.5	1.5	6.9
21.4	2.2	82.5	1.5	4.6
28.2	3.5	83.9	1.6	6.7
35.0	4.7	87.4	1.7	6.9
41.9	5.7	91.3	1.7	5.2
48.9	6.6	92.5	1.6	5.2

water flow varies with net pressure in accordance with Eq. 4.1 and that salt flow is essentially independent of pressure. The latter observation is somewhat surprising in view of the low observed salt rejections, which are probably not the result of boundary-layer effects, since in such a case the salt flux would increase and the membrane constant decrease with increasing pressure. The results are also not consistent with an assumption of an imperfect membrane unless one also assumes that the size of the imperfections is a decreasing function of pressure. From the permeability of cellulose triacetate to water reported in Table 4–6, i.e., 1.5×10^{-7} g\cm-sec, one can calculate an effective thickness of the Skiens and Mahon membrane of 0.70 μ, or about 1.2% of the total thickness. We conclude that this is a modified cellulose triacetate membrane with somewhat poorer performance in desalination, the result, perhaps, of the difficulties of adapting the Loeb-Sourirajan technique to the triacetate.

In a series of publications,[74–76] Sourirajan has reported some results on the use of porous cellulose acetate membranes in water desalination. The membranes used in this study were prepared by the Schleicher & Schuell Company and are designated UA-Superdense. Sourirajan studied the effect of varying the porosity of these membranes by heat treatment on the semipermeability to a large number of aqueous salt solutions, with the result that even these relatively porous membranes can be highly selective to some species: A membrane giving 82.5% rejection of 0.5 M NaCl at 102 atm gave 99.5% rejection of 0.5 M Na$_2$SO$_4$ at the same pressure. In the limit of high heat treatment these membranes are only slightly inferior in selectivity to the modified membranes, i.e., 96.5% rejection of 0.84% NaCl solution at an applied pressure of 100 atm. One can show from the reverse-osmosis results that the water flow follows Eq. 4.1 quite well for the highly selective membranes. However, the water flux through the most selective membranes is relatively low. In the original report of these studies,[6] a water flux of 1.1 $\times$ 10^{-4} g/cm^2-sec, or 2.3 gpd/ft^2 at 102 atm was reported, but in more recent reports Sourirajan states that membranes with much higher flow rates can be prepared with salt rejections at 102 atm in the 50-to-90% range. Sourirajan noted that the product of the observed water-permeation rates through these membranes and the viscosity of water is essentially independent of temperature over the range 10 to 25°C, indicating substantial viscous flow. His results include a large amount of data on the relative semipermeability to various salts as well as organic solutes.

Sourirajan interprets the water-flow and salt-rejection mechanisms quite differently than we have here. He considers the fact that salts are known to be negatively adsorbed in the first molecular layer or so of an air-water interface. He assumes an analogous situation at the solution-membrane interface and employs the Gibbs adsorption isotherm to account for the observed selectivity. Water is assumed to flow through pores, the radii of which are smaller than the thickness of the demineralized water layer, in order to effect salt exclusion. Salt transport occurs through pores larger than this critical size. In order to account for the results it is postulated that the size, number, and distribution of pores can vary. One weakness of this theory is that it fails to predict adequately the effect of pressure, salt type, or salt concentration on the flux and desalination observed in reverse osmosis. According to the Sourirajan theory, as extended by Glueckauf,[88] salt rejection should vary rather strongly with salt concentration. The data for the relatively highly selective membranes show only a weak trend in this direction and are actually in excellent agreement with predictions based on Eq. 4.3. Furthermore, Scatchard[89] has extended the Sourirajan approach to account for differences in dielectric behavior between the membrane-water and the water-air interfaces. This more exact treatment predicts that the distribution of salt in the aqueous phase within the first few angstroms of the membrane-water interface does not affect salt rejection.

All of the membranes reported on in this section thus far have had the property of being basically highly porous, with an effective thickness much less than the apparent thickness. They have the advantage of simplicity of preparation in that one prepares the membrane and its support simultaneously. However, they suffer somewhat from inflexibility of design — it is difficult to change reproducibly and accurately either the effective thickness of the membrane or the porosity of the substructure. Some interesting experiments have been carried out by Francis[90] on the preparation of very thin films of cellulose acetate without supporting substructure. His membranes are cast from an appropriate solution onto water, where they are spread to extreme thinness. Membranes with fairly good semipermeability to sodium chloride and with a thickness of ~ 0.1 μ have been prepared by this method.

More recently, thin films have been prepared in our Laboratory by drawing a clean glass plate out of a dilute solution of cellulose acetate in a suitable solvent.[91] The film dries on the plate on standing in air and is subsequently removed from the plate by floating it off on water. This technique is an extension of the method originally used by Carnell and Cassidy[92,93] for other polymer systems. Useful films as thin as 600 Å have been reproducibly prepared in this way. The salt rejection achieved with these thin films improves with the cleanliness of the solutions and the casting conditions. Two of the membranes prepared in this way have given "theoretical" salt rejection. In reverse-osmosis tests at 1560 psi with 0.9% NaCl feed solution, the observed salt rejection on two 2800-Å-thick samples of 39.8%-acetyl cellulose acetate was 99.81%, and the water flux was about 9.5 gpd/ft^2.[94] The theoretical rejection under these conditions is 99.83%. It is also interesting that only these two membranes out of the many tested did not contain observable imperfections. A search for imperfections was made by adding ethyl violet to the brine; imperfections were distinguished by the presence of a stain in the porous support. All previous membranes, both of the thin-film and modified types, did contain imperfections detectable by this method.

These latter findings offer strong support for the conclusions already drawn about the importance of membrane imperfections, and they offer a good rationalization of the intrinsic solute-permeability coefficients and the salt rejections observed in practice.

4.4 Summary

In this chapter we have presented working equations for the transport of water and solute species across cellulose acetate membranes; these were developed on the assumption that the membranes are essentially diffusion barriers. A number of observations on the transport properties of dense membranes were in accordance with these equations, and it has been found that water flow can be described quite well in both dense and modified membranes, but that salt flow cannot be described as simply. The equilibrium and transport properties of cellulose acetates of varying degree of substitution appear to be fairly well known, based on direct-osmosis and reverse-osmosis measurements and on sorption measurements, all carried out on dense membranes. These measured values are believed to be intrinsic properties of cellulose acetate, and it is anticipated that they will apply to modified membranes as well. Some reservations go with this statement, however. It is certainly expected that changes in polymer microstructure will have a significant effect on the permeability coefficients; it is perhaps surprising that these coefficients have been found relatively constant in spite of several variations in the membrane history.

Based on intrinsic permeability measurements, the salt rejection of sodium chloride has been predicted to be about 99.7% at a net pressure of 60 atm, although in fact a salt rejection as high as this has never been reported for modified membranes (and achieved only recently with thin films); salt leakage through imperfections is the apparent reason for the discrepancy. In spite of a good deal of research on the mechanism of salt leakage, our understanding remains incomplete, even though a combined-diffusion-plus-viscous-flow model of salt transport fits the observations fairly well.

The morphology of the membrane will of course determine its water-flow behavior by defining the effective thickness. The most successful method for producing effectively very thin membranes thus far is that of Loeb and Sourirajan.[6] Membranes so prepared have been shown to possess a very thin dense layer on one surface, on the order of 0.2 μ thick. The remainder of the membrane consists of a porous mass, the pore size being in the range of a few tenths of a micron. It appears from osmosis measurements that the dense layer has the transport properties of cellulose acetate and that the porous substructure contributes very little resistance to flow, at least at low pressures. From an analysis of the time- and pressure-dependent behavior of water flow and salt rejection through these membranes, it appears that the resistance to water and, perhaps, salt flow increases with time and pressure. This can be a serious limitation in the use of these membranes.

At least two other novel attempts to prepare very thin membranes are in progress and it would appear that still others are in order.

Membrane lifetime has been studied in association with hydrolysis-kinetics measurements, and it has been found that membrane failure can be brought about by heterogeneous hydrolysis, which is particularly rapid in basic media. A membrane lifetime of a year or more can probably be expected with the use of pH control.

Some problem areas remain in the field of transport theories; in the improvement in membrane fabrication with respect to both reproducibility and improved salt rejection; and, in the case of the Loeb-Sourirajan membrane, in the elimination of compaction effects. These problem areas are the active subjects of research in several laboratories, and we can expect further improvements in the performance of membranes prepared from this very promising material.

References

1. Barrer, R. M., *Diffusion in and Through Solids*, Cambridge University Press' 1951, Chap. X.
2. Jost, W., *Diffusion in Solids, Liquids, Gases*, Academic Press, New York, 1960, p. 298.
3. Simonds, H. R., A. J. Weith, and M. H. Bigelow, editors, *Handbook of Plastics*, 2nd ed., Van Nostrand, Princeton, N. J., 1949, p. 581.
4. Breton, E. J., Jr., *Water and Ion Flow Through Imperfect Osmotic Membranes*, Office of Saline Water, Research and Development Progress Report No. 16, PB 161391 (1957).
5. Reid, C. E., and E. J. Breton, *J. Appl. Polymer Sci.* **1**, 133 (1959).
6. Loeb, S., and S. Sourirajan, UCLA Department of Engineering Report 60-60 (1960); *Advan. Chem. Ser.* **38**, 117 (1962).
7. Eastman Chemical Products, Inc., Circular *Cellulose Acetate*.
8. Moore, W. R., and B. M. Tidswell, *J. Appl. Chem. (London)* **8**, 235 (1938).
9. Genung, L. B., *Anal. Chem.* **36**, 1817 (1964).
10. Malm, C. J., L. J. Tanghe, and G. D. Smith, *Ind. Eng. Chem.* **42**, 730 (1950).
11. Gearhart, W. M., Eastman Chemical Products, Inc., Kingsport, Tenn., private communication.
12. Dobry, A., *Bull. soc. chim. France* **3**, 312 (1936).
13. Biget, A.-M., *Ann. chim.* **5**, 66 (1950).
14. Borgin, K., *TAPPI* **36**, 284 (1953).
15. Crisp, D. J., *J. Coll. Sci.* **1**, 49, 161 (1946).
16. Baker, W. O., C. S. Fuller, and N. R. Pape, *J. Amer. Chem. Soc.* **64**, 776 (1942).
17. Spence, J., *J. Phys. Chem.* **45**, 401 (1941).
18. Boyer, R. F., and R. S. Spencer, in *Advances in Colloid Science* Vol. II Interscience, New York, 1946, p. 1.
19. Daane, J. H., and R. E. Barker, *Polymer Letters* **2**, 343 (1964).
20. Ferry, J. D., *Viscoelastic Properties of Polymers*, John Wiley & Sons, New York, 1961.
21. Richards, W. T., *J. Chem. Phys.* **4**, 449 (1936).
22. Laidler, K. J., and K. E. Shuler, *J. Chem. Phys.* **17**, 851 (1949).
23. Lonsdale, H. K., U. Merten, and R. L. Riley, *J. Appl. Polymer Sci.* **9**, 1341 (1965).
24. Michaels, A. S., H. J. Bixler, and R. M. Hodges, Jr., M.I.T. Dept. of Chem. Engr., Report 315-1 DSR 9409 (1964).
25. Clark, W. E., *Science* **138**, 148 (1963).
26. Reid, C. E., Univ. of Florida, Gainesville, Fla., private communication.
27. Reid, C. E., and H. G. Spencer, *J. Phys. Chem.* **64**, 1587 (1960).
28. Vos, K. D., and A. P. Hatcher, General Atomic Division, General Dynamics Corporation, San Diego, Calif., private communication.
29. Reid, C. E., and J. R. Kuppers, *J. Appl. Polymer Sci.* **2**, 264 (1959).
30. Birkhimer, E. A., and P. Harriott, 35th National Meeting of American Institute of Chemical Engineers, Houston, Texas, Feb. 8, 1965.
31. Mauersberger, H. R., ed., *Textile Fibers*, 6th ed., John Wiley & Sons, New York, 1954, pp. 886–7.
32. Long, E. A., and L. J. Thompson, *J. Polymer Sci.* **15**, 413 (1955).

33. Thomas, A. M., *J. Appl. Chem.* 1, 141 (1951).
34. Kovacs, A., *J. chim. phys.* 45, 258 (1948).
35. Korte-Falinski, M., *ibid.* 59, 27 (1962).
36. Taylor, R. L., D. B. Herman, and A. R. Kemp, *Ind. Eng. Chem.* 28, 1255 (1936).
37. Thomas, C. R., and R. E. Barker, Jr., *J. Appl. Polymer Sci.* 7, 1933 (1963).
38. Hauser, P. M., and A. D. McLaren, *Ind. Eng. Chem.* 40, 112 (1948).
39. Binnings, R. C., R. J. Lee, J. F. Jennings, and E. C. Martin, *ibid.* 53, 45 (1961).
40. Michaels, A. S., R. F. Baddour, H. J. Bixler, and C. Y. Choo, *Ind. Eng. Chem. Process Design Develop.* 1, 14 (1962).
41. Stannett, V., and H. Yasuda, *J. Polymer Sci.* B1, 289 (1963).
42. Newsome, P. T., and S. E. Sheppard, *J. Phys. Chem.* 36, 930 (1932).
43. Tankard, J., *J. Textile Inst.* 28, T263 (1937).
44. Wang, J. H., *J. Amer. Chem. Soc.* 73, 510 (1951).
45. Olander, D. R., *A. I. Ch. E. J.* 7, 175 (1961).
46. Ref. 3, pp. 79–80.
47. Lonsdale, H. K., U. Merten, R. L. Riley, and K. D. Vos, *Reverse Osmosis for Water Desalination*, Annual Report April 16, 1964–April 15, 1965. Office of Saline Water, Research and Development Progress Report No. 150.
48. Ferry, J. D., *Chem. Rev.* 18, 373 (1936).
49. Elford, W. J., *Proc. Roy. Soc.* B106, 216 (1930).
50. Elford, W. J., *J. Path. and Bact.* 34, 505 (1931).
51. Elford, W. J., *Trans. Far. Soc.* 33, 1094 (1937).
52. Grabar, P., *Compt. rend.* 198, 1640 (1934).
53. Vaughan, M. F., *Nature* 183, 43 (1959)
54. Riley, R. L., J. O. Gardner, and U. Merten, *Science* 143, 801 (1964).
55. Riley, R. L., U. Merten, and J. O. Gardner, *Desalination*, 1, 30 (1966).
56. Loeb, S., UCLA Department of Engineering Report 63-32 (1963).
57. Loeb, S., UCLA Department of Engineering Report 62-26 (1962).
58. Loeb, S., and S. Manjikian, UCLA Department of Engineering Report 63-22 (1963).
59. Keilin, B., *The Mechanism of Desalination by Reverse Osmosis*, Office of Saline Water, Research and Development Progress Report 117, PB 166395 (Aug. 1964).
60. Keilin, B., *The Mechanism of Desalination by Reverse Osmosis*, Office of Saline Water, Research and Development Progress Report 84, PB 181571 (Nov. 1963).
61. Kesting, R. E., *J. Appl. Polymer Sci.* 9, 663 (1965).
62. Kesting, R. E., M. K. Barsh, and A. L. Vincent, *ibid.* 9, 1873 (1965).
63. Vincent, A. L., M. K. Barsh, and R. E. Kesting, *ibid.* 9, 2363 (1965).
64. Banks, W., and A. Sharples, *The Mechanism of Desalination by Reverse Osmosis, and its Relation to Membrane Structure*, Final Report to the Office of Saline Water for the Period January 1963–December 1964 (1965); *J. Appl. Chem.* 16, 28 (1966).
65. Loeb, S., and J. W. McCutchan, *Ind. Eng. Chem. Prod. Res. Dev.* 4, 114 (1965).
66. Loeb, S., UCLA Department of Engineering Report 62-41 (1962).
67. Manjikian, S., UCLA Department of Engineering Report 65-13 (1965).
68. Loeb, S., UCLA Department of Engineering Report 61-42 (1961).
69. Blunk, R., UCLA Department of Engineering Report 64-28 (1964).
70 Loeb, S., and S. Manjikian, UCLA Department of Engineering Report 63-37 (1963).
71. Loeb, S., and S. Manjikian, *Ind. Eng. Chem. Proc. Des. Dev.* 4, 207 (1965).
72. *Investigation and Preparation of Polymer Films to Improve the Separation of Water and Salts in Saline Water Conversion.* Office of Saline Water, Research and Development Progress Report No. 69, PB 181467 (1962).
73. Skiens, W. E., and H. I. Mahon, *J. Appl. Polymer Sci.* 7, 1549 (1963).

74. Sourirajan, S., *Ind. Eng. Chem. Fundamentals* **2**, 51 (1963).
75. Sourirajan, S., *ibid.* **3**, 206 (1964).
76. Sourirajan, S., *J. Appl. Chem.* **14**, 506 (1964).
77. Robinson, R. A. and R. H. Stokes, *Electrolyte Solutions*, 2nd ed., Butterworths, London, 1959.
78. Vos, K. D., and A. P. Hatcher, General Atomic Division, General Dynamics Corporation, unpublished results.
79. Kirk, R. E., and F. Othmer, editors, *Encyclopedia of Chemical Technology* Vol. 11, Interscience Encyclopedia Inc., New York, 1953, p. 651.
80. Tuwiner, S. C., *Diffusion and Membrane Technology*, Reinhold Publishing Co., New York, 1962, p. 376.
81. Kraus, K. A., R. J. Raridon, and W. B. Baldwin, *J. Amer. Chem. Soc.* **86**, 2571 (1964).
82. Sourirajan, S., and T. S. Govindan, *Proc. First Intn'l. Desalination Symp.*, Paper SWD/41, Washington, D. C., Oct. 3–9, 1965.
83. Experimental data were provided by S. Loeb, Univ. of California, Los Angeles.
84. Vos, K. D., F. Burris, and R. L. Riley, *J. Appl. Polymer Sci.* **10**, 825 (1966).
85. Vos, K. D., A. P. Hatcher, and U. Merten, *Ind. Eng. Chem. Prod. Res. Dev.* **5**, 211 (1966).
86. Ticknor, L. B., *J. Phys. Chem.* **62**, 1483 (1958).
87. Certain experimental data were supplied by H. I. Mahon, Dow Chemical Company, Pittsburg, California.
88. Glueckauf, E., *Proc. First Intn'l. Desalination Symp.*, Paper SWD/1, Washington, D. C., Oct. 3–9, 1965.
89. Scatchard, G., *J. Phys. Chem.* **68**, 1056 (1964).
90. Francis, P. S., *Fabrication and Evaluation of New Ultrathin Reverse Osmosis Membranes*, First Annual Report, Sept. 28, 1964 through Sept. 27, 1965, Office of Saline Water, Research and Development Progress Report No. 177 (Feb. 1966).
91. Merten, U., H. Lonsdale, R. L. Riley, and K. Vos, *Reverse Osmosis for Water Desalination*, Final Report to Office of Saline Water, under contract 14-01-0001-250, to be published.
92. Carnell, P. H., and H. G. Cassidy, *J. Polymer Sci.* **55**, 233 (1961).
93. Carnell, P. H., *J. Appl. Polymer Sci.* **9**, 1863 (1965).
94. Riley, R. L., General Atomic Division, General Dynamics Corporation, private communication.

5. Mass Transport in Reverse Osmosis

P. L. T. Brian

In all processes for water desalination, the water and the salt to be separated must ultimately diffuse apart by molecular diffusion. Thus, at the phase boundary where the separation is effected there will be a salt-concentration boundary layer, the salt concentration at the phase boundary exceeding that in the bulk brine. This salt-concentration polarization is generally assumed to have a negligible effect upon desalination by distillation, while on the other hand concentration-polarization effects are known to be important in desalination by electrodialysis. Since reverse osmosis is similar to desalination by electrodialysis in that both processes use a membrane as the phase boundary that effects the separation, and since the hydrodynamics of brine flow past the membrane in reverse osmosis will probably be similar to that in electrodialysis, it can be expected that concentration-polarization effects might be important in desalination by reverse osmosis.

In water desalination by reverse osmosis, the salt concentration at the membrane surface builds up to a value exceeding the bulk salt concentration, and the concentration gradient that is established causes the salt to diffuse away from the membrane surface. This salt-concentration polarization produces several effects detrimental to the desalination process. The osmotic pressure that must be overcome is that corresponding to the salt concentration at the membrane surface, and the concentration polarization causes this effective osmotic pressure to exceed the osmotic pressure of the bulk salt solution. Thus, the required operating pressure of the reverse-osmosis cell is increased by the polarization

161

effect, and the pumping power requirements are increased correspondingly. In addition, the concentration polarization has a detrimental effect upon the salinity of the product water because this salinity will generally increase as the salt concentration at the membrane surface increases. The reality of these two effects is evident in the experimental data presented in Chapter 3. Furthermore, the deterioration of the membrane may be hastened by increased water salinity, and concentration polarization will aggravate this effect. Finally, most saline waters contain at least one salt at a concentration level not far below its solubility limit. Therefore, excessive concentration polarization may cause precipitation of salts at the surface of the osmotic membrane.

Concentration polarization in reverse-osmosis desalination is subject to reasonably reliable mathematical analysis. In the pages that follow a theoretical treatment of salt-diffusional effects is presented for both laminar and turbulent flow of brine within tubular membranes of circular cross section and within the channels between parallel flat membranes. The results of these theoretical analyses are then examined, and their implications to reverse-osmosis system design explored.

5.1 Theoretical Analysis for Laminar Flow

Differential Equation for Parallel Flat Membranes

Consider a case in which brine flows within the channel between two parallel, flat osmotic membranes, as shown in Fig. 5–1. The width of the

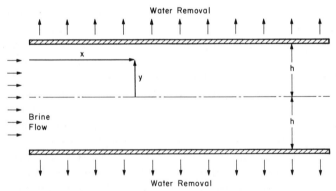

Fig. 5–1 Parallel flat membranes.

membranes is assumed to be very large relative to the membrane spacing, and product water is assumed to be permeating both the upper and the lower membranes; thus the brine flow will be assumed to be two-dimensional and symmetrical about the midplane of the channel of half-thickness h. This implies that the flow is assumed to be laminar, and natural convection effects are assumed to be negligible. The analysis is for brine containing a single salt with a diffusion coefficient D_2 that is independent of concentration. The volume change upon mixing salt solutions of different concentrations is also assumed negligible.

At the channel inlet, the salt concentration is assumed to be uniform over the channel cross section and equal to the feed concentration, c_2^i. As the brine flows down the channel and product water is removed through the membranes, a salt-concentration profile will develop and the salt concentration at the membrane surface c_2' will increase with increasing distance down the channel. A salt material balance on a differential volume element yields the following partial differential equation:

$$\frac{\partial}{\partial x}\left(uc_2\right) + \frac{\partial}{\partial y}\left(vc_2 - D_2\frac{\partial c_2}{\partial y}\right) = 0, \tag{5.1}$$

where u and v are fluid-velocity components in the x and y directions, respectively. In writing this equation, steady-state operation is assumed, and thus time derivatives are absent. Both diffusion and convection of salt in the transverse direction are included, but diffusion in the longitudinal direction is assumed negligible. The boundary conditions are

$$\text{At} \quad x = 0, \text{ any } y: \quad c_2 = c_2^i; \tag{5.2}$$

$$\text{At} \quad y = 0, \text{ any } x: \quad \frac{\partial c_2}{\partial y} = 0; \tag{5.3}$$

$$\text{At} \quad y = h, \text{ any } x > 0; \quad vc_2 - D_2\frac{\partial c_2}{\partial y} = F_2. \tag{5.4}$$

Equation 5.3 expresses the assumption of symmetry with respect to the channel mid-plane, and Eq. 5.4 relates conditions at the membrane surface to the salt flux F_2 through the membrane. It is convenient to define a membrane salt-rejection efficiency as unity minus the ratio of the salt flux through the membrane to the convective flux of salt to the membrane surface:

$$r = 1 - \left(\frac{F_2}{vc_2}\right)_{y=h}. \tag{5.5}$$

By combining Eqs. 5.4 and 5.5, the third boundary condition can be rewritten as

$$\text{At} \quad y = h, \text{ any } x > 0: \quad D_2\frac{\partial c_2}{\partial y} = rvc_2. \tag{5.6}$$

In order to solve the differential equation, the velocity field must first be specified. Berman[1] has obtained a solution for the velocity field in the case of a homogeneous fluid flowing between parallel porous walls with a uniform withdrawal flux through the walls:

$$u = \left(\frac{3}{2}\right)(\overline{u})\left(1 - \frac{y^2}{h^2}\right)\left[1 - \frac{N_F}{420}\left(2 - 7\frac{y^2}{h^2} - 7\frac{y^4}{h^4}\right)\right]; \tag{5.7}$$

$$v = v'\left[\left(\frac{y}{2h}\right)\left(3 - \frac{y^2}{h^2}\right) - \frac{N_F y}{280h}\left(2 - \frac{3y^2}{h^2} + \frac{y^6}{h^6}\right)\right]. \tag{5.8}$$

With the simplifications employed in the present analysis, these velocity-field equations apply to the reverse-osmosis desalination system for the case in which the permeation flux is constant, independent of longitudinal position. The term v' represents the transverse velocity adjacent to the membrane surface and is essentially equal to the volumetric production rate of product water per unit of membrane surface area, because the water concentration in the saline solution can be assumed to be constant and approximately 1 gram/cc with negligible error. The term $N_F = hv'/\nu$, with ν the kinematic viscosity of the solution, is a permeation Reynolds number based upon the half-width of the channel and the permeation velocity; it will generally be so small in reverse-osmosis desalination applications that the terms involving this quantity in Eqs. 5.7 and 5.8 can be neglected. With this simplification, the velocity-field equations become

$$u = \left(\frac{3}{2}\right)(\bar{u})\left(1 - \frac{y^2}{h^2}\right); \tag{5.9}$$

$$v = (v')\left(\frac{y}{2h}\right)\left(3 - \frac{y^2}{h^2}\right). \tag{5.10}$$

No solution has been obtained for the velocity-field equations for a case in which the permeation velocity v' varies with longitudinal position. But Eq. 5.9 reveals that the effect of a constant permeation velocity upon the longitudinal velocity component is simply to decrease the average longitudinal velocity $\bar{u}$ as water is withdrawn through the membrane; the parabolic profile is not distorted by a constant permeation velocity. Thus, it seems reasonable to assume that Eq. 5.9 would describe the longitudinal velocity profile adequately even for a case in which the permeation velocity varies with longitudinal position. Similarly, Eq. 5.10 shows that the transverse velocity at any point is equal to the permeation velocity multiplied by a cubic function of transverse position. It seems reasonable to assume that Eq. 5.10 would adequately describe the transverse velocity profile, even though v' were varying with x. Therefore, in the analysis to follow Eqs. 5.9 and 5.10 are used to describe the velocity field, whether or not the permeation velocity varies with longitudinal position. The use of Eqs. 5.9 and 5.10 over the entire channel implies the additional assumption that the parabolic longitudinal velocity profile is already established at the channel inlet.

It is convenient to rewrite Eqs. 5.1, 5.2, 5.3, 5.6, 5.9, and 5.10 in dimensionless form:

$$\frac{\partial}{\partial X}(UC) + \frac{\partial}{\partial Y}\left(VC - \alpha_0 \frac{\partial C}{\partial Y}\right) = 0; \tag{5.11}$$

At $X = 0$, any Y: $C = 1$;   (5.12)

At $Y = 0$, any X: $\dfrac{\partial C}{\partial Y} = 0$;   (5.13)

At $Y = 1$, any $X > 0$: $\alpha_0 \left(\dfrac{\partial C}{\partial Y} \right) = rVC$;   (5.14)

$$U = \tfrac{3}{2}(1 - \Delta)(1 - Y^2);$$ (5.15)

$$V = V' \left(\frac{Y}{2} \right)(3 - Y^2).$$ (5.16)

The dimensionless quantities are defined by the relations:

$$U = \frac{u}{\overline{u}^i}; \qquad V = \frac{v}{v'^i}; \qquad X = \left(\frac{v'^i}{\overline{u}^i} \right) \cdot \left(\frac{x}{h} \right);$$

$$Y = \frac{y}{h}; \qquad C = \frac{c_2}{c_2^i}; \qquad \alpha_0 = \frac{D_2}{v'^i h}.$$

Here the superscript i indicates that the quantity is evaluated at the channel inlet. In particular, $\overline{u}^i$ is the average value of u across the channel width at the inlet. The term Δ represents the volumetric fraction of the feed stream that has been removed through the membrane at a given longitudinal position. In converting Eq. 5.9 to Eq. 5.15 the average longitudinal velocity has been related to the inlet velocity in terms of the fractional water removal Δ. The symbol V' represents the permeation velocity at any longitudinal position divided by the permeation velocity at the channel inlet. The relationship between V' and Δ is given by the over-all water–material balance

$$\Delta = \int_0^X V' \, d\underline{X}, \qquad\qquad (5.17)$$

where $\underline{X}$ is a dummy variable in the definite integral.

Solution for a Constant Permeation Velocity

For the case of a constant permeation velocity, V' is equal to unity and Eq. 5.17 simplifies to

$$\Delta = X. \qquad\qquad (5.18)$$

With these simplifications, and with a salt-rejection efficiency equal to unity, an infinite-series solution to Eqs. 5.11 through 5.16 was obtained by Sherwood, Brian, and Fisher.[2,3] The principal result obtained was C', which represents the salt concentration at the membrane surface divided by the salt concentration in the feed brine. This quantity was determined as a function of the fractional water removal and the normalized salt diffusion coefficient $\alpha = D_2/v'h$. The infinite-series solution was obtained for only three values of α; therefore Brian[4] later solved the problem by a finite-difference method and obtained the solution for a large number of values of α. The finite-difference solution was found to be in excellent agreement with the infinite-series solution for the three values of α for which the latter was available, and thus the solutions can be considered reliable.

Dresner[3,5] obtained an approximate solution that is valid near the channel entrance:

$$\Gamma = \frac{\Delta}{3\alpha^2} + 5\left[1 - \exp\left(-\sqrt{\frac{\Delta}{9\alpha^2}}\right)\right], \quad \text{for} \quad \frac{\Delta}{3\alpha^2} \geq 0.02;$$

$$\Gamma = 1.536\left(\frac{\Delta}{3\alpha^2}\right)^{\frac{1}{3}}, \qquad \text{for} \quad \frac{\Delta}{3\alpha^2} \leq 0.02. \tag{5.19}$$

The polarization Γ is defined as

$$\Gamma \equiv C'(1 - \Delta) - 1, \tag{5.20}$$

and $(1 + \Gamma)$ is equal to the salt concentration at the membrane surface divided by the mixing-cup average salt concentration at the same longitudinal position. Dresner also obtained an approximate solution for the "far-downstream" concentration polarization:

$$\Gamma = \frac{1}{3\alpha^2} \tag{5.21}$$

Figure 5–2 presents the results of the finite-difference solution obtained by Brian,[4] plotted in a manner suggested by Dresner's approximate solution, Eq. 5.19. For any value of α, Γ is seen to increase with Δ and then to level out at an asymptotic value of Γ. The asymptote corresponds to the "far-downstream solution" for the polarization, and it is approached at relatively low values of Δ when α is large. In contrast, at low values of α, the asymptotic polarization is approached only as Δ

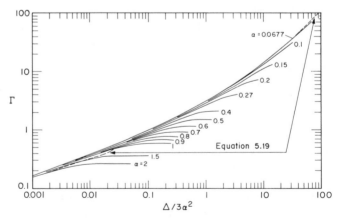

Fig. 5–2   Solution for constant flux and complete salt rejection. Parallel flat membranes. (Reproduced from Ref. 4 by permission of the American Chemical Society.)

nears unity. When the value of Γ is substantially below the asymptotic value, the solution corresponds to the entrance-region solution; Fig. 5–2 reveals that in the entrance region Γ is a unique function of $\Delta/3\alpha^2$. Furthermore, the approximate solution represented by Eq. 5.19 is shown as the dashed curve in Fig. 5–2; it is in good agreement with the finite-difference solution in the entrance region. At high values of $\Delta/3\alpha^2$ the agreement between the finite-difference solution and the approximate solution is excellent. At values of $\Delta/3\alpha^2$ near 0.02, the meshing point for the two approximate expressions, Eq. 5.19 yields values of Γ that are approximatley 17% lower than those of the finite-difference solution.

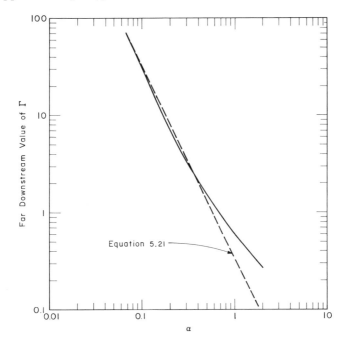

Fig. 5–3   Far-downstream solution, parallel flat membrane.

Figure 5–3 shows how the far-downstream solution varies with α. The solid curve represents the finite-difference solution[4] and the infinite-series solution,[2,3] and the dashed curve, the approximate solution[3,5] given by Eq. 5.21. For values of α between 0.0677 and 0.4, it is shown that Eq. 5.21 accurately predicts the far-downstream value of Γ. At larger α values, Eq. 5.21 falls beneath the true solution, and the error becomes quite appreciable.

The finite-difference solution presented by Brian[4] includes results for membranes with incomplete salt rejection. It was assumed that the salt-rejection efficiency r is independent of salt concentration and thus does not change as the salt concentration at the membrane surface builds up. This is a simplifying assumption; it is likely that the salt-rejection efficiency for most real osmotic membranes will vary with the salt concentration at the membrane surface, probably decreasing as the salt concentration increases. But since the manner in which this efficiency varies has not been well established for real membranes, it seemed most appropriate to carry out the theoretical analysis assuming that the membrane salt-rejection efficiency remains constant. This should be adequate in a general way for indicating the effect of incomplete salt rejection. Figures 5–4 and 5–5 present these results for salt-rejection efficiency values of 90 and 80%, respectively. The coordinates plotted here are the same as those of Fig. 5–2; this method of plotting renders the solution essentially independent of α in the entrance region. The variable Γ is defined by Eq. 5.20, but when the salt-rejection efficiency is less than unity, it no longer represents the concentration polarization relative to the mixing-cup average concentration. Nevertheless, it is still simply related to C' by Eq. 5.20, and the insensitivity of the solution to the value of α in the entrance region facilitates interpolation with respect to α. This is therefore an efficient method of presenting the results, even though Γ has no simple physical meaning when the salt-rejection efficiency is less than unity.

The effect of Δ upon C' and Γ shows an interesting variation with salt-rejection efficiency that is not readily visualized in Figs. 5–2, 5–4, and 5–5. When the salt-rejection efficiency is unity, C' approaches infinity as Δ approaches unity, but Γ approaches an asymptotic value, the "far-downstream" solution. On the other hand, when the salt-rejection efficiency is less than unity, C' approaches an asymptotic value as Δ approaches unity. In this case Γ, as defined by Eq. 5.20, falls off rather sharply as Δ tends toward unity. This behavior is understandable be-

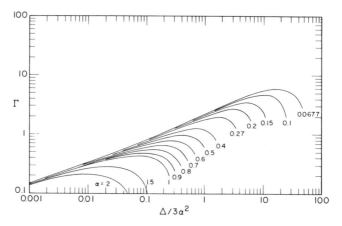

Fig. 5–4   Solution for constant flux, $r = 0.9$. Parallel flat membranes. (Reproduced from Ref. 4 by permission of the American Chemical Society.)

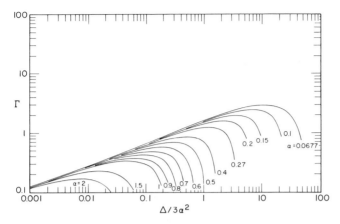

Fig. 5–5 Solution for constant flux, $r = 0.8$. Parallel flat membranes. (Reproduced from Ref. 4 by permission of the American Chemical Society.)

cause for a membrane with a salt-rejection efficiency less than unity the salt flux through the membrane increases with C' until finally salt is carried through the membrane as fast as it is convected to the membrane surface. At this point C' will no longer increase as Δ increases, and consequently Γ will fall off.

Variable Permeation Flux

The idealization of a constant permeation flux will not be closely approached in reverse-osmosis desalination of brines of relatively high salinity. Merten[6] reports that the permeation velocity can be expressed by

$$v' = A(\Delta p - \Delta \pi), \tag{5.22}$$

where Δp is the pressure drop across the membrane, $\Delta \pi$ the difference between the osmotic pressures of the saline solution at the membrane surface and the product water, and A the membrane-permeability constant. Therefore, for a given pressure drop across the membrane, the permeation velocity will fall off as the salt concentration at the membrane surface increases, thereby increasing the osmotic pressure at the membrane surface. Assuming that osmotic pressure is directly proportional to salt concentration and that Δp is essentially constant, Eq. 5.22 can be normalized with respect to the permeation velocity at the channel inlet and rewritten as

$$V' = 1 - \beta \gamma. \tag{5.23}$$

The constant β, defined as

$$\beta \equiv \frac{r\pi^i}{\Delta p - r\pi^i} \tag{5.24}$$

is a measure of that fraction of the pressure driving force that is represented by the osmotic pressure of the feed solution. The concentration polarization γ is defined as

$$\gamma \equiv C' - 1. \tag{5.25}$$

Thus the term $\beta\gamma$ in Eq. 5.23 represents the decrease in the permeation velocity due to the concentration polarization at the membrane surface.

Equation 5.23 represents a nonlinear coupling between the concentration polarization at the membrane surface and the permeation flux that produces the polarization. This nonlinear problem, represented by Eqs. 5.11 through 5.17 plus Eq. 5.23, was solved by Brian[4] using a finite-difference method. The solid curves in Figs. 5-6 through 5-8

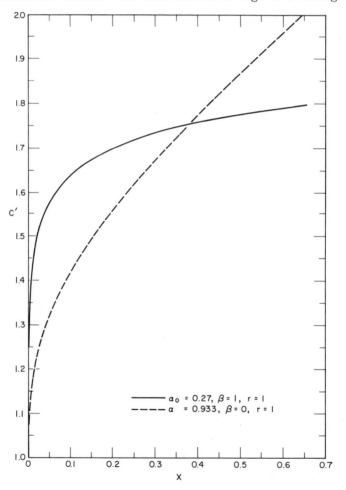

Fig. 5-6   Concentration at membrane surface versus longitudinal position. (Reproduced from Ref. 4 by permission of the American Chemical Society.)

present the results for $\alpha_0 = 0.27$, $\beta = 1$, and $r = 1$. The value of $\alpha_0 = 0.27$ corresponds to a permeation velocity at the channel inlet equal to 10 gpd/ft² if the membrane spacing is 0.1 inch, or it corresponds to a permeation velocity of 100 gpd/ft² if the membrane spacing is only 0.01 inch. The value of $\beta = 1$ corresponds to an applied pressure drop across the membrane equal to twice the osmotic pressure of the feed brine. The results shown in Figs. 5–6 through 5–8 present the normalized salt concentration at the membrane surface, the normalized permeation velocity, and the fractional water removal, respectively, all plotted versus the normalized longitudinal position. At $X = 0.656$, approximately 19% of the water has been removed, as shown in Fig. 5–8. It should be noted that X is defined so that it would be numerically equal

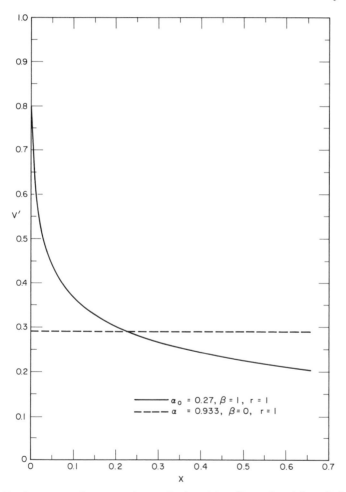

Fig. 5–7   Permeation flux versus longitudinal position. (Reproduced from Ref. 4 by permission of the American Chemical Society.)

to the fractional water removal if the permeation velocity had remained constant at its value at the channel inlet. Thus the average value of the normalized permeation velocity $\overline{V}'$ is simply the ratio of Δ to X; in this case it is given by

$$\overline{V}' = \frac{0.19}{0.656} = 0.2895. \tag{5.26}$$

Correspondingly, the average value of α is

$$\bar{\alpha} = \frac{0.27}{0.2895} = 0.933. \tag{5.27}$$

The dashed curves in Figs. 5–6 through 5–8 present the constant-flux solution for $\alpha = 0.933$ and $r = 1$, corresponding to a membrane operat-

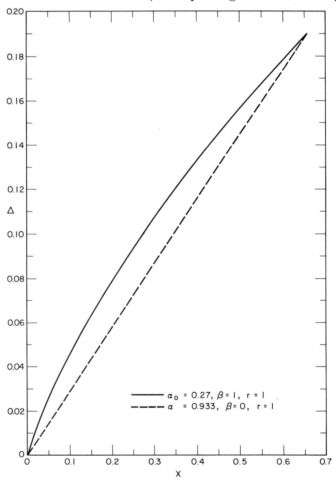

Fig. 5–8   Water removal versus longitudinal position. (Reproduced from Ref. 4 by permission of the American Chemical Society.)

ing with a constant permeation velocity equal to the average permeation velocity of the variable-flux membrane represented by the solid curves in Figs. 5–6 through 5–8. The normalized permeation velocity, normalized with respect to the permeation velocity at the inlet of the channel for the variable-flux case, is shown plotted versus normalized longitudinal position in Fig. 5–7. For the variable-flux case, V' is unity at the channel inlet and falls to 0.203 at $X = 0.656$. For the corresponding constant-flux case, V' is constant at 0.2895. Figure 5–8 shows how the fractional water removal compares for the two membranes: For the constant-flux membrane, Δ versus X is a straight line, but this relationship is nonlinear for the variable-flux membrane. However, for both membranes, 19% of the water is removed at a normalized longitudinal position of 0.656. Figure 5–6, contrasting the salt-concentration polarization for these two cases, shows that the salt concentration at the phase boundary builds up more rapidly for the variable-flux case and then flattens out; thus, near the channel inlet the variable-flux membrane has a higher concentration polarization than the constant-flux membrane, while the opposite is true near the channel outlet. This is to be expected because the permeation flux is higher for the variable-flux membrane near the channel inlet, while the constant-flux membrane has the higher permeation flux near the channel outlet.

Figure 5–6 shows that the longitudinal profile of the concentration polarization for the constant-flux membrane is substantially different from that for the variable-flux membrane. Indeed, at the channel outlet, C' has slightly exceeded 2 for the constant-flux membrane. This could never happen with the variable-flux membrane, because a value of C' exceeding 2 would correspond to a negative permeation velocity when $\beta = 1$. Nevertheless, it is interesting to inquire how the average value of the concentration polarization for the constant-flux case compares with that for the variable-flux case and how useful the constant-flux solution might be for the approximate design of a variable-flux system. Therefore, for the constant-flux example shown in Figs. 5–6 through 5–8, the average value of the concentration polarization up to $X = 0.656$ was computed according to

$$\bar{\gamma} = \left(\frac{1}{X}\right) \int_0^X (C' - 1)\, d\underline{X} \qquad (5.28)$$

and the resulting value was found to be 0.6725. This value can be used with Eq. 5.23, modified to the average form

$$\beta_{\text{calc}} = \frac{1 - \overline{V}'}{\bar{\gamma}}, \qquad (5.29)$$

in order to form the basis of a design procedure based upon the constant-flux solution. When the values of 0.2895 and 0.6725 are inserted for $\overline{V}'$ and $\bar{\gamma}$, respectively, in Eq. 5.29, the calculated value of β is 1.057, 6%

greater than the actual value. This corresponds to a required pressure drop of 1.95 times the osmotic pressure of the feed solution, instead of the actual value of exactly twice the osmotic pressure of the feed solution. Thus the average concentration polarization over the length of the membrane channel is very nearly the same for the constant-flux and the variable-flux solutions, even though this example is a rather severe test because the permeation flux fell off by a factor of almost five from the channel inlet to the outlet.

The integration required in Eq. 5.28 can be conveniently avoided by using the point value of the polarization halfway down the channel as an approximation of the average value for the constant-flux membrane. For the present case, this approximation to the average value of γ is obtained by reading the dashed curve in Fig. 5–6 at a value of $X = 0.328$. This yields a value of 0.702, approximately 4.5% higher than that found by integrating over the channel length. With this value inserted in Eq. 5.29, the calculated value of β is found to be 1.01, an error of only 1%, as compared with almost 6% when the integral average value of γ was used.

The solid curve in Fig. 5–9 shows the longitudinal profile of the concentration polarization for a case where $\alpha_0 = 0.27$, $\beta = 1$, and $r = 0.9$. At $X = 0.656$, $C' = 1.768$, and therefore the permeation flux has fallen to 23% of its value at the channel inlet. At this point $\Delta = 0.211$, and therefore $\overline{V}' = 0.322$ and $\bar{\alpha} = 0.838$. The normalized average concentration of the product water, $\overline{C}''$, can be computed by

$$\overline{C}'' = \frac{(1 - r)}{\Delta} \int_0^X V'C' \, d\underline{X}; \qquad (5.30)$$

at $X = 0.656$, $\overline{C}''$ is found to be 0.164. The dashed curve in Fig. 5–9 shows the longitudinal profile of concentration polarization for a constant-flux membrane with a 90% salt-rejection efficiency operating at a flux equal to the average permeation flux for the variable-flux membrane represented by the solid curve. The comparison between the constant-flux and the variable-flux results is similar to that shown in Fig. 5–6. By use of Eq. 5.28, the value of $\bar{\gamma}$ at $X = 0.656$ for the constant-flux example is found to be 0.651; together with $\overline{V}' = 0.322$ in Eq. 5.29 this yields a calculated value of $\beta = 1.04$, only 4% greater than the actual value. The value of γ at the midpoint of the channel, $X = 0.328$, is read from the dashed curve in Fig. 5–9 as 0.682. Substituting this for $\bar{\gamma}$ in Eq. 5.29 yields a calculated value of $\beta = 0.994$, only 0.6% lower than the actual value. Thus, the use of the constant-flux solution to calculate the required pressure drop for the membrane is just as accurate when the salt rejection is 90% as it was in the previous example with complete salt rejection.

The constant-flux solution can also be used to predict the salinity of

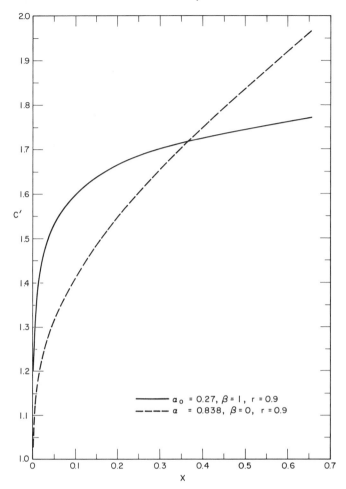

Fig. 5–9   Concentration at membrane surface versus longitudinal position. (Reproduced from Ref. 4 by permission of the American Chemical Society.)

the product water. For the special case in which the permeation flux is constant, Eq. 5.30 simplifies to

$$\bar{C}'' = (1 - r)(\bar{\gamma} + 1). \tag{5.31}$$

Using $\bar{\gamma} = 0.651$ in Eq. 5.31 results in a value of 0.165 for $\bar{C}''$; this is within 0.6% of the actual value. If, instead of using the integral average value of γ, the value of γ at the channel midpoint is used, the resulting value of $\bar{C}''$ is 0.168, 2.5% greater than the actual value.

The preceding examples plus a number of others examined by the author show that the constant-flux solution is very useful for obtaining accurate predictions of the extra osmotic-pressure requirements and of the increased product water salinity due to concentration polarization at the membrane surface. Furthermore, the general conclusion that the average polarization over the length of the membrane is relatively insensitive to the manner in which the permeation flux varies can be expected to apply to cases not yet treated, such as the tubular membranes to be discussed later. Consider also a brine containing a mixture of salts with different rejection values; the computer program developed by Brian[4] and the finite-difference results obtained do not apply to this case. But the approximate procedure can be applied to each salt separately to determine its average polarization, and the extra osmotic-pressure requirement and the product-water salinity can be computed from the average polarization for each salt. The problem of salt-rejection efficiency varying with concentration or that of osmotic pressure not being exactly proportional to concentration can be handled in a similar manner. Strictly speaking, when several salts are involved the diffusion of the individual ions and their electrical interactions must be considered,[7,8] but the error involved in using salt diffusivities will be rather small if the mobilities of the different ions are approximately equal, as in seawater.

Approximate Design Curve

Figure 5–2 showed that Γ is a unique function of α and Δ for a constant-flux membrane with complete salt rejection. The variation of Γ with α for constant values of Δ equal to 0.05 and 0.25 is shown in Fig.

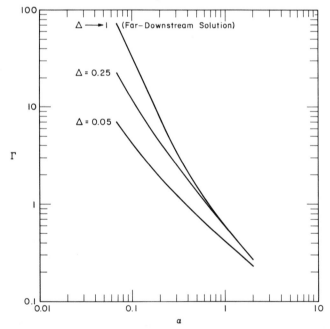

Fig. 5–10   The variation of Γ with α at constant Δ. Parallel flat membranes, $r = 1$.

5–10, as is the curve for Δ approaching unity, which corresponds to the far-downstream solution. As discussed earlier, the polarization obtained at Δ = 0.25 is a good approximation to the average polarization over a membrane in which 50% of the inlet water is removed. Similarly, that at Δ = 0.05 is a good approximation to the average polarization over a membrane in which 10% of the water is removed. Similar curves for other salt-rejection efficiencies can be constructed with the aid of Figs. 5–4 and 5–5; such curves are useful for direct estimates of average polarization values made to assess the effects of concentration polarization upon extra osmotic-pressure requirements and upon product-water salinity, as outlined earlier. For a fixed percentage of water removal the average polarization as determined in this manner varies with membrane spacing and permeation velocity but not with brine-flow velocity. To be sure, brine-flow velocity affects the average polarization if the channel length is kept constant, but the length required for a given percentage of water removal varies with brine flow velocity and cancels this effect.

Tubular Membranes

The problem of concentration polarization for brine flow in a tubular membrane of circular cross section and tube radius h is quite similar to that outlined for brine flow in the channels between parallel flat membranes; the mathematical details will not be reproduced here. For the case of a constant permeation flux and complete salt rejection, an infinite-series solution has been obtained by Fisher, Sherwood, and Brian.[3,9] Results obtained for three different values of α are shown in Fig. 5–11, plotted in the same coordinates as those employed in Fig. 5–2. In Fig. 5–11 this method of plotting yields a single curve for the

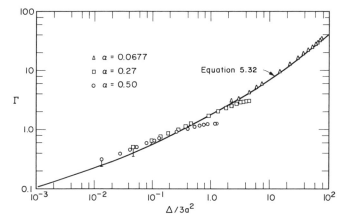

Fig. 5–11 Solution for laminar flow in round tubes, constant flux and complete salt rejection. (Reproduced from Ref. 3 by permission of the American Chemical Society.)

entrance-region solution, independent of the value of α, just as it did in the case of parallel flat membranes. Furthermore, an approximate solution for the entrance region can be obtained from Eq. 5.19 by examining the analogy between the tubular and the parallel flat membranes. Near the channel entrance, where the concentration boundary layer is a small fraction of the tube radius, the round-tube results should agree with those for the parallel flat membranes if the values of v', x, D_2, and (du/dy) at the wall are the same for both cases. Because of the difference in the velocity profiles for the two cases this similarity is achieved when the value of Δ/α^2 for the round tube is $\frac{8}{3}$ that for the flat membranes. Therefore the equation analogous to Eq. 5.19 which forms an approximate solution for the entrance region for the tubular membrane is[3],[9]

$$\Gamma = \frac{\Delta}{8\alpha^2} + 5\left[1 - \exp\left(-\sqrt{\frac{\Delta}{24\alpha^2}}\right)\right], \quad \text{for} \quad \frac{\Delta}{8\alpha^2} \geq 0.02;$$

$$\Gamma = 1.536\left(\frac{\Delta}{8\alpha^2}\right)^{\frac{1}{3}}, \quad \text{for} \quad \frac{\Delta}{8\alpha^2} \leq 0.02.$$

(5.32)

This equation is plotted in Fig. 5–11 for comparison with the infinite-series solution and is a reasonably good approximation to the solution in the entrance region.

Figure 5–12 shows the variation of Γ with α for $\Delta = 0.05$ and 0.25 and for Δ approaching unity. This graph is similar to Fig. 5–10 for flat membranes, and it can be used to obtain an approximation to the average polarization over the length of a tubular membrane.[9]

5.2   Theoretical Analysis for Turbulent Flow

Perhaps the simplest model for the concentration boundary layer in turbulent flow is the film-theory model. The boundary layer is idealized as a thin, liquid film in which eddy motion is assumed to be negligible and therefore mass transport takes place by molecular diffusion alone. This thin film separates the membrane surface from the bulk brine solution, which is assumed to be so turbulent that concentration gradients are absent. Steady-state operation is assumed and longitudinal mass transport within the film is assumed negligible. Therefore, mass transport within the film is one-dimensional. Figure 5–13 shows the geometry of the film-theory model. With these simplifications, the differential equation describing salt transport is given by

$$F_2 = -D_2\frac{dc_2}{dy} + vc_2.$$

(5.33)

With the film-theory simplifications, the salt flux F_2 is constant throughout the film and is related to the membrane salt-rejection efficiency by

$$F_2 = (1 - r)v'c_2'.$$

(5.34)

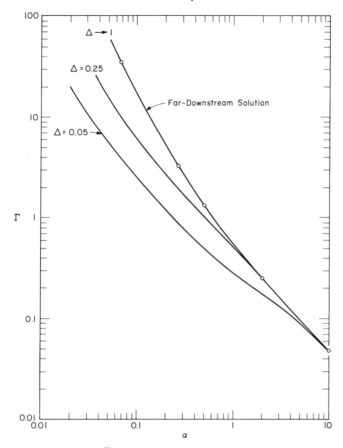

Fig. 5–12   The variation of Γ with α at constant Δ. Round tubular membrane, $r = 1$.

Likewise, with the film-theory simplifications and the assumption that the water concentration in the brine solution is essentially constant and equal to 1 gram/cc, the transverse velocity v is essentially constant throughout the film and equal to the permeation velocity

$$v = v'. \tag{5.35}$$

Combining Eqs. 5.33 through 5.35 yields

$$-D_2 \frac{dc_2}{dy} + v'c_2 = (1 - r)v'c_2'. \tag{5.36}$$

Integrating this differential equation across the film results in

$$\frac{c_2'}{c_2^b} = \frac{\exp\left(\dfrac{v'\delta}{D_2}\right)}{r + (1 - r)\exp\left(\dfrac{v'\delta}{D_2}\right)}, \tag{5.37}$$

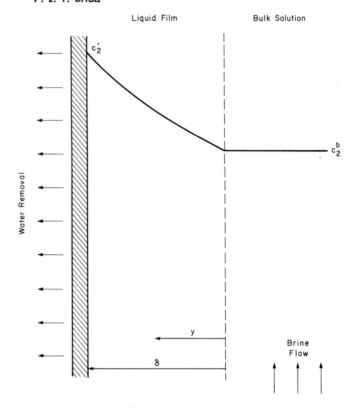

Fig. 5–13   Film-theory model.

where c_2^b is the salt concentration in the bulk solution. Now δ is unknown because it represents the thickness of the fictitious film. Therefore, it is customary in a film-theory analysis such as this to eliminate the film thickness from the final answer by using the mass transfer coefficient between the wall and the bulk fluid that would exist for the same flow system and the same Reynolds number but in the absence of the transpiration velocity through the boundary layer. This mass-transfer coefficient k^0 is simply found in terms of the film-theory model:

$$k^0 = \frac{D_2}{\delta}. \tag{5.38}$$

Using Eq. 5.38 to eliminate δ from Eq. 5.37 yields

$$\frac{c_2'}{c_2^b} = \frac{\exp\left(\dfrac{v'}{k^0}\right)}{r + (1 - r)\exp\left(\dfrac{v'}{k^0}\right)}. \tag{5.39}$$

It is often convenient to express the mass-transfer coefficient in terms of the Chilton-Colburn j factor:

$$j_D \equiv \left(\frac{k_0}{\overline{u}}\right) N_{Sc}^{\frac{2}{3}};$$ (5.40)

then, Eq. 5.39 can be written in the form

$$\frac{c_2'}{c_2^b} = \frac{\exp\left[\left(\frac{v'}{j_D \overline{u}}\right) N_{Sc}^{\frac{2}{3}}\right]}{r + (1 - r) \exp\left[\left(\frac{v'}{j_D \overline{u}}\right) N_{Sc}^{\frac{2}{3}}\right]}.$$ (5.41)

The Chilton-Colburn j factor is related to the friction factor f for the brine flow past the membrane surface by the Chilton-Colburn analogy

$$j_D = \frac{f}{2}.$$ (5.42)

Equations 5.39 and 5.41 express the film-theory prediction for the salt concentration build-up at the membrane surface in terms of the permeation flux, the fluid mechanical parameters, and the Schmidt number N_{Sc} for salt diffusion. For $r =$ unity, this result was previously given by Sherwood, Brian, and Fisher[2,3] and by Merten, Lonsdale, and Riley.[11] Equation 5.41 can be put into another form involving the product water salinity c_2'', instead of the salt-rejection efficiency:

$$\frac{c_2' - c_2''}{c_2^b - c_2''} = \exp\left[\left(\frac{v'}{j_D \overline{u}}\right) N_{Sc}^{\frac{2}{3}}\right].$$ (5.41a)

The film-theory model contains a number of simplifying assumptions known to be incorrect, but the effect of these assumptions upon the film-theory predictions are often found to be rather small. For example, the film-theory model is equivalent to the assumption that the eddy diffusivity due to turbulent motion is zero within the film and infinite within the turbulent bulk. In actuality the eddy motion persists right up to the wall and the eddy diffusivity approaches zero only at the wall itself. Furthermore, for mass transfer at high Schmidt numbers, the nonzero value of the eddy diffusivity near the wall has an important effect upon the mass-transfer rate. Nevertheless, when an eddy-diffusion model is used instead of the film-theory model, the result is identical with that expressed by Eq. 5.39.[2,3] This will be demonstrated in the analysis that follows.

Consider an eddy-diffusion model of mass transfer between the membrane and the bulk brine, as shown in Fig. 5–14. Let the eddy diffusivity be an arbitrary function of transverse distance

$$\epsilon = \epsilon(y).$$ (5.43)

In this case the transverse coordinate y is measured from the outer edge of the concentration boundary layer toward the membrane surface. Of course the outer edge of the boundary layer is arbitrarily defined, and this point is chosen sufficiently far from the membrane surface that

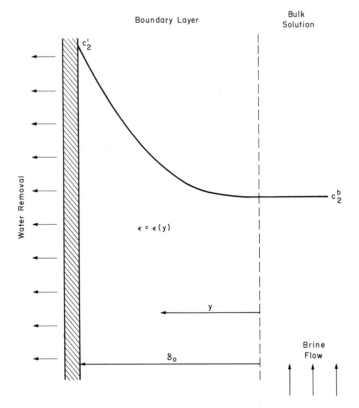

Fig. 5–14   Eddy-diffusion model.

choosing it larger would have a negligible effect upon the final result. If longitudinal mass transport within the boundary layer is assumed negligible, as in the film-theory model, the differential equation for the eddy-diffusion model is

$$-[D_2 + \epsilon(y)]\frac{dc_2}{dy} + v'c_2 = (1 - r)v'c_2'. \tag{5.44}$$

For this model the mass-transfer coefficient in the absence of a transpiration velocity is given by

$$\frac{1}{k^0} = \int_0^{\delta_0} \frac{dy}{D_2 + \epsilon(y)}, \tag{5.45}$$

where δ_0 is the thickness of the concentration boundary layer and is therefore the value of y at the membrane surface. To demonstrate that the result of the eddy-diffusion model is the same as that for the film-theory model, irrespective of the nature of the variation of the eddy diffusivity with distance from the membrane surface, it is convenient to transform the differential equation, Eq. 5.44, with the following transformation of independent variable using the dummy variable y:

$$\eta \equiv \frac{\int_0^y \{d\underline{y}/[D_2 + \epsilon(\underline{y})]\}}{\int_0^{\delta_0} \{d\underline{y}/[D_2 + \epsilon(\underline{y})]\}} = k^0 \int_0^y \frac{d\underline{y}}{D_2 + \epsilon(\underline{y})}. \tag{5.46}$$

This transformation reduces Eq. 5.44 to

$$-k^0 \frac{dc_2}{d\eta} + v'c_2 = (1 - r)v'c_2'. \tag{5.47}$$

Integration of Eq. 5.47 across the boundary layer, from $\eta = 0$ to $\eta = 1$, yields Eq. 5.39 directly.

The preceding analysis shows that the film-theory result expressed in Eq. 5.39 is identical with that of the eddy-diffusion model, no matter what the eddy-diffusivity function may be. Of course, the eddy-diffusivity model as well as the film-theory model contained the assumption that longitudinal mass transport within the boundary layer is negligible. This is not rigorously true, and indeed the magnitude of the transfer coefficient between the wall and the bulk varies somewhat with the manner in which the flux varies with longitudinal position. But on the whole such effects are quite small in turbulent flow, and for mass transfer at high Schmidt numbers, such as those of aqueous salt solutions, the concentration boundary layer is generally so thin relative to the dimensions of the bulk fluid that the effect of longitudinal mass transport within the boundary layer is quite small indeed.

Average Polarization Over the Channel Length

Equations 5.39 and 5.41 can be used to predict the ratio of the salt concentration at the membrane surface to that in the bulk solution at a given longitudinal position. It would be useful to have a simple method for obtaining the average polarization over the length of the channel so the extra osmotic-pressure requirement due to concentration polarization can be readily obtained. One such method is to use the technique that was shown to be quite accurate for the laminar-flow case, namely to approximate the average value of the concentration polarization over the channel length by the point value of the polarization at the stage where the water removal is half completed. Consider, for example, turbulent flow of brine in a tubular membrane in which half of the inlet water is being removed. At the point where the water removal is half completed, the average longitudinal velocity is 75% of the inlet velocity and the bulk salt concentration is equal to 1.333 times the salt concentration in the feed brine. On the assumption that the average polarization over the channel length can be approximated by the polarization at the point at which the water removal is half completed, the result, provided the membrane completely rejects the salt, is

$$\frac{\bar{c}_2'}{\bar{c}_2^i} = 1.333 \exp\left[\left(\frac{\bar{v}'}{0.75\,\bar{u}^i}\right)\left(\frac{2}{f}\right)N_{Sc}^{\frac{1}{3}}\right], \qquad (5.48)$$

where $\bar{c}_2'$ and $\bar{v}'$ are the average values over the channel length of the salt concentration at the wall and of the permeation velocity, respectively. The friction factor in Eq. 5.48 is evaluated at a Reynolds number corresponding to the average velocity, $0.75\,\bar{u}^i$.

In order to appraise the accuracy of Eq. 5.48, the average concentration polarization over the channel length was computed for turbulent flow in a round tubular membrane with 100% salt-rejection efficiency. Equations 5.41 and 5.42 were used to evaluate the concentration polarization at a given point, and it was assumed that the friction factor varies as the -0.2 power of the average longitudinal velocity. With these equations, the integration down the tube was accomplished by a finite-difference method that accounted for the decreasing longitudinal velocity as water was withdrawn through the membrane and also for the decreasing permeation velocity as the salt concentration at the membrane surface increased. The calculations were all for a membrane in which 50% of the inlet water was removed, but calculations were performed for several different values of β, as defined by Eq. 5.24.

The results are shown in Fig. 5–15, where the abscissa represents the true integral average value of the concentration polarization, and the ordinate the approximate value given by Eq. 5.48. The lowest ordinate value covered is 0.333. This corresponds to an infinite mass-transfer

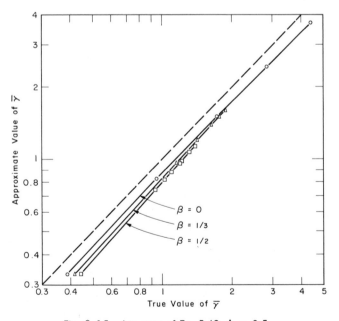

Fig. 5–15   Accuracy of Eq. 5.48, $\Delta = 0.5$.

coefficient, and the concentration ratio 1.333 represents the average increase in the bulk concentration due to water removal. At the other end of the scale, ordinate values of up to almost 4 are included; this probably covers the range of polarization ratios of interest. The curve for $\beta = 0$ represents the case of a constant permeation flux. For this case Eq. 5.48 predicts values of $\bar{\gamma}$ that are approximately 14% below the true values. For a value of β equal to $\frac{1}{3}$, Eq. 5.48 predicts values of $\bar{\gamma}$ approximately 19% below the true values, and for β equal to $\frac{1}{2}$ the error increases to approximately 22%. It is probable that the value of β actually employed in a practical reverse-osmosis desalination system will generally be less than one half. Indeed, a value of β as high as unity corresponds to an operating-pressure drop equal to twice the osmotic pressure of the feed solution; in such a case 50% of the water could not be removed. Therefore, the range of all β values of practical importance is presented in Fig. 5–15.

The results in Fig. 5–15 show that Eq. 5.48 predicts values of $\bar{\gamma}$ that are 14 to 22% lower than the actual values, at least for $\bar{\gamma}$ near unity. Because of its simplicity, Eq. 5.48 should prove useful for making approximate calculations of the average concentration polarization over the channel length. Greater accuracy may be achieved without performing a numerical integration down the channel, by using Eq. 5.48 together with correction factors obtained from Fig. 5–15.

5.3   Average Polarization Values

Theoretically predicted values of the average concentration polarization over the length of the membrane are presented in Figs. 5–16 through 5–19 for round tubular membranes in which 50% of the water

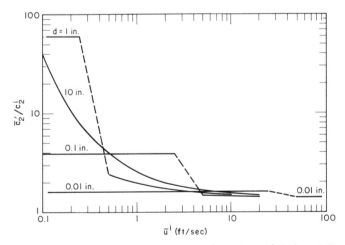

Fig. 5–16   Average polarization for $\bar{v}' = 10$ gpd/ft², $\Delta = 0.5$.

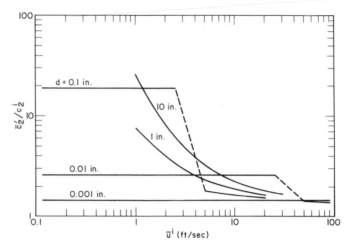

Fig. 5–17   Average polarization for $\bar{v}' = 50$ gpd/ft^2, $\Delta = 0.5$.

is removed from the inlet brine. The membranes are assumed to reject the salt completely. The figures show the effects of brine-inlet velocity and tube diameter upon the average polarization ratio, and each graph is for a different value of the average permeation velocity. Flow was assumed to be laminar for values of the Reynolds number at the channel inlet less than 2100, and turbulent for values at the channel outlet greater than 2100. Since half of the water is removed through the membrane, there is a range representing a factor of 2 in inlet velocity which separates these two regions; in this transition zone a dashed line is drawn to connect the laminar and turbulent flow solutions. In laminar flow, the average polarization ratio was obtained from the middle curve in

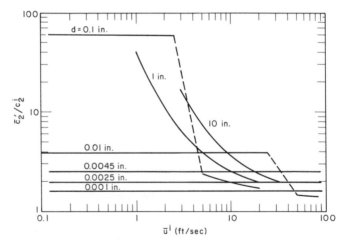

Fig. 5–18   Average polarization for $\bar{v}' = 100$ gpd/ft^2, $\Delta = 0.5$.

Fig. 5–12; it thus represents the polarization ratio for a constant-flux membrane at the point at which 25% of the inlet water has been removed. The turbulent-flow results were computed using Eq. 5.48 and correction factors from the curve for $\beta = 0$ in Fig. 5–15. Since the curves in Fig. 5–15 vary but little with β, these results are good approximations to the turbulent-flow solution in general. In making these calculations, the salt-diffusion coefficient was assumed to be 1.62×10^{-5} cm^2/sec, and the Schmidt number was assumed to be 560.

Similar results could also be obtained for parallel flat membranes. In the turbulent regime, mass-transfer coefficients for channels of noncircular cross section are often approximated by using results for round tubes of the same mean hydraulic radius. With this assumption, the turbulent-flow results of Figs. 5–16 through 5–19 can be applied to the case of parallel flat membranes if d is interpreted as the equivalent diameter, which is equal to twice the membrane spacing. The laminar-flow solutions, on the other hand, will be different for the case of parallel flat membranes. Comparing the middle curves of Figs. 5–10 and 5–12 shows that the concentration polarization for a tubular membrane is greater than that for parallel flat membranes if the mean hydraulic radii are equal (that is, if the spacing of the flat membranes is half the diameter of the tubular membrane). On the other hand, if the spacing of the flat membranes is equal to the diameter of the tubular membrane, the concentration polarization will be greater for the flat membranes.

Figures 5–16 through 5–19 show that the average polarization ratio is fixed for a given permeation velocity and tube diameter in the laminar regime but that the polarization ratio can be decreased by increasing the brine velocity in the turbulent regime. The average polarization ratio can be decreased by decreasing the tube diameter in either the

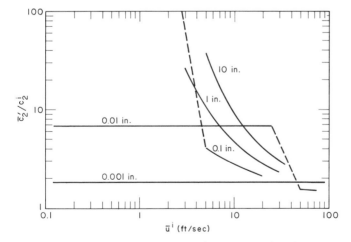

Fig. 5–19 Average polarization for $\bar{v}' = 200$ gpd/ft^2, $\Delta = 0.5$.

laminar or the turbulent range, but the effect is generally greater in the laminar range. The effect of permeation velocity is quite pronounced. In the turbulent regime an increase in the permeation velocity by a factor of 2 requires an increase in the brine velocity by a factor of approximately 2.4 in order to maintain the polarization ratio constant. In the laminar-flow regime, increasing the permeation velocity by a factor of 2 requires a decrease in the tube diameter by a factor of 2 to maintain a constant polarization ratio.

Experimental Confirmation

The theoretical results for laminar flow were developed from first principles and can be expected to be valid as long as the several assumptions upon which they were based remain valid. For turbulent flow, the models used are unquestionably crude models of the details of the turbulent boundary layer, but here an experimental mass-transfer coefficient k^0 is used in the result, and experience suggests that the result will be reliable. Nevertheless, experimental confirmation of these theoretical results is clearly desirable.

The turbulent-flow result has been checked by Sherwood, Brian, and Fisher.[10,12,13] Experimental results obtained for a rotating cylindrical osmotic membrane were compared with Eq. 5.41a in which j_D values for turbulent transport to a rotating cylinder were used. The agreement between theory and experiment was very satisfactory.

To check the theoretical results for laminar flow, careful experiments must be performed, in which entrance effects must be minimized because the theoretical results are based upon the assumption of a well-developed velocity profile at the leading edge of the membrane. As yet, no experimental measurements are available for testing the theoretical results for laminar flow.

Spongy Membrane Surface

At this point it should be emphasized that these theoretical results are based upon the assumptions that the membrane surface adjacent to the saline solution is smooth and that this surface is the point of salt rejection. If, instead, the salt-rejection point were within the membrane and an outer layer of the membrane were permeable to the salt, then this layer of membrane would represent an additional salt-diffusional resistance in series with the hydrodynamic boundary layer. For turbulent flow the effect of such a resistance could be included in Eq. 5.39 by adding the diffusional resistance of the membrane layer to the term $1/k^0$. This additional resistance cannot be decreased by increasing the brine-flow velocity.

Consider, for example, a 1-inch tubular membrane with $\bar{v}' = 100$ gpd/ft². At $\bar{u}^i = 10$ ft/sec, the average polarization ratio is 2.53, as shown in Fig. 5–18. The average mass-transfer coefficient at this point is equivalent to a stagnant layer of brine 0.0007 inch thick. If 10% of a membrane 0.002 inch thick were an outer layer permeable to salt, this would represent a diffusional resistance equal to that of the hydrodynamic boundary layer at $\bar{u}^i = 10$ ft/sec, assuming that the effective diffusivity of salt in the membrane layer were only one third of that in the brine. This would raise the average polarization ratio from 2.5 to 4.6, and even at very high brine-flow velocities it would only come down to a limiting value of 2.5.

These considerations emphasize the need for having membranes that are free of any spongy salt-permeable layer on the surface adjacent to the saline solution. Fortunately, it appears that membrane developments to date have avoided this problem.

5.4 Influence upon Reverse-Osmosis System Design

Using the theoretical predictions of concentration polarization presented in the preceding pages, Brian[14] has given an analysis of the effects of concentration polarization upon reverse-osmosis system design. Although it is not a complete economic balance, and thus is preliminary and general in nature, it adds perspective and insight into the influence that concentration polarization will have upon the design of reverse-osmosis desalination systems. The discussion given here differs from that of reference 14 only in that the numerical results are based upon Fig. 5–15 for $\beta = 0$ instead of upon Eq. 5.48 and, in addition, a small error in the calculation of frictional pressure drop has been corrected. The analysis is presented in terms of a tubular reverse-osmosis membrane, but the results would be qualitatively similar for parallel flat membranes, and the essential conclusions would not be changed. Its focus is upon the desalination of seawater, with an osmotic pressure of approximately 350 psi. The osmotic membrane is assumed to reject the salt completely, and a water removal of 50% is assumed throughout the discussion.

Consider first a tubular membrane with an average permeation velocity of 100 gpd/ft². For a specified allowable value of the average salt concentration at the membrane surface, the required inlet brine velocity versus the tube diameter can be read directly from Fig. 5–18. For example, Table 5–1 shows the required inlet brine velocity as a function of tube diameter if the allowable value of $\bar{c}_2'/c_2^i$ is equal to 2. For tube diameters of 0.001 and 0.0025 inch, the laminar-flow value of the average polarization ratio is less than 2, and thus any inlet brine velocity can be used. For the other tube diameters, the laminar flow solution is greater

Table 5–1   Operating Conditions for $\bar{c}_2'/c_2^i = 2$ at $\bar{v}' = 100$ gpd/ft^2

Tube diameter (in.)	Required $\bar{u}^i$ (ft/sec)	Frictional pressure drop (psi)	Approx. length	Approx. number of tubes for 10^6 gpd
0.001	Any {0.18	1	0.15''	3 × 10^9
	value {1.8	100	1.5''	3 × 10^8
0.0025	Any {0.18	0.4	0.36''	5 × 10^8
	value {1.8	40	3.6''	5 × 10^7
0.01	50	19,700	33'	120,000
0.1	9	84	61'	6,000
1	19	385	1,200'	30
10	31	893	21,000'	$\frac{1}{6}$

than 2, and thus the inlet brine velocity must be high enough to produce turbulent flow.

The frictional pressure drop was computed for each of the cases listed in Table 5–1. The pressure-drop values reported represent values due to skin friction alone. There is also a pressure rise due to the decreased momentum of the flowing stream and a pressure drop due to losses in headers, bends, and fittings. These effects tend to cancel each other and in most cases are quite small compared with the skin-friction losses. Thus, the values reported were based upon skin friction only; they should be sufficiently accurate for the present purpose. For the laminar-flow pressure-drop calculation, Poiseuille's law was used with a value of velocity equal to $0.75\ \bar{u}^i$. For the turbulent-flow pressure drop the friction factor was read corresponding to the average velocity, $0.75\ \bar{u}^i$; this was used with a velocity head calculated in terms of a mean-square velocity assumed to be equal to $\frac{7}{12}(\bar{u}^i)^2$, which would be exact if the permeation flux were uniform with longitudinal position. The table also shows the tube length required to remove 50% of the inlet water and the approximate number of tubes in parallel that would be required for a plant producing one million gallons per day of fresh water.

The values in Table 5–1 reveal an interesting functional relationship between the tube diameter and the frictional pressure drop required to keep the average concentration polarization ratio less than a factor of 2. For a 10-inch tube a pressure drop of 893 psi is required, but this can be reduced to only 84 psi by reducing the tube diameter to 0.1 inch. If a tube diameter of 0.01 inch is used, the required frictional pressure drop is almost 20,000 psi, because in this case turbulent flow must be maintained in order to keep the average polarization ratio less than a factor of 2. For tube diameters of 0.001 and 0.0025 inch, any inlet velocity will achieve the desired polarization; therefore two inlet-velocity values are shown in the table to demonstrate the effect of inlet velocity upon the frictional pressure drop, the required length, and the number of tubes required to produce one million gallons per day of fresh water. The results suggest that a reasonable design, provided the average polarization ratio is to be kept to less than a factor of 2, would be turbulent flow in a tube of diameter between 0.1 and 0.5 inch. This would result in a frictional pressure between 80 and 300 psi, and both the tube length and the number of tubes required seem reasonable from the point of view of constructing an assembly of a shell and a tube bundle. The low concentration polarization and a reasonable frictional pressure drop below 100 psi can also be achieved with laminar flow in a tube of diameter 0.001 or 0.0025 inch, and thus a hollow-fiber approach such as suggested by Mahon[15] appears promising. However, a consideration of the number of tubes and of the very short tube length required suggests that turbulent flow in a tube of 0.1-inch diameter is a more likely design point than laminar flow in a tube of 0.0025-inch diameter. Furthermore, the suspended solids and colloidal material usually present in the feed brine would probably present a plugging problem for such small tubes or narrow passages, making the problem of cleaning the system a severe one. Of course, the optimum design must be determined by a complete economic balance, and this analysis does not claim such completenes. Nevertheless, the present considerations do show that the frictional pressure drop can be kept to a reasonably low value by employing turbulent flow in a tube between 0.1 and 0.5 inch in diameter, and thus there seems to be little incentive to attempt the development of fabrication techniques for large bundles of very short tubes of very small diameter.

It should here be mentioned that the average polarization ratio can be kept below 2 for laminar flow in a 0.01-inch diameter (or larger) tube if the water removal in a single pass is less than 50% and therefore a number of passes are used with remixing of the brine between passes. The same effect can also be obtained by boundary-layer removal techniques and by the use of turbulence promoters or other devices to promote radial mixing at frequent intervals down the channel. For laminar flow in a 0.01-inch-diameter tube with a flux rate of 100 gpd/ft^2, approximately sixty passes or remixing points would be required to keep $\bar{c}_2'/c_2^t$ below 2. Table 5–2 shows how the operating conditions for such a system would vary with brine velocity. The frictional pressure-drop values are computed for a single smooth pipe, neglecting the header or remixing losses associated with operation with sixty passes; thus, the actual frictional pressure drop may be much greater than the values shown. The results in Table 5–2 show that reasonable *total* tube lengths can be obtained with a 0.01-inch diameter tube, but the length per pass appears to be unreasonably small. Of course, the development of easy, inexpensive methods for liquid remixing could render such a system workable, but from the present viewpoint operation with turbulent flow with a

Table 5–2　Operating Conditions for 0.01-inch-diameter Tube with $\bar{v}' = 100$ gpd/ft² in Laminar Flow with Sixty Remixing Points

$\bar{u}^i$ (ft/sec)	Frictional pressure drop (psi)	Approx. length Total	Approx. length Per pass	Approx. number of tubes for 10^6 gpd
1	3	$8''$	$\frac{1}{8}''$	5×10^6
2	12	$16''$	$\frac{1}{4}''$	3×10^6
4	48	$32''$	$\frac{1}{2}''$	1.3×10^6
8	192	$64''$	$1''$	0.7×10^6

tube diameter between 0.1 and 0.5 inch appears to be more attractive. If an average value of c_2'/c_2^i of 2.5 is allowable, the required inlet velocities are lower and the frictional pressure-drop penalty is decreased, as shown in Table 5–3. Here, too, a very reasonable design can be achieved with turbulent flow in a tube of diameter between 0.1 and 0.5 inch. In this case a frictional pressure drop below 50 psi can be achieved, and the required tube lengths and tube bundle sizes appear to be quite reasonable.

The Balance Between Polarization and Friction

The optimization of the design of a reverse-osmosis desalination plant will involve a balance between investment and energy costs; these are the considerations that will dictate the optimum permeation flux.

If the installation and replacement costs of the membrane per unit of surface area are low or if the membrane-permeability constant is low, the optimum permeation flux will likewise be low, and concentration-polarization effects will be small. Higher membrane costs or higher permeability values, however, will shift the optimum design to higher

Table 5–3　Operating Conditions for $\bar{c}_2'/c_2^i = 2.5$ at $\bar{v}' = 100$ gpd/ft²

Tube diameter (in.)	Required $\bar{u}^i$ (ft/sec)	Frictional pressure drop (psi)	Approx. length	Approx. number of tubes for 10^6 gpd
0.001	Any {0.18	1	$0.15''$	3×10^9
	value {1.8	100	$1.5''$	3×10^8
0.0045	Any {0.2	0.27	$0.72''$	1.4×10^8
	value {2.0	27	$7.2''$	1.4×10^7
0.01	50	19,700	$33'$	120,000
0.1	5	17.5	$33'$	12,000
1	10.3	70	$700'$	50
10	18.2	212	$12,000'$	$\frac{1}{3}$

flux rates, and polarization effects will become more important. The present analysis is focused upon flux rates of 50 to 200 gpd/ft² because this is the range in which concentration polarization effects are quite significant and because future developments in membrane technology may be expected to produce membranes that can be operated at such high rates.

For any given value of the permeation flux in the turbulent-flow regime there is a trade-off between frictional pressure drop and osmotic pressure requirements. It is the balancing of these two factors, along with other considerations, that will dictate the allowable value of the average concentration polarization. The other considerations have been mentioned previously; they include polarization effects upon the salinity of the product water, the life of the membrane, and the precipitation of salts at the membrane surface. No attempt will be made here to present a quantitative evaluation of these effects. If, however, it is assumed that these effects are not of major consequence, the optimum value of the average concentration polarization will be that at which the balance between frictional pressure loss and required osmotic pressure minimizes the pumping-power requirements for the system. It appears worth while to explore this balance in more detail in order to see what values of the average polarization will minimize the pumping-power requirement for a given value of the permeation flux.

The pressure at which the brine must be delivered to a reverse-osmosis cell is equal to the sum of the pressure drop due to the membrane permeation resistance, the frictional pressure drop, and the osmotic-pressure requirement. The pressure drop due to membrane permeation resistance is equal to the permeation flux divided by the permeation constant of the membrane. It will vary somewhat with longitudinal position because the permeation flux varies as the osmotic pressure increases with distance down the channel. The required osmotic pressure can be thought of as the sum of the osmotic pressure of the bulk salt solution plus an extra increment in osmotic pressure due to the salt-concentration boundary layer which is the focus of the present discussion. These quantities will also vary with longitudinal position; it is their average values over the length of a channel that are of principal concern.

Consider for example the case presented in Table 5–3, in which the average value of the salt concentration at the membrane surface is 2.5 times the concentration of the feed brine. If the osmotic pressure of the feed solution equals 350 psi (approximately the value for seawater), and if osmotic pressure is directly proportional to salt concentration, the average osmotic pressure will be 2.5 times 350, or 875 psi. Of course the average osmotic pressure of the bulk brine is greater than that of the feed brine, because the brine becomes concentrated as the water is removed. The average value of the osmotic pressure of the bulk solution is obtained by reading the lowest abscissa value in Fig. 5–15. For $\beta = 0$, this value is $\bar{\gamma} = 0.386$ and represents the integral average value of γ for an infinite mass-transfer coefficient. Thus, even if the salt diffusivity were infinite and no concentration polarization were present, an average osmotic-pressure requirement of $1.386 \times 350 = 485$ psi would have to be overcome. Thus, in this case the extra osmotic pressure due to concentration boundary-layer effects is equal to $875 - 485$, i.e., 390 psi. This extra osmotic-pressure requirement is reduced to 215 psi if the average value of c_2'/c_2^i is 2 instead of 2.5, but the frictional pressure-drop requirements to keep the polarization at the lower level of 2 are somewhat greater, as can be seen by comparing Table 5–1 with Table 5–3.

It is important to recognize that, to a close approximation, only half of the frictional pressure-drop requirement represents an increased demand in the pressure at which the brine must be delivered to the reverse-osmosis cell. This is because the frictional pressure drop due to brine flow down the channel is distributed over the entire channel length, and thus approximately half of it represents additional pressure for overcoming the membrane permeability resistance and the osmotic pressure requirement in the front half of the brine flow channel. To recognize that this is so, imagine an ideal situation in which the osmotic-pressure requirement is negligibly small and frictional pressure drop is absent, and assume that 1000 psi are required to overcome the membrane-permeation resistance. Here the pressure in the brine solution will be essentially independent of longitudinal position and will be equal to 1000 psi more than the discharge pressure of the product water. Now if the channel is redesigned so as to produce a frictional pressure drop of 200 psi, the delivery pressure required of the system increases from 1000 psi to approximately 1100 psi; it does not increase to 1200 psi. In this case the pressure would vary from 1100 to 900 psi from the channel inlet to the channel outlet, resulting in an increased permeation flux near the channel inlet and a decreased permeation flux near the channel outlet, but the average permeation flux would be essentially the same as in the case of a membrane with no frictional pressure loss operating at 1000 psi. Thus the penality to be paid for having a high brine velocity is only half of the frictional pressure drop, not all of it.

In contrast, the additional osmotic-pressure requirement due to the average concentration polarization represents an additional requirement on the pressure at which the feed brine must be supplied to the reverse-osmosis cell. All of this additional pressure requirement represents extra pumping-power requirement unless the concentrated brine-waste stream is expanded through a turbine to recover the energy represented by its high pressure. If this could be done with perfect efficiency, then approximately half of the pumping energy represented by the osmotic-pressure requirement — including the extra osmotic pressure due to concentration polarization — could be recovered from the concentrated brine-waste stream. Since it seems unlikely that this energy recovery will be economically feasible, at least in plants of smaller size, it will here be assumed that 100% of the extra osmotic-pressure requirement represents an additional power requirement.

Figure 5–20 shows the effect of brine-inlet velocity upon the sum of the extra osmotic-pressure requirement plus half of the frictional pressure drop for several values of the tube diameter in the turbulent range, assuming an average permeation flux of 100 gpd/ft². For each tube diameter there is a value of the brine-inlet velocity that minimizes this extra delivery-pressure requirement. At higher velocities, frictional pressure drop predominates, but at lower velocities concentration polarization effects result in an increased osmotic pressure. The figure shows that the optimum brine inlet velocity is equal to approximately 10, 15,

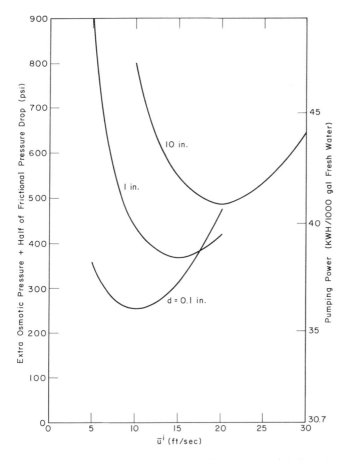

Fig. 5–20 Minimum pumping power for $\bar{v}' = 100$ gpd/ft², $\Delta = 0.5$.

and 20 ft/sec for tube diameters of 0.1, 1, and 10 inches, respectively. At these velocities the average values of c_2'/c_2^i are approximately 1.96, 2.16, and 2.38 for tube diameters of 0.1, 1, and 10 inches, respectively, according to Fig. 5–18. Thus for a permeation flux of 100 gpd/ft^2 the brine-delivery pressure is minimized at inlet-velocity values that correspond to average polarization ratios in the vicinity of 2. It is probable, therefore, that a practical design for a reverse-osmosis plant operating at a permeation flux of 100 gpd/ft^2 will correspond approximately to the results shown in Table 5–1, and the most suitable design is probably operation with turbulent flow in a tube of 0.1- to 0.5-inch diameter.

Figure 5–20 reveals that the minimum in the curve of delivery pressure versus inlet brine velocity is reasonably sharp and that the minimum delivery pressure decreases with decreasing tube diameter. In order to put the ordinate values into perspective, however, it should be remembered that two fixed pressure requirements must be added to the ordinate values to yield the pressure at which the brine feed must be delivered to the reverse-osmosis cell. One such value is the average osmotic pressure of the bulk brine solution; this corresponds to 485 psi if the inlet osmotic pressure is 350 psi, approximately the value for seawater. The second value is the average pressure drop required to overcome the membrane permeation resistance. For the cellulose acetate membrane tested by Loeb and Manjikian[16] on a brackish-water feed, a water-flux rate of almost 50 gpd/ft^2 was achieved with a permeation pressure drop in the vicinity of 500 psi, but this membrane did not have a salt-rejection value sufficiently high for use with seawater. Nevertheless, it may be assumed that a membrane with this permeability can be developed for seawater operation; thus the permeation pressure drop would be approximately 1000 psi for a flux rate of 100 gpd/ft^2. With this assumption, 1485 psi must be added to the ordinate values in Fig. 5–20 to obtain the required brine-delivery pressure. When these delivery pressures are converted into pumping-power requirements by assuming a 70% over-all efficiency of the brine pump and motor, the pumping power expressed in kwh/1000 gallons of fresh water is shown on the right-hand ordinate scale. If the membrane-permeability constant were assumed twice as great, the pumping-power requirement would be decreased by approximately 10 kwh/1000 gallons. In any event, the pumping-power penalty resulting from the salt concentration polarization effect has a minimum value of approximately 5 kwh/1000 gallons for the 0.1-inch diameter tube.

Results for other permeation flux rates. Figure 5–21 presents calculated values of the additional delivery-pressure requirement for a membrane operating in the turbulent region at a permeation flux of 50 gpd/ft^2. As in Fig. 5–20, the right-hand ordinate scale presents the total pumping-power requirement assuming a 70% over-all efficiency and also a membrane permeability constant equal to that found by Loeb and Manjikian, so that the pressure drop due to permeation resistance is 500 psi. With a permeability equal to twice this value, the pumping-power requirement would be approximately 5 kwh/1000 gallons less. According to Fig. 5–21 the pumping-power penalty due to the salt-concentration polarization has a minimum value of approximately 3 kwh/1000 gallons for turbulent flow in a 0.1-inch-diameter tube, and even for a 10-inch-diameter tube the penalty is only approximately 6 kwh/1000 gallons. Table 5–4 summarizes the operating conditions for each tube size at its point of minimum delivery pressure. The design conditions for a tube of diameter between 0.1 and 0.5 inch appear to be convenient, and the delivery-pressure penalty due to concentration polarization is between 160 and 220 psi, corresponding to approximately 3 to 5 kwh/1000 gallons.

The sum of the extra osmotic-pressure requirement plus half of the

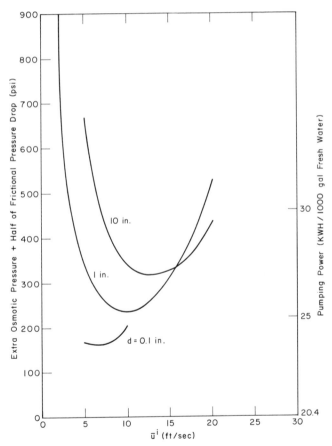

Fig. 5–21   Minimum pumping power for $\bar{v}' = 50$ gpd/ft², $\Delta = 0.5$.

Table 5-4   Conditions at Minimum Delivery Pressure for $\bar{v}' = 50$ gpd/ft²

Tube diameter (in.)	$\bar{u}^i$ (ft/sec)	$\bar{c}_2'/c_2^i$	Extra osmotic pressure (psi)	Frictional pressure drop (psi)	Approx. length	Approx. number of tubes for 10⁶ gpd
0.1	7	1.72	118	86	95'	8000
1	10	1.88	172	128	1,400'	55
10	12.5	2.08	244	148	16,000'	½

frictional pressure drop for a membrane operating in the turbulent region at an average permeation flux of 200 gpd/ft² is shown in Fig. 5–22. The right-hand ordinate scale shows the pumping-power requirement, assuming a 70% over-all efficiency. In calculating the pumping power, 2485 psi was added to the pressure-requirement values shown on the left-hand

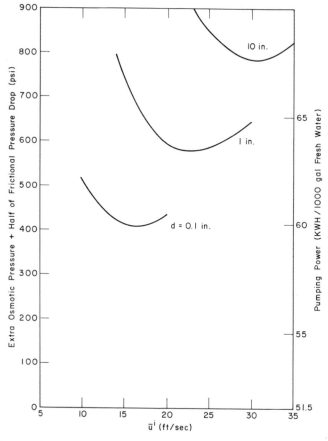

Fig. 5-22   Minimum pumping power for $\bar{v}' = 200$ gpd/ft², $\Delta = 0.5$.

ordinate scale in order to obtain the brine-delivery pressure. This value was based on the assumption that the permeation pressure drop was 2000 psi, which corresponds to a membrane permeability equal to that found by Loeb and Manjikian. If the membrane permeability were twice this value, a 1000-psi pressure drop would be required to overcome the permeation resistance of the membrane, and approximately 20 kwh/1000 gallons would be subtracted from the total power requirement shown. It is improbable that such a high permeation flux rate would be used unless a membrane were to be developed with a permeability much greater than that found by Loeb and Manjikian. The delivery-pressure penalty due to concentration polarization is minimized at approximately 410 psi for a 0.1-inch-diameter tube; this corresponds to a pumping-power penalty of approximately 8.5 kwh/1000 gallons. For a 1-inch-diameter tube, the pumping power penalty is approximately 12 kwh/1000 gallons. Figure 5–22 shows that the minimum in the curve for a 0.1-inch diameter is well out in the turbulent range (a brine inlet velocity of 5 ft/sec is the minimum for turbulent flow in a 0.1-inch-diameter tube), and it may be that turbulent flow in a tube of diameter smaller than 0.1 inch is indicated for operation at this high flux rate.

Table 5–5   Conditions at Minimum Delivery Pressure for $\bar{v}' = 200$ gpd/ft^2

Tube diameter (in.)	$\bar{u}^i$ (ft/sec)	$\bar{c}_2'/c_2^i$	Extra osmotic pressure (psi)	Frictional pressure drop (psi)	Approx. length	Approx. number of tubes for 10^6 gpd
0.1	17	2.22	291	236	60'	3300
1	22	2.64	440	280	750'	25
10	31	2.95	547	476	10,000'	$\frac{1}{5}$

Table 5–5 summarizes the operating conditions for each tube diameter at the point of minimum delivery pressure. As before, the tube length and the number of tubes required appear to be at their most reasonable values when the tube diameter is in the range between 0.1 and 0.5 inch, where the pumping-power penalty due to concentration polarization is between 8 and 11 kwh/1000 gallons and the average concentration polarization is between 2.2 and 2.5. The relatively higher pumping-power penalty as well as other possible adverse effects of these higher polarization values might dictate the use of diameters smaller than 0.1 inch in this case, but on the whole it seems that concentration-polarization effects can be made small enough to be tolerated even at the relatively high water-flux rate of 200 gpd/ft^2. Thus the feasibility of operating at such a high flux rate will depend upon obtaining a membrane with a high permeability constant.

Brackish water. The preceding discussion was based upon an osmotic pressure of 350 psi for the feed brine and a membrane salt rejection of 100%. For desalting brackish water with an osmotic pressure in the vicinity of 25 psi, the extra osmotic pressure due to concentration polarization will not be a major factor unless the polarization ratio is quite large. Furthermore, a salt-rejection value of 90% will probably suffice for such an operation, and Eq. 5.39 indicates that the polarization ratio will be somewhat reduced at the lower salt-rejection value. Thus lower brine inlet velocities and thus lower frictional pressure drops can be used for brackish-water desalination. But even for operation with brackish water it is likely that polarization-ratio values greatly in excess of 3 will not often be tolerated. In this case it would not be the extra osmotic pressure that would limit the polarization ratio but rather the precipitation of salts at the membrane surface and possibly the effect of polarization on the apparent membrane salt-rejection efficiency. Thus the maximum value of c_2'/c_2^i, occurring at the channel outlet, would probably be of greater interest than the average value. But salt precipitation will not always result when c_2' exceeds the solubility limit, and experimental results on the effect of salt precipitation will be needed to clarify this effect.

Symbol List

Symbols first appear in equation indicated, or in text shortly preceding or following this equation.

A	membrane-permeability constant, gpd/ft²-psi	5.22
c_2	salt concentration, g/cm³	5.1
$\bar{c}_2'$	average salt concentration at channel wall, g/cm³	5.48
c_2''	product water salinity at given longitudinal position, g/cm³	5.41a
C	normalized salt concentration, c_2/c_2^i	5.11
$\bar{C}''$	average normalized concentration of product water	5.30
d	tube diameter, inches	Fig. 5–16
D_2	molecular-diffusion coefficient of salt, cm²/sec	5.1
f	friction factor for brine flow past membrane surface	5.42
F_2	salt flux through membrane, g/cm²-sec	5.4
h	half-width of channel, or radius of tube, cm	Fig. 5–1
j_D	Chilton-Colburn mass transfer j-factor	5.40
k^0	mass-transfer coefficient in absence of transpiration, cm/sec	5.38
N_F	permeation Reynolds number, hv'/ν	5.7
N_{Sc}	Schmidt number for salt diffusion, ν/D_2	5.40

p	pressure, psi	5.22
r	salt rejection, $[1 - (F_2/v'c_2')]$	5.5
u	velocity component in the x direction, cm/sec or ft/sec	5.1
$\bar{u}$	average value of u over the channel width at a given value of x, cm/sec	5.16
U	normalized velocity in the x direction, $u/\bar{u}^i$	5.11
v	velocity component in the y direction, cm/sec	5.1
$\bar{v}'$	average value of v' over the channel length, cm/sec	5.48
V	normalized velocity in the y direction, $v/v^{i'}$	5.11
$\bar{V}'$	average value of V' over the channel length	5.26
x	longitudinal distance from channel inlet, cm	Fig. 5–1
X	normalized longitudinal distance from inlet, $(v^{i'}/\bar{u}^i)\,(x/h)$	5.11
y	transverse distance from bulk fluid toward membrane surface, cm	Fig. 5–1
Y	normalized transverse distance, y/h	5.11
α	normalized salt-diffusion coefficient for constant permeation flux, $D_2/v'h$	5.19
α_0	normalized salt-diffusion coefficient for variable permeation flux, $D_2/v^{i'}h$	5.11
$\bar{\alpha}$	average normalized salt-diffusion coefficient, $D_2/\bar{v}'h$	5.27
β	ratio of inlet-solution osmotic pressure to net driving force for water permeation, $r\pi^i/(\Delta p - r\pi^i)$	5.23
γ	concentration polarization, $C' - 1$	5.23
$\bar{\gamma}$	average value of γ, calculated according to Eq. 5.28	
Γ	a measure of concentration polarization defined by Eq. 5.20	
δ	film thickness in film theory, cm	5.37
δ_0	boundary-layer thickness in eddy-diffusion theory, cm	5.45
Δ	fractional water removal at a given longitudinal position	5.15
Δp	pressure drop across membrane, psi	5.22
$\Delta \pi$	difference in osmotic pressure across membrane, psi	5.22
ϵ	eddy diffusivity, cm²/sec	5.43
η	transformed variable defined by Eq. 5.46	
ν	kinematic viscosity of solution, cm²/sec	5.7
π	osmotic pressure, psi	5.22

Commonly used superscripts

$'$	variable evaluated at channel wall	5.8
b	variable evaluated in bulk solution	5.37
i	variable evaluated at channel inlet	5.2

References

1. Berman, A. S., *J. Appl. Phys.* **24**, 1232 (1953).
2. Sherwood, T. K., P. L. T. Brian, and R. E. Fisher, M.I.T. Desalination Research Laboratory, Report 295-1 (August 1963).
3. Sherwood, T. K., P. L. T. Brian, R. E. Fisher, and L. Dresner, *Ind. Eng. Chem. Fundamentals* **4**, 113, (1965).
4. Brian, P. L. T., *ibid.* **4**, 439 (1965). Also, M.I.T. Desalination Research Laboratory, Report 295-7 (May 1965).
5. Dresner, L., Oak Ridge Nat'l. Lab. Report 3621 (May 1964).
6. Merten, U., *Ind. Eng. Chem. Fundamentals* **2**, 229 (1963).
7. Sherwood, T. K., and J. C. Wei, *A. I. Ch. E. J.* **1**, 522 (1955).
8. Vinograd, J. R., and J. W. McBain, *J. Am. Chem. Soc.* **63**, 2008 (1941).
9. Fisher, R. E., T. K. Sherwood, and P. L. T. Brian, M.I.T. Desalination Research Laboratory, Report 295-5 (January 1965).
10. Fisher, R E., Sc.D. Thesis, Department of Chemical Engineering, M.I.T. (1965).
11. Merten, U., H. K. Lonsdale, and R. L. Riley, *Ind. Eng. Chem. Fundamentals* **3**, 210 (1964).
12. Sherwood, T. K., P. L. T. Brian, and A. F. Sarofim, M.I.T. Desalination Research Laboratory, Report 295-8 (December 1965).
13. Sherwood, T. K., P. L. T. Brian, and R. E. Fisher, article submitted to *Ind. Eng. Chem. Fundamentals*.
14. Brian, P. L. T., "Influence of Concentration Polarization on Reverse Osmosis System Design," *Proc. First Intn'l. Desalination Symp.*, Paper SWD/79, Washington, D. C., October 3–9, 1965.
15. Mahon, H. I., *Proceedings of Desalination Research Conference*, p. 345, Nat'l. Acad. Sci., Publ. 942 (1963).
16. Loeb, S., and S. Manjikian, *Ind. Eng. Chem. Process Design and Development* **4**, 207 (1965).

6. Engineering of Reverse-Osmosis Plants

Donald T. Bray

As a chemical process develops there is a gradual transition from the original idea to research, to development, and finally to commercial production of a product. The reverse-osmosis process is somewhere between the research and the development stages at the present state of its evolution. It is at this point that one must start giving serious attention to the engineering aspects of the concept. It is the purpose of this chapter to discuss the present status of engineering and plant design for the reverse-osmosis process.

Because reverse osmosis has yet to be applied in large-scale plants, published information on engineering aspects is still extremely limited. Several organizations have, however, run pilot-plant experiments, and we will use the separator units used in these pilot-plant designs as examples of possible membrane configurations. Details of the pilot-plant operating experience will be found in Chapter 7. There are also available two engineering studies of larger reverse-osmosis systems. These are included in the report by McCutchan, et al., published in December 1963,[1] and that of Lonsdale, et al.,[2] published in May 1964. In the following discussions we will draw on the results obtained in these studies; but because recent progress in the engineering area has been rapid, we will also draw particularly heavily on our own experience and on a recent preliminary design study[3] done within our own organization.

Saline-water conversion plants are frequently divided into two classes: those designed for seawater conversion and those designed for brackish-water conversion. This distinction is particularly useful in considerations of the reverse-osmosis process, because brackish waters are often suffi-ciently dilute to permit the use of substantially lower operating pressures than must generally be utilized in seawater conversion, and because the lower feed-water salinities permit the use of higher permeability and less selective membranes than must be chosen for seawater. The pressure at which brackish-water reverse-osmosis systems should be operated depends upon the quality of water to be treated as well as upon the design details of the plant. For our present purposes we will think of brackish-water systems as being those that operate at system pressures up to about 600 psi, and we will think of seawater systems as those that operate at pressures up to 2000 psi.

As has been pointed out in Chapters 3 and 4, the quality of the product water obtained from a reverse-osmosis system depends upon the charac-teristics of the feed, the system operating pressure, and the membrane characteristics. Existing technology is good enough so that most brackish waters can be treated in a single-stage reverse-osmosis process and water that meets normal standards for potable water can be produced. However, the same cannot be said for seawater; product salinities of the order of 1000 to 1500 ppm are probably as good as can be anticipated with present membrane technology and single-stage operation. Several methods can be proposed for reducing this salt content further; in particular, part or all of the first-stage water can be treated in a second reverse-osmosis plant similar to the brackish-water systems. The use of a second stage seems sufficiently unattractive economically and the probability of membrane technology improving seems sufficiently great to justify the design assumption of single-stage operation for future large-scale seawater plants. We will, in general, adopt the single-stage approach in our discussions.

6.1   Basic Plant Requirements

Flow Diagram

The basic process flow diagram for a single-stage reverse-osmosis plant is shown in Fig. 6–1. Feed water, assumed to be free of silt and gross debris, enters the feed sump. Chlorine is periodically added to the inlet feed line. From the feed sump the solution is brought to sufficient pressure to force it through filters. Between the feed sump and the main pump a pH controller regulates an acid-injection system to govern the pH of the feed. After filtration the water is pumped to system pressure and enters the membrane separator unit. Within this unit, part of the water is forced through the membrane, becoming the product water. This water then flows through porous-membrane backing material until it reaches an outlet port where it leaves the unit at near-atmospheric

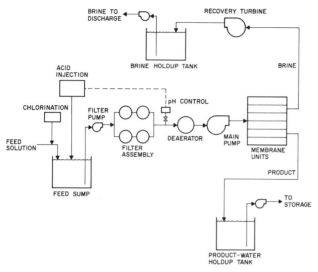

Fig. 6–1   Basic flow diagram for a single-stage reverse-osmosis plant.

pressure. The remaining water, together with most of the salt and all of the suspended solids, leaves the unit at a pressure slightly lower than that at the main pump outlet and then passes through a recovery turbine to brine discharge.

Several modifications of this basic diagram are possible. In smaller-size plants the recovery turbine is not economically justified and is omitted. The feed-water pretreatment suggested here is minimal and may not suffice in all cases. Deaeration has not been called for because there is no experimental evidence to indicate that the presence of dissolved gases, including CO_2, in the feed water is detrimental to the reverse-osmosis system. It is assumed that all parts of the system will be built of materials whose corrosion resistance is sufficiently good at ambient temperatures and at the system pH so that deoxygenation is not necessary. This last point is, however, an economic question, and it may be that deaeration will eventually prove to be a desirable step. In addition, some brackish waters may contain sufficient iron and other materials to lead to scale formation on the membrane surfaces if these materials are not removed in a pretreatment step.

Water recovery in a reverse-osmosis system can be limited by either of two conditions: In seawater, it is the increase in osmotic pressure of the feed water leading to decreased flows that sets the limit on discharge concentration. In most brackish waters, on the other hand, osmotic pressure will not be a serious problem and discharge concentrations will be governed by the degree of concentration permissible before precipitation of calcium sulfate or other slightly soluble salts begins. Ion-exchange softening or other methods of preventing calcium sulfate precipitation may be desirable as a means of increasing water recovery in such cases.

Feed-brine flow within the separator unit can be either laminar or turbulent. It now appears that designs with turbulent flow conditions will become of greatest interest as membrane fluxes are improved. For these conditions, as shown in Chapter 5, reasonably high flow rates of feed water across the membrane surface must be maintained to prevent excessive buildup of salts in the boundary layers. These velocities can be obtained only in two ways: For a given percentage water removal and necessary conditions of turbulence, either the water must be passed over a sufficiently long run of membrane surface by series connections, or the brine must be recycled through the system until the required amount of water is removed. In general, the former approach introduces no special design problems and is to be preferred, since recycling means the addition of pumps and associated components to the system and results in a higher average brine concentration in a system for a given brine outlet concentration.

Materials of Construction

The choice of construction materials is dictated by pressure, corrosion, and economic requirements. It appears that in the near term reverse-osmosis systems will be operated at ambient temperature on a feed saturated with air at atmospheric pressure, and having a pH of 3 to 7. Pressures may range up to 2000 psi. Corrosion data are meager for this particular set of conditions. Operating data in this area, especially for seawater feeds, are needed. It is possible that future units may operate at temperatures up to 150°F with cellulose acetate membranes and perhaps far higher with still-to-be-developed membrane materials. Such a change would of course greatly intensify the corrosion problem.

For relatively noncorrosive conditions, such as exist for some brackish-water and waste-water feeds, carbon steel pipe and fittings are acceptable. For seawater systems, however, there has been a tendency to use expensive alloys, such as Monel or 316 SS, on smaller pipes and fittings in the high-pressure portion of the plant and to coat or line carbon steel for the larger pipes or tanks. For system pressures of 500 psi or below, tubes of glass-fiber-reinforced epoxy are available that can be used as high-pressure piping or as the pressure-container vessels for spiral-wound modules. Development work is in progress to fabricate this type of tube for use at much higher pressures. Each situation should be examined to determine the most economical solution for a given design approach and feed.

For low-salt-content feed the designer generally has the choice of carbon steel, copper, or plastic (such as PVC) for the low-pressure portion of the plant. This section will operate in most systems at less than

100 psi and generally at less than 50 psi. For higher salt-content feed, such as seawater, plastic piping is preferred for the low-pressure portion of the plant.

Special note should be made of the use of glass-fiber-reinforced epoxy. This material has excellent corrosion resistance as well as considerable strength. It is receiving increasing attention in all three major membrane-assembly approaches. Development work to fit this material better into reverse-osmosis desalination systems of the future can be expected.

Chemical Pretreatment

Control of the *p*H is probably the most important feed pretreatment. It is desirable to keep the *p*H between about 3 and 7 because of membrane-lifetime considerations (see Chapter 4). It is further necessary in most natural waters to add acid to prevent the precipitation of calcium carbonate or magnesium hydroxide during the concentration of the feed stream within the membrane unit. It is perhaps fortunate that both these requirements are in the same direction, and it appears that a feed *p*H between 5 and 6 may be a good compromise between chemical costs, membrane lifetime, calcium carbonate precipitation, and corrosion. The amount of acid needed depends on the degree of alkalinity of the feed water.

Periodic chlorination or other bactericide additions to the feed supply are necessary to reduce the growth of organisms within the plant. The amount and frequency of treatment will depend on the source of feed water, but in any case is expected to be of minor cost importance. Chlorine in small doses apparently does not cause significant damage to cellulose acetate membranes. Feeds with 1 to 2 ppm residual chlorine have been used for periods of several months with no apparent detrimental effect.[4] Further unpublished work carried out within our organization on continuous closed-cycle loop operation with residual chlorine levels varying from less than 1 to about 50 ppm for 400 hours showed no effect on membrane water flux or salt rejection.

Filtration and Clarification

The required degree of filtration is primarily a function of the design of the brine-flow passages within the membrane unit. The different approaches to membrane configuration to be discussed here vary widely in the degree of filtration required. The biggest problem appears to be the mechanical plugging of the brine-flow channels, and hence the guiding criterion is related to the sizes of the smaller brine-flow passages. The shapes of suspended solids are also important. Long stringy particles tend to give more trouble than granular particles when peg or cross stringer spacers or turbulence promoters are used. Fine particles or emulsions of heavy greases or waxes may present a special problem if this material tends to stick to either the membrane or any brine side spacer. Slimy or gelatinous deposits such as iron oxide may be yet another problem.

In general, one can expect that filtration to a size one fifth that of the minimum brine-flow passage dimension would suffice, but experimental data on this assumption are meager, and this item remains one of the major unknowns in plant design. The author's experience indicates, however, that with brine-side openings of 0.010 inch or more, small particulate matter in the millimicron up to a few micron size range does not remain in the unit or tend to accumulate at the membrane surface. Formation of precipitates within the membrane assembly is a real problem and one that cannot be controlled by feed filtration per se.

The type of filter needed to achieve the desired filtration will depend on plant size and allowable maximum particle size. For laboratory test units and small demonstration models where convenience and not cost is the main criterion, replaceable cartridge filters that remove particles greater than five microns have proved very useful. For larger plants however we have, in order of decreasing costs, diatomaceous-earth filters for 1 to 10 μ filtration, sand filters for 10 to 25 μ, and screen strainers above 25 μ.

In Section 6.2 we will discuss a number of membrane separator units. For normal feed pretreatment, present information suggests that screen strainers should suffice in the large-tube design. The plate-and-frame and the spiral-wound module concepts will require filtration of a quality that can be furnished by sand filters. The small-tube approach will probably require diatomaceous-earth filtration. If special feed pretreatment is needed to remove some component, such as iron, then the type of filter used may be determined by pretreatment requirements and not by the type of separator unit employed.

For systems using sand filtration, the discharge brine stream is an excellent back-flush medium. This water has already been filtered, and its use therefore markedly reduces the probability of small slugs of unfiltered feed water reaching the membrane units.

High-Pressure Pumps and Turbines

The main pressure pumps are expected to be the major capital equipment and maintenance cost item over the long run. There is a very large variety of pumps available in today's market. In spite of this, suitable equipment is readily available only for laboratory units, where cost and maintenance requirements are of secondary importance, and for high-volume, low-pressure systems. Centrifugal pumps are generally preferred because of lower maintenance requirements. However, for low flow volumes this type of pump is restricted to low-pressure uses because of capital costs and pumping efficiency. For high-pressure applications (1000 psi and over) plant capacities approaching 500,000 gpd are needed before centrifugal pumps become acceptable. For intermediate pressures of 400 to 1000 psi, minimum plant capacities of 100,000 to 200,000 gpd are indicated before the use of centrifugal pumps becomes feasible. For plants with capacities below these values (e.g., test loops, pilot plants, and demonstration units), piston pumps are generally used.

The feed-water conditions in reverse-osmosis systems are not now encountered industrially on a large scale. The water is at high pressure, it may be saturated with air (at atmospheric pressure), and its pH may be adjusted to a value of 3 to 7. Its total solids content will range up to seawater concentrations. Very little data exist on the use of pumps of either piston or centrifugal types for medium- and high-pressure use under these conditions. When large reverse-osmosis desalination plants become a reality, development work on pumps specifically intended for this application appears warranted.

Industrial experience on recovery turbines is less than that on pumps. A recent study[3] showed that recovery turbines are not economically justified for brine-discharge volumes of less than about 500,000 gpd. For brackish-water plants recovering 90% of the water in the feed, this means that a plant size of about 5 million gpd would be needed before a recovery turbine is used. The problems and experience relating to corrosion are similar to those noted above for pumps.

Sumps and Storage Tanks

The minimum sizes of the feed sump and the product-water storage tank are governed by the time it takes to shut the system down on low-level signals or start up a pump on high-level signals. A sump tank of a few minutes' pumping capacity for the pump involved should suffice. Product-water storage capacity consistent with the usage requirements must of course be provided separately. If the reject brine is to be used for sand-filter back flush, a brine holdup tank of a size commensurate with the back-flush requirements must be provided.

Plant Controls

The main control signals for the plant are expected to be system pressure, product water quality, pH, pressure drop across the membrane assembly, and brine flow velocity. Control of pH has already been alluded to and is critical in that a pH above 3 or below 8 must be maintained at all times. System pressure would be controlled about an operating point with suitable pressure-actuated bypass and relief valves. The product-water quality would be monitored from the unit as a whole, and for larger plants from subsections as well. On a signal indicating an excessively high salt content, the affected section would be shut down or the product stream from the section would be diverted back to the feed sump. In all current design concepts it is relatively easy to provide for the monitoring of small sections of the separator units to locate trouble spots. Correct brine flow is needed to prevent excessive salt buildup with subsequent poorer quality water and/or precipitation within the module. Hence, separate control of this variable may be desirable.

6.2 Separator Units

Design Objectives

The characteristics of the reverse-osmosis membrane and of the unit in which it is contained largely determine the engineering design of a reverse-osmosis plant. In Chapters 3 and 4, the characteristics of the membrane per se have been described in detail, but little has been said concerning the practical design of membrane-containing separator units.

In the final analysis the design of a separator unit must be judged on the basis of its effect on total water costs. The unit itself contributes directly to these costs through capital cost of the unit, purchase price of expendable components, and installation cost of expendable components. Furthermore, its design feeds back on over-all costs by affecting operating pressures, required brine flow rates, space requirements, filtration requirements, and so on. Three problems that have received special attention in the designs proposed to date are the provision of suitable boundary-layer conditions within the unit, the efficient removal of product water from the unit after it has passed through the membrane, and the possibility of minimizing volume requirements in the high-pressure portion of the reverse-osmosis system through high-density membrane packing.

There are under study today at least four different approaches to the assembly of the membrane-containing units of reverse-osmosis systems. Each of these differs in the method of assembly and support for the membrane material itself. We will term these design concepts plate and frame, large tube, small tube, and spiral-wound module. There are other possible approaches, but these four represent the most advanced concepts.

The details of three of these arrangements, as now utilized in pilot plants, will be discussed in Chapter 7. Here we shall consider only their general features.

Design Concepts

Plate-and-frame. This arrangement is patterned after the conventional filter press. Circular sheets of membrane are placed on each side of a porous supporting disk. Many such disks, each with two membranes, are then stacked next to each other with a spacer washer around the periphery between each pair of disks. In the version on which most of the development work to date has been done, the whole assembly is held together by external tie bolts between sufficiently thick end plates. The system pressure is carried by these tie bolts and by the disk rims and spacer rings. The brine flow takes place in the space between the disks, and the product-water flows through the membrane into the porous supporting structure and radially outward (or inward) to a product-water takeoff outlet. This system has the advantage that it is simple, rugged, that much practical experience already exists in plate-and-frame technology and that when membrane material fails, only the membrane itself needs replacement. It has the disadvantages of difficult brine-flow patterns, the need for appreciable manual labor in membrane assembly and replacement, and high equipment costs. The membrane packing density in current designs is 50 to 100 square feet of membrane per cubic foot of pressure vessel. This approach has been pursued by Loeb and his co-workers at UCLA[1,5] and by the Aerojet-General Corporation.[6,7,8]

Large tube. This approach utilizes a porous-wall tube with the membrane on the inside wall either cast in place or precast and inserted. The porous tube either can be supported by an outer tube or can be its own pressure tube. Brine flow is axial inside the tube. Product-water flow is through the membrane, to an outlet hole in the supporting tube wall and then through the porous wall. The water emerges at near-atmospheric pressure and is collected for transfer to storage. This concept has several advantages: The porous support wall can serve simultaneously as the pressure-containing unit, the brine-flow passage geometry is cylindrical and well defined, and filtration requirements are minimal. The principal disadvantages of this approach are in the cost of the tubes and in the large number of individual tubes that must be handled. Further, the method of membrane replacement has not yet been clarified.

In one embodiment of this arrangement, first reported by Havens Industries,[9] the porous support tube is of glass-fiber-reinforced epoxy. Loeb and his co-workers reported on a similar unit using 1-inch-diam copper tubes with small holes drilled 3 inches apart in the tube wall.[10] The cost problem is at least partially overcome with the epoxy tubes, but economical production of tubes smaller than about 0.5-inch diam appears to be indicated for this type of membrane arrangement. Packing densities of

10 to 100 ft²/ft³ are obtainable, but packing densities are not too important in this concept since the tube wall itself serves as the pressure
vessel and the densities are still sufficiently high to keep over-all plant
volume small.

Small tube. This approach utilizes small-diameter tubes, where the
walls of the tube serve both as the membrane material and as the pressure containing unit. The original work in this area was reported by
Mahon of the Dow Chemical Company.[11] Little recent data are available. Tube diameters are in the range of 5 to 100 μ with diameter-to-wall
ratios 4 to 5. Tubes are arranged in bundles with the ends sealed in
headers by some material such as epoxy. The brine flow is inside the
tubes. The product water flows through the walls of the tubes and is
collected at near-atmospheric pressure for transfer to storage. Work has
been reported only for dense cellulose acetate membranes, but because
of the large surface area per unit plant space (10,000 to 20,000 ft²/ft³
tube bundle) it may be possible to utilize this material in place of high-
flux membranes. The advantages of this approach are the large surface
areas per unit plant volume, the elimination of the need for a membrane-
support material, and the possibility of achieving high water fluxes
before boundary-layer problems become limiting. Its disadvantages are
the need for good feed-water filtration (probably a diatomaceous-earth
filter), the enormous multiplicity of tubes, which will require the detec-
tion and sealing of faulty tubes during assembly, and the need for
short tube lengths for high-flux membranes. It seems likely that even
with the present relatively thick-walled dense cellulose acetate, the
tubes will be restricted to use at relatively low system pressures ($<$ 500
psi).

Spiral-wound module. The spiral-wound concept can be visualized as
follows: A piece of membrane is folded over a porous product-water-
side backing material and a tube is placed between the two layers at the
fold. The resulting sandwich is then sealed along both sides and one
end as well as around the central tube where the tube leaves the sandwich. The central tube wall has perforations in the area between the
glue regions. This unit is then simply rolled up by wrapping the leaf
around the tube. Before rollup, a highly porous brine-side spacer screen
is placed on one membrane surface so that, as the assembly is rolled,
adjacent brine-side surfaces are spaced apart. The rolled-up unit, called
a module, is then placed in a pressure tube, generally a piece of pipe,
and sealed between the outer wrap of the module and the inside of the
pipe to prevent short-circuit flow of the brine around the module during
operation. The brine is forced through the brine-side spacer in a direction
parallel to the axis of the roll. As it flows through the module, part of the
water is forced through the membrane and into the porous product-
water-side backing material. Once in the backing material it flows spi-

rally inward to the central tube, through the slots, into the center tube at essentially atmospheric pressure, and then out through a sealing connection in the pressure-pipe cap end. This concept has the advantage of providing a relatively high membrane-packing density of between 250 and 500 ft^2/ft^3, and a controlled brine-side spacing. The design lends itself to factory assembly and easy field replacement of light-weight units. Its disadvantages lie in the need for the product water to flow appreciable distances in a porous medium before it can be removed from the module, and in the need for a reasonably good filtration to prevent plugging of the brine-side spacer. Further, when membrane replacement is performed it becomes necessary to replace not only the membrane material itself but the rest of the materials of the module. The cost savings gained by factory fabrication and simplified installation must be balanced against the added material costs. This concept has been developed at the General Atomic Division of General Dynamics Corporation.[3,12]

Membrane Packing Density

As noted in the previous section, considerable variation exists in the membrane packing density for the various conceptual approaches. The intrinsic worth of high packing density is dependent on specific conditions. One aspect relates to the over-all physical size of the complete water plant (excluding storage). For all concepts, plant packing densities of 5 to 10 ft^2 of membrane per ft^3 plant space are obtainable. For 10 gpd/ft^2 of membrane, a plant covering one acre utilized for 30 ft in height could produce 6 to 12 million gpd. Thus plant-area requirements for the reverse-osmosis process are small regardless of approach, and the advantage of one approach over the other in this regard is minimal. The major point here is the small plant space requirements for reverse osmosis as compared with those for other methods of desalination.

Another aspect relates to capital cost of the membrane-containing unit. Since the tube designs utilize, or can utilize, the membrane-support structure as the pressure container, any comparison between approaches should consider the membrane, its support, and the pressure container as a complete unit. The pressure vessels for the plate-and-frame, for the spiral-wound module, and perhaps for the large-tube approach would be considered as capital equipment. Since one hopes to build future reverse-osmosis plants for well under one dollar per gpd capacity, allowed charges to the pressure container alone should probably be less than 10 cents per gpd capacity. From these data and the materials of construction needed for the system pressure and feed-water type, one can estimate a desirable minimum packing density. Packing densities much in excess of this minimum are not overly beneficial except for special applications. With internally coated carbon steel pressure vessels of careful design for operation at 800 to 1500 psi, a reasonable allowed cost for vessel construction might be $100/ft³ of pressure volume. In this event, and with a water flux of 10 gpd/ft², minimum packing densities of 100 ft²/ft³ of pressure vessel space are indicated.

Brine-Side Considerations

The design of the brine path through the separator unit determines the pumping-power requirement to reduce salt buildup in the boundary layer to acceptable values as well as the clogging susceptibility of the unit by particulate matter. The concentration buildup at the membrane surface can be reduced by suitably decreasing the thickness of the laminar boundary layer for turbulent flow (by increasing the velocity) or reducing the channel width for laminar flow. Since these measures increase the pressure drop, there is a practical limit to how far one can go in these directions. Thus, the allowable salt buildup and pumping-power requirements are closely coupled, a fact which presents an optimization condition for each feed and represents one of the major selections in plant design. These problems are discussed in detail from the theoretical point of view in Chapter 5, where the designer will find much data fundamental to good plant design.

In actual assemblies, the variation of channel dimensions from point to point, and the introduction of spacers that promote turbulence can complicate the calculational problem. The following paragraphs present some data on the spiral-wound module and compare it with the theoretical calculations of Chapter 5. The brine-side spacer used for this illustration is a 12 × 12 mesh polyethylene screen made from circular 0.013 inch-diam monofilaments at 90° to each cross strand and 45° to the axial direction of the module. The filaments do not bend around the cross strands but go straight across. The over-all thickness of the screen is about 0.026 in. and the over-all porosity about 0.875. If the brine flow follows the 45° bias, then the effective flow channels are about 0.013 × 0.070 inch in cross section, and the brine flows about 1.41 ft for each foot of module length. Under these conditions, calculations of the pressure drop are presented in Fig. 6–2 for laminar flow conditions, together with measured values. The data were taken at pressures of 50 to 100 psi and 66°F with San Diego tap water. As can be seen, the experimental values agree well with the calculations at low velocities but deviate significantly at the higher flow rates. Figure 6–2 indicates the start of deviation from laminar flow at apparent Reynolds numbers less than 100. These Reynolds numbers are so low that the usual calculational methods for pressure drop based on turbulent flow conditions are not applicable.

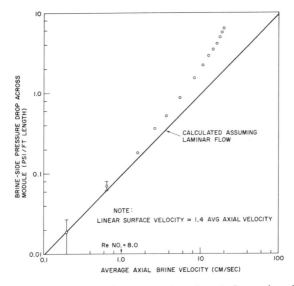

Fig. 6–2   Typical brine-side pressure drop for spiral-wound modules.

Examination of the module-fabrication procedures and materials of assembly indicate further potential difficulties of the calculational approach. When the module is rolled, tension is applied to the leaves to obtain a tight wrap. This tension forces the brine-side spacer screen into the membrane surface, causing a reduction in brine-flow channel cross-sectional area that can easily amount to 25%. Then when the unit is placed into operation, the brine-side pressure will tend to compress the product-water-side backing material and the membrane itself. At higher pressures this can amount to a 25% increase in brine-flow channel cross-sectional area. Further variation exists in the size of the screen monofilaments (measurements of 0.010 to 0.014 inch have been made) and in the corresponding value for thickness and porosity. Thus, while the calculational methods already described can be very helpful in design considerations, they cannot substitute for experimental data in many practical instances.

Product-water cost is determined, of course, by over-all plant economics. Within the brine-side regime, there is a balance to be struck between pumping requirements (pressure drop), water recovery, amount of membrane surface required, and product-water quality. As the brine velocity increases, the pumping requirements increase but the salt buildup at the membrane surface is reduced. The change in the salt concentration right at the surface can be determined by measuring the salt content of the product water as compared to the bulk of the brine and assuming that any increase in this value at lower brine flow rates is due to this

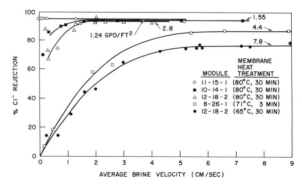

Fig. 6–3   Effect of brine velocities on Cl⁻ rejection, heat-treated membrane.

buildup. Figure 6–3 presents some data for spiral-wound modules using brine-side spacers similar to that described above for pressure-drop data. Here the calculated percent Cl⁻ rejection is based on the average of the feed-in brine-out salt concentrations. Except for the 1.24-gpd/ft² curve, the percent water removal was about 5% per module (one foot long) per pass.

These data were obtained in a nominal 300-psi closed-cycle recirculating loop using NaCl solutions, except for run 8-26-1 where a mixture of salts was used. Salt concentrations were in the range of 1500 to 2700 ppm. Temperature was ambient (75° to 80°F). In order to obtain different water fluxes, the membranes used were given different heat treatments, as noted.

The 1.24-gpd/ft² curve does not show any decrease in rejection at the lower flows. For this flux, the rate of diffusive back flow of salt is sufficiently rapid compared to its rate of arrival at the membrane surface so that the membrane surface concentration is only slightly higher than the bulk concentration, and the difference could not be detected with the analytical techniques used. The fall-off in salt rejection at low brine flows becomes evident at the higher water fluxes.

At the higher brine velocities given in Fig. 6–3, the percent rejection approaches a maximum value, depending on the particular membrane used, indicating that salt concentration at the membrane surface is only slightly higher than that in the bulk of the stream. If one assumes that the salt-flux increase at lower brine velocities is directly proportional to the salt-concentration increase at the membrane surface, one can determine from Fig. 6–3 a relationship between degree of polarization, brine velocity, and product-water flux. Figure 6–4 shows a plot of brine velocity versus product-water flux for a membrane-surface to bulk-stream concentration ratio of 1.1 in the module tested.

Comparison of these results at low velocities with the laminar-flow theory of Chapter 5 shows satisfactory agreement. For example, Fig.

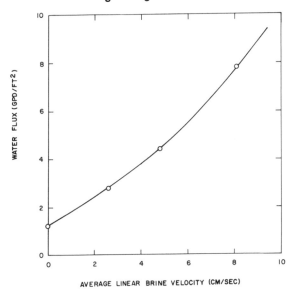

Fig. 6–4 Water flux versus brine velocity at membrane-surface to bulk-stream concentration ratio of 1.1.

5–10 predicts an α of 5.5 for a Γ of 0.1, i.e., a membrane-surface to bulk-stream concentration ratio of 1.1 in the case of complete salt rejection and 5% water removal. Using $D_2 = 1.6 \times 10^{-5}$ cm²/sec and $h = 0.033$ cm, this α value corresponds to a membrane flux v' of 0.9×10^{-4} cm/sec or 1.9 gpd/ft². The point on the curve in Fig. 6–4 which corresponds to 5% water removal in the experimental module is at $v' = 1.5$ gpd/ft² (and an average brine velocity of 0.5 cm/sec), in reasonable agreement with the predicted result, particularly in view of the fact that the spacer present in the brine channel makes its representation as two parallel flat membranes only an approximation.

Precipitation of slightly soluble compounds. Should the brine become supersaturated in one or more of its constituents, there is danger of precipitation within the membrane unit. If this occurs, the surface of the membrane can become coated with a lightly adhering scale that reduces the water flux, perhaps due to a simple blocking action. The seriousness of this phenomenon depends on several factors, but primarily on the type of brine-flow channels, the constituents involved, the degree of supersaturation, and the kinetics of precipitation. The residence time in the membrane units is of the order of seconds so that considerable supersaturation may be permissible. If precipitation occurs in the module, however, data indicate that at least part of it accumulates on the membrane surface and tends to reduce product-water flow. Greatly increased brine flows for short times apparently do not dislodge the scale. Some modular designs should be much better suited than others to cope with this situation with the large-tube approach for tube sizes in the range of 0.1- to 0.5-inch diam apparently having some inherent advantages. Further experience in this area is needed.

Product-Water-Side Considerations

Backing material. In all except the small-tube approach the membrane is supported by some porous material, hereinafter called the product-water-side backing material.

The size and shape of the pore structure of this backing material is a compromise between the need for a thick layer of large pores for minimum pressure loss, fine pores for membrane support, and economics. Current cellulose acetate membrane will support itself for short times at 1500 psi over holes or channels of dimensions about equal to the membrane thickness (see Chapter 4 on physical properties). When the pressure is applied more slowly and the membrane allowed to creep, considerable elongation occurs before rupture — several hundred percent has been observed. Therefore, if the hole or pit is shallow, such as in a sand or felt layer, advantage can be taken of this characteristic. It appears that the backing material in contact with the undersurface of the 0.004-inch-thick current membrane should not have holes greater than 0.001- to 0.002-inch diam. When larger holes are used for the bulk of the backing-material layer, a surface coating or protective layer with smaller holes should be used. Also, economics as related to packing density and material cost dictate as thin a layer as possible for the composite product-water-side backing material. Even with the multilayer approach, pore sizes greater than about 0.005 inch do not appear practical, and a more realistic maximum size is 0.002- to 0.003-inch diam. In the plate-and-frame approach porous metal, porous reinforced plastic plate, and slotted solid plates have been used.[8] In the large-tube approach it is a nominally solid glass-fiber-reinforced epoxy tube with holes penetrating the tube wall at closely spaced intervals, and in the spiral-wound module it is a porous plastic cloth or sand type layer.

Pressure losses. In the plate-and-frame, the spiral-wound, and one of the large-tube approaches the product water is forced directly through the membrane film into the porous backing layer. Once in this backing layer the product water must flow parallel to the membrane surfaces to a product-water outlet. In the other large-tube approach the product water, after being forced through the thin "working" layer of the membrane, must flow within the porous section of the membrane in a direction parallel to this working layer until it finds a "hole" in the wall of the epoxy tube. In all four cases a certain amount of pressure drop occurs. This in effect lowers the average net driving force across the membrane layer and hence lowers the water flux for a given system pressure. The seriousness of this varies with the approach and the specific design. In the spiral-wound concept it is a principal limitation on module design.

The pressure-loss equations for three cases of interest are given. All cases assume that the water flux is constant over the membrane surfaces (i.e., the product-water-side pressure loss is small compared to the net driving force across the membrane), and that membranes are on both sides of the porous product-water-side layer of thickness w.

Case 1. Circular plate with product-water flow inward to a centrally located removal port:

$$\Delta p = KR_0^2 \left\{ \ln\left(\frac{R_0}{r_0}\right) - \frac{1}{2}\left[1 - \left(\frac{r_0}{R_0}\right)^2\right]^2 \right\}, \tag{6.1}$$

where

$$K = \frac{H\mu}{g_c} v' \tag{6.2}$$

and

$$H = \frac{32\sigma^2}{\beta D_h^2 w}. \tag{6.3}$$

Here v' is the water velocity through the membrane and a function of membrane properties and system operating conditions; R_0 is the outer radius and line of zero net product-water flow; r_0 is the radius of the product-water exit port; μ is the product-water viscosity; g_c is the gravitational constant; and σ, β, and D_h are the tortuosity factor, fractional open area, and hydraulic diameter of the product-water-side material, respectively.

The constant H, as defined by Eq. 6.3, is called herein the product-water-side pressure-loss constant. It depends only on the physical properties of the backing material and its thickness w, and hence characterizes the material. Preliminary experiments have shown that for round particles these values of H can be suitably calculated from Eq. 6.3 by assuming a value of D_h of one third to one fourth of the diameter of the particle involved, provided no large amount of plastic deformation takes place.

Case 2. Circular plate with flow outward toward the product-water removal rim:

$$\Delta p = Kr_0^2 \left\{ \frac{1}{2}\left[\left(\frac{R_0}{r_0}\right)^2 - 1\right] - \ln\left(\frac{R_0}{r_0}\right) \right\}; \tag{6.4}$$

as r_0 becomes small or vanishes,

$$\Delta p = \frac{KR_0^2}{2}. \tag{6.5}$$

Case 3. Sheet flow between two parallel boundaries toward a product-water-removal tube:

$$\Delta p = KL_0^2, \tag{6.6}$$

where L_0 is the distance from the line of no product-water flow to the product-water outlet tube.

Equations 6.1 and 6.4–6.6 give the maximum pressure drops within the backing material. In order to apply these values, one must calculate an average over the entire membrane area. In the case of Eq. 6.6, for instance, a suitable integration shows that

$$\bar{\Delta p} = \frac{2\Delta p}{3}, \tag{6.7}$$

where $\bar{\Delta p}$ is the area averaged pressure drop within the product-water backing material above the pressure in the product-water outlet tube.

Since the backing material must support large pressure loads, H can vary with time under pressure due to compression of the backing material. This is particularly true with plastics, as can be seen from the data in Table 6–1. The plastic in this case was two layers of 100 × 100 mesh

Table 6–1   Variation of H (of Eq. 6.3) with Time
for a Nylon-Cloth Backing Material

System pressure = 300 psi nominal
Temperature = ambient (~75°F)
Thickness = 0.008 inch
Initial porosity = 70%

Time at pressure (hours)	H (ft^{-3})
0	3.5 × 10^{13}
50	9.9 × 10^{13}
100	12.4 × 10^{13}
200	16.2 × 10^{13}

nylon cloth, each 0.004 inch thick, made from 0.002-inch-diam filament and having about 70% initial porosity. Both sides were covered with a 0.004-inch-thick layer of Dacron felt made from 0.0003-inch-diam mono-filament. Because of the smaller hydraulic radii in the Dacron felt, nearly all of the water flow was in the nylon cloth. As can be seen, the pressure loss increased with time. This is due to plastic creep of the nylon fila-ments where they cross each other. A small amount of compression lowers both porosity and hydraulic radius, and inspection of Eq. 6.3 shows that this has an inverse fourth-power effect on H. Thus, it is necessary to pick a backing material suitably noncompressible for long-term operation at the system pressure of interest. Runs with a 0.020-inch layer of spherical glass beads in the size range from 0.003- to 0.006-inch diam gave an H value of about 1.5 × 10^{13} ft^{-3} which did not change appreciably with time at 1500 psi.

In the large-tube approach where the porous section of the membrane is the flow path, the maximum long-term system pressures may be limited due to the compression of the membrane material itself. The pore size in the porous section of the membrane is small — a fraction of a micron. Therefore, H values are very high, but are compensated for by short product-water flow distances.

To obtain a feeling for the design limitations imposed by these product-water-side losses, consider a system operating with a net driving force of 50 atm using a membrane with a water flux constant of 1×10^{-5} g/cm²-sec-atm. Then, for a typical set of design parameters and dimensions normally associated with the preceding three approaches and assuming we can tolerate about 10% loss in our driving force, the following comments can be made: For the large-tube approach using glass-fiber-reinforced epoxy tubes, the critical parameter is the distance between holes in the tube wall. Using values of initial pore sizes and porosities reported for a typical membrane[2] one can estimate that the holes in the wall should not be more than about 0.100 inch apart. While this is large compared with the hole spacings, membrane compaction at elevated pressures can reduce this allowable distance markedly. For the plate-and-frame approach the critical parameter is the equivalent diameter of the flow passages. Using 3-ft-diam plates 0.100-inch thick with product-water outlet continuous around the rim, the net average equivalent diameter of the pores D_h should be ≥ 0.0004 inch. If the product-water flow is inward to a central hole 1 inch in diameter, then a $D_h \geq 0.0008$ inch is needed. The achievement of these pore sizes does not appear difficult. If, however, there is a limited number of product-water exit ports around the rim so that the product-water flow must channel into these, or the central hole becomes small and has apertures only at specific locations, then serious spreading losses can occur and the design needs to be carefully analyzed. With the spiral-wound module, the critical parameters are pore size and length of the flow path. Using 0.020-inch layers of the best noncompressible material found to date (spherical glass beads 0.003- to 0.006-inch diam), product-water flow distances of about 1.4 ft can be used.

For the large-tube approach using holes drilled in metal tubes, the critical parameters are thickness of the porous membrane-support layer, its equivalent pore sizes and the distance between holes. Using a 0.010-inch-thick layer of 0.0015- to 0.003-inch-diam spherical glass beads and a hole diameter of 0.050 inch, the distance between holes should be ≤ 4 inches.

Pressure drop within the membrane. This problem has already been alluded to in discussing the large-tube approach (glass-fiber-reinforced epoxy) where some horizontal flow is encountered. In this case definite limitations on the length of the flow path exist. However, in all cases except the small-tube approach using dense cellulose acetate, the water must flow through the porous section of the membrane before it can enter the porous backing material, the minimum flow distance being about 0.004 inch for current membranes. Given the porosity and pore-size distribution as reported,[2] one can readily estimate that no serious pressure loss will occur across this section of the membrane except under unusual conditions of rather complete compaction of the membrane. Membranes do compact under use at higher pressure. Presumably the larger pores collapse first with the remaining ones, becoming progressively harder to collapse. Good, long-term compaction data have not yet appeared in the literature. Present knowledge on this phenomenon is covered in Chapter 4.

6.3   Optimization of System Parameters

The basic premise of good design is the selection of the system equipment and process parameters that will result in a product water meeting specifications at minimum cost over a given plant lifetime. Comments on optimizations of brine-side and product-water-side parameters have been given. This section deals with optimization considerations of the plant as a whole. Since large reverse-osmosis plants have yet to be built, selection of system parameters must be based primarily on analytical techniques — i.e., parametric studies. Two such studies are available.[1,2] Much development work has been done since these studies were made, and the ground rules for selection of parameters have changed. A report on economic considerations of the membrane assembly unit for the plate-and-frame is available.[8]

Early in 1965 General Atomic made a new parametric study of a 1-million-gpd reverse-osmosis plant operating on seawater feed and utilizing the spiral-wound concept; their results will be used to illustrate this section.[3] However, the general approach will apply almost equally well to optimization of large-tube and the plate-and-frame units, and many of the numerical results will be similar. A more important aspect of the study at this time is the comparison that it affords between reverse-osmosis systems and other methods of desalination.

Certain unique characteristics of reverse-osmosis systems need to be kept in mind and used to best advantage in design. The low energy requirements and the use of electricity as the source of power (mechanical power may also be used) allows physical separation of the plant from the power source. Thus the plant can be located to its best over-all advantage. The operational characteristics of the system are well suited to automatic control; therefore operational labor costs will be minimal. The plants are capable of rapid response to changes in load or power-input demands. They can be started up and shut down in seconds and are limited only by the response time of the major system components such as the main pumps. Thus, they are well suited for use with off-peak or nonfirm power if this use is economically justified. Further, because of the low temperatures, corrosion problems are less severe and the scaling problems are of a different nature than those encountered in distillation processes.

Membranes currently available can give potable water from a sea-water feed in a one-stage operation only with difficulty. This fact results not from the fundamental properties of the cellulose acetate membrane but from the method of producing membranes and fabricating the membrane assembly and from limitations on the operating pressure of the system. For example, with seawater feed at 1500 psi, Cl^- rejection calculated from the values of $D_{1m}c_{1m}$ and D_2K, as given in Chapter 4 for cellulose acetate of 39.8% acetyl content, is about 99.7%. With such a membrane, a product-water-to-brine flow ratio of 1.0 would result in water containing 150 ppm total solids. However, actual membranes run between 97% and 99% rejection under these conditions, and give product water with 500 to 1500 ppm total dissolved salts. Thus, membranes made to date have salt fluxes 3 to 10 times the value calculated on the basis of the transport properties of cellulose acetate and necessitate two-stage operation with its attendant additional costs. The approach used in this study was first to investigate a single-stage operation, assuming that the product water had the same worth regardless of quality, followed by consideration of a second stage using as feed product water of varying salt content resulting from the first stage. While the second-stage feed was not directly coupled to any given set of conditions for the first stage, the first stage was designed with 25% excess capacity to give a net plant output from the second stage of 1 million gpd with a product-water-to-brine flow ratio of 4.

The final criteria of selection were the "relative" costs of water from the systems having different parameters. To arrive at this point, the costs were broken down into annual capital charges, pumping power, operation and maintenance, and membrane replacement.

Basic Flow Systems

The basic flow diagram for the system, excluding the relationship of a second stage, is as shown in Fig. 6–1. The system was broken down into subassemblies which for the first-stage unit consisted of the following:

Subassembly	*Parameters Affecting Costs*
Seawater feed	Flow ratio
Chlorinator	Fixed
pH control	Flow ratio

Subassembly	Parameters Affecting Costs
Filter	Flow ratio
Deaerator	Flow ratio
Main pump	Flow ratio, pressure
Module pressure vessel	Flow ratio, pressure
Recovery turbine/generator	Flow ratio, pressure
Product-water transfer	Fixed
Land and building	Fixed

Systems were considered for pressures p of 720, 960, 1440, and 2160 psi. At each pressure, product-water-to-exit-brine flow ratios R of 0.5, 1.0, 1.5, and 2.0 were used. Thus 16 different flow systems were considered. Installed costs were determined separately for each subassembly of each system.

These pressures were selected to correspond with the allowable pressures at which standard-size carbon steel pipe could be used for the module pressure vessels. Flow rates represent values of R around 1.0, which have been found to be near optimum in past studies.[1,2]

Technical Ground Rules

1. The membrane water permeability was considered a parameter. The zero-time reference membrane constant A_0 was chosen as 1×10^{-5} g/cm²-sec-atm, and the final steady-state value at operating pressure was taken as a function of pressure. Specifically, three straight-line plots of log A (membrane constant) versus pressure were used, each passing through one point at 150 psi with $A = A_0 = 1 \times 10^{-5}$ g/cm²-sec-atm and another at 1500 psi with $A = 0.5 \times 10^{-5}$, 0.7×10^{-5} or 0.9×10^{-5} g/cm²-sec-atm. These values of 0.5, 0.7, and 0.9 are called f values hereafter. The $f = 0.5$ value represents the best fit to data available as of December 1964.

2. The salt flux for the assembled module was assumed to be five times the theoretical minimum (see Chapters 3 and 4).

3. The summation of brine-side and product-water-side pressure losses were taken as 10% of the system pressure. These losses were applied analytically by assuming that all the loss occurred within the brine side of the membrane unit.

4. The operating temperature was assumed to be 70°F in all cases.

5. The osmotic pressure used for a given feed solution was taken as $\pi = 0.0115\ c$, where π is given in psi and c in ppm of total salts.

6. For calculation of water fluxes and salt rejections, the module assembly was considered to be a single large module in which an average between inlet and outlet conditions was used to obtain both pressure and salt-concentration differences across the membrane. This assumption was checked by breaking down one system into 10

longitudinal sections, averaging each section, and then computing the values for the entire assembly. These numbers were quite close to the ones obtained assuming a single large unit.

7. The membrane module design used was based on the spiral-wound concept. For this study, a module 10.5 inches in diam by 60 inches long containing 1800 ft² of membrane was used. In light of more recent thinking, this may be too large a module and the membrane packing per unit volume may be somewhat higher than we would expect for the first million-gpd plants.

8. Pressure containers were 12-ft sections of 12-inch-diam Schedule 80 carbon steel pipe internally coated to prevent corrosion and flanged on each end. Each vessel contained two modules.

Economic Ground Rules

1. Whenever possible, standard equipment items were selected, and price estimates or quotations were obtained from one or more vendors or fabricators. Where equipment sizes did not fit a particular condition, the next larger size or higher pressure unit was chosen. The installed costs for each subassembly included equipment, installation labor, installation materials, foundations, supports, piping, instrumentation, contingencies, engineering, subcontractor's overhead and profits, and contractor's overhead and profits.

2. For single-stage evaluation it was assumed that all water produced had the same economic value, even though most of the systems resulted in water with a salt content above the 500-ppm limit for potable water. This assumption favors lower system pressures.

3. A plant load factor of 0.9 was used.

4. Power cost was taken at 0.7 mill/kw-hr. Turbine-recovered power was also credited at this rate.

5. Plant operation was assumed to be under the control of one operator plus extra help for equipment maintenance and two men for two months per year for membrane replacement. The major unknown concerns maintenance requirements resulting from the corrosive nature of the water being handled.

6. Membrane-replacement costs C_{mr} were considered a parameter and expressed as $/ft² of membrane surface per year of membrane life or $/ft²-year. Membrane-replacement costs are a function of both manufacturing and replacement labor costs and of membrane lifetime. In Chapter 4 it is shown that with the proper pH adjustment, membrane lifetimes of years are obtainable. Module manufacturing and replacement costs are currently high, but the next few years should see this sharply reduced; membrane-replacement costs of $.25/ft²-year look realistic for the future.

7. Annual capital charges were taken as 9.4%. This is composed of 4% interest on plant investment, amortization over a 20-year life on a sinking-fund basis at 4%, and 2% for local taxes and insurance.
8. Other cost assumptions follow those established by the Office of Saline Water costing procedures[13] or give similar water-cost results.

Results

The capital costs are summarized in Table 6–2 and plotted in Fig. 6–5 for $f = 0.5$. The breakdown of these total capital costs into fixed, flow-dependent, and flow- and pressure-dependent subassemblies for the case $f = 0.5$ is given in Tables 6–3 and 6–4. The costs for each subassembly include engineering, contingencies, and profit with different values assigned to each subassembly depending on its technical status. Analysis of these data, as illustrated by Fig. 6–5, indicate the optimum pressures from a capital-cost standpoint to be around 1500 psi, and optimum water recoveries over 70%. It appears that the capital cost of the first single-stage reverse-osmosis seawater plant of 1-million-gpd capacity will be less than $1/gpd capacity. Of this about 30% will be in the mem-

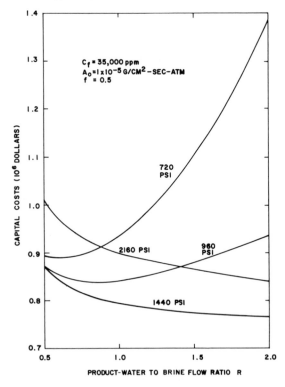

Fig. 6–5   Capital cost for single-stage one-million-gpd plant as function of *p* and *R*.

Table 6–2   Total Capital Cost for Single-Stage One-Million-Gpd Reverse-Osmosis Seawater-Conversion Plant as Function of p, R, and f
$A_0 = 1 \times 10^{-5}$ g/cm²-sec-atm

System pressure (psi)	f	Capital cost (dollars)			
		$R = 0.5$	$R = 1.0$	$R = 1.5$	$R = 2.0$
720	0.9	813,100	828,480	960,020	1,174,600
	0.7	845,260	871,570	1,015,560	1,257,280
	0.5	892,260	933,810	1,103,500	1,384,640
960	0.9	786,350	739,270	756,420	785,340
	0.7	817,850	779,080	803,440	841,440
	0.5	870,350	838,790	878,680	932,970
1440	0.9	779,590	688,300	622,610	641,540
	0.7	811,790	727,290	700,340	685,320
	0.5	868,130	790,780	772,030	761,920
2160	0.9	878,190	734,480	706,200	669,210
	0.7	952,610	787,940	757,290	723,360
	0.5	1,058,040	894,850	865,160	837,070

Table 6–3   Breakdown of Single-Stage One-Million-Gpd Plant Capital-Cost Data. Fixed Costs and Flow-Dependent costs
$A_0 = 1 \times 10^{-5}$ g/cm²-sec-atm; $f = 0.5$

Fixed costs
(dollars)

Land and building	52,040
Chlorinator assembly	5,360
Product-water transfer assembly	26,720
Total	84,120

Flow-dependent costs

Cost item	Capital cost (dollars)			
	$R = 0.5$	$R = 1.0$	$R = 1.5$	$R = 2.0$
Brine feed assembly	46,760	40,960	40,960	37,170
pH-control assembly	14,250	12,570	11,890	11,590
Filter assembly	69,350	55,410	48,790	48,790
Deaerator assembly	51,110	31,940	31,900	31,700
Total (R dependent)	181,470	140,880	133,540	129,250

Table 6-4   Breakdown of Single-Stage One-Million-Gpd Plant Capital-Cost Data
Flow- and pressure-dependent costs.
$A_0 = 1 \times 10^{-5}$ g/cm²-sec-atm; $f = 0.5$

Cost item	System pressure (psi)	Capital cost (dollars)			
		$R = 0.5$	$R = 1.0$	$R = 1.5$	$R = 2.0$
Main pump assembly	720	185,890	157,300	169,700	149,220
	960	214,410	190,480	172,350	149,480
	1440	276,620	246,190	220,440	191,520
	2160	364,080	278,860	261,470	234,560
Module pressure-vessel assembly	720	367,090	495,000	664,300	972,910
	960	301,950	355,920	427,320	511,750
	1440	218,280	239,900	261,310	289,140
	2160	273,830	280,110	284,820	293,360
Recovery turbine/generator assembly	720	73,690	56,510	51,840	49,140
	960	88,400	67,390	61,350	58,370
	1440	107,640	79,690	72,620	67,890
	2160	154,540	110,880	101,210	95,780
Total (R and p dependent)	720	626,670	708,810	885,840	1,171,270
	960	604,760	613,790	661,020	719,400
	1440	602,540	565,780	554,370	548,550
	2160	792,450	669,850	647,500	623,700

Table 6-5   Single-Stage Salt Concentration in Product Water and Brine

System pressure (psi)		Salt concentration* (ppm)			
		$R = 0.5$	$R = 1.0$	$R = 1.5$	$R = 2.0$
720	c_P†	2,963	4,677	6,621	8,555
	c_B	51,019	65,323	77,569	87,890
960	c_P	1,537	2,197	3,228	4,683
	c_B	51,731	67,803	82,658	95,633
1440	c_P	787	1,007	1,305	1,735
	c_B	52,106	68,993	85,543	101,528
2160	c_P	386	531	697	882
	c_B	52,307	69,469	86,455	103,236

* Salt-permeation constant assumed 5 × "theoretical" value for 39.8 wt-% acetyl cellulose acetate (see Chapter 4).
† c_P = product-water concentration; c_B = brine concentration.

brane-containing subassembly. Further, about 80% of plant cost is a function of size so that increasing plant size greatly assists the over-all water-cost economics until much larger size plants are reached.

Salt concentrations in the product water and exit brine for the assumed salt rejection are given as a function of pressure and R in Table 6–5. It can be seen that the product water generally has over 500 ppm of salt, most of which is NaCl. These concentrations, however, should be taken as indicative of present membrane technology and not of the future state of the art.

Table 6–6   Pumping-Power Requirements for Single-Stage One-Million-Gpd Plant as Function of p and R

System pressure (psi)	Pumping-power requirements* (kw-hr/1000 gal)			
	$R = 0.5$	$R = 1.0$	$R = 1.5$	$R = 2.0$
720	14.0	10.5	9.3	8.7
960	18.2	13.7	12.2	11.4
1440	26.5	20.0	17.8	16.7
2160	38.9	29.4	26.2	24.6

* Pump efficiency (including motor) assumed to be 81%. Recovery-turbine efficiency (including generator) assumed to be 66%.

The tabulated values include power for a 60-psi head required for filtration of the seawater feed and other minor plant duties. This is in addition to the 10% allowance for brine-side and product-water-side pressure losses.

Pumping-power requirements are given in Table 6–6 for the four pressures and R ratios with the pump and turbine efficiencies noted. For 1440 psi, $R = 1.0$, 20 kw-hr/1000 gal are required. Without a recovery turbine this would be about 28 kw-hr/1000 gal. With higher flux membranes, the power consumption under optimum plant conditions would be lowered and 12 to 15 kw-hr/1000 gal seem like future goals for large size plants.

Table 6–7   Product-Water Cost for Single-Stage One-Million-Gpd Plant as Function of p and R
$A_0 = 1 \times 10^{-5}$ g/cm²-sec-atm; $f = 0.5$; $C_{mr} = 50$ cents/ft²-year

System pressure (psi)	Water cost (cents/1000 gal)			
	$R = 0.5$	$R = 1.0$	$R = 1.5$	$R = 2.0$
720	114.3	136.9	179.3	250.0
960	89.5	93.2	105.5	122.8
1440	81.1	75.6	76.4	79.5
2160	91.0	79.2	76.5	76.4

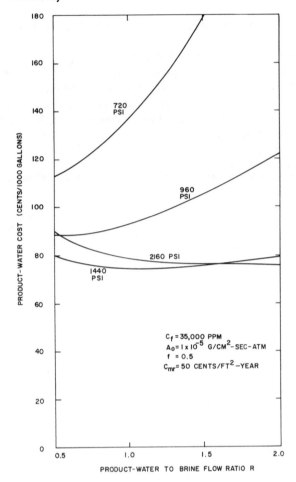

Fig. 6–6   Product-water cost for single-stage one-million-gpd plant as function of p and R.

Water costs for single-stage seawater-feed operation are given in Table 6–7 and shown graphically in Fig. 6–6 as a function of pressure and R for $f = 0.5$, C_{mr} \$.50/ft²-yr, and $A_0 = 1 \times 10^{-5}$ g/cm²-sec-atm. The contributions of the various items that go into making up these costs are shown in Fig. 6–7 for $P = 1440$ psi. The effect of varying A_0, C_{mr}, and f can be seen from Table 6–8 and in Figs. 6–8, 6–9, and 6–10 for the case of $P = 1440$ psi and $R = 1.0$.

Since the product-water quality was insufficient to meet the U. S. Public Health Service standards under the salt-rejection conditions assumed, the economics of second-stage operation on the first-stage product water were investigated. Much of the feed pretreatment and postmembrane unit equipment is not needed for this stage. Therefore,

Table 6–8   Product-Water Cost for Single-Stage One-Million-Gpd Plant as Function of A_0, f, and C_{mr}
$p = 1440$ psi; $R = 1.0$

Membrane constant A_0 (g/cm²-sec-atm)	f	Water cost (cents/1000 gallons)				
		$C_{mr} = 10$	$C_{mr} = 25$	$C_{mr} = 50$	$C_{mr} = 75$	$C_{mr} = 100$
0.5×10^{-5}	0.5	66.9	82.8	109.3	135.9	162.4
	0.7	60.4	72.1	91.6	111.0	130.5
	0.9	56.6	65.9	81.4	96.8	112.3
1.0×10^{-5}	0.5	54.3	62.3	75.6	88.9	102.1
	0.7	51.1	56.9	66.7	76.4	86.1
	0.9	49.2	53.8	61.5	69.2	77.0
1.5×10^{-5}	0.5	50.1	55.4	64.3	73.1	82.0
	0.7	47.9	51.8	58.3	64.8	71.3
	0.9	46.7	49.8	54.9	60.1	65.2
2.0×10^{-5}	0.5	48.0	52.0	58.6	65.3	71.9
	0.7	46.6	49.5	54.2	59.2	64.1
	0.9	45.4	47.8	51.6	55.5	59.3
3.0×10^{-5}	0.5	45.9	48.6	53.0	57.4	61.9
	0.7	44.8	46.8	50.0	53.3	56.5
	0.9	44.2	45.7	48.3	50.9	53.5
4.0×10^{-5}	0.5	44.9	46.8	50.2	53.5	56.8
	0.7	44.1	45.6	48.0	50.5	52.9
	0.9	43.6	44.7	46.7	48.6	50.5

capital costs are relatively low and not representative of brackish-water systems. Further, the salt constituent is primarily NaCl, and large concentration factors (large R ratios) can be used without danger of salt

Table 6–9   Capital Cost for Second Stage of One-Million-Gpd Plant
$R = 4.0$; $A_0 = 1.0 \times 10^{-5}$ g/cm²-sec-atm; $f = 0.5$

System pressure (psi)	Capital cost (dollars)			
	$c_f{}^* = 1000$	$c_f = 3000$	$c_f = 5000$	$c_f = 7000$
720	206,200	214,400	224,600	239,000
960	234,400	242,600	250,800	261,800
1440	272,500	275,900	282,800	289,600
2160	350,200	355,300	360,300	365,400

* c_f = feed-water concentration (ppm).

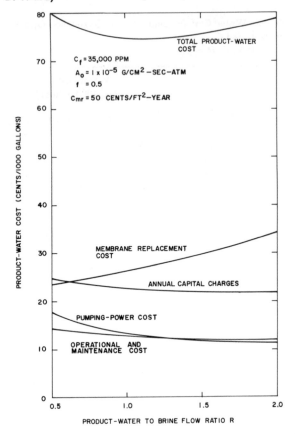

Fig. 6–7 Itemized product-water cost for single-stage one-million-gpd plant for
$p = 1440$ psi and $R = 1$.

precipitation within the module. Representative capital costs for the
second stage unit are given in Table 6–9 for $R = 4.0$, $A_0 = 1 \times 10^{-5}$

Table 6–10   Product-Water Cost for Second Stage of One-Million-Gpd Plant
$R = 4.0$; $f = 0.5$; $A_0 = 1 \times 10^{-5}$ g/cm²-sec-atm; $C_{mr} = 50$ cents/ft²-
year

System pressure (psi)	Water cost (cents/1000 gals)			
	$c_f{}^* = 1000$	$c_f = 3000$	$c_f = 5000$	$c_f = 7000$
720	34.2	36.8	40.1	44.2
960	33.3	35.0	37.0	39.4
1440	35.2	36.1	37.2	38.4
2160	42.4	43.1	43.8	44.5

* c_f = feed-water concentration (ppm).

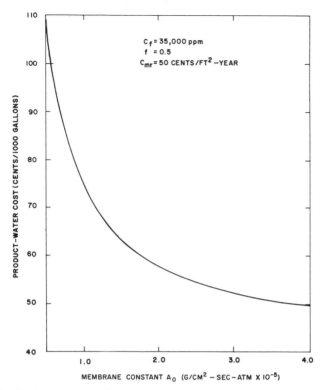

Fig. 6–8   Product-water cost for single-stage one-million-gpd plant as function of A_0

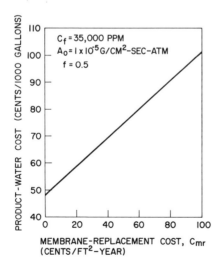

Fig. 6–9   Product-water cost for single-stage one-million-gpd plant as function of C_{mr}.

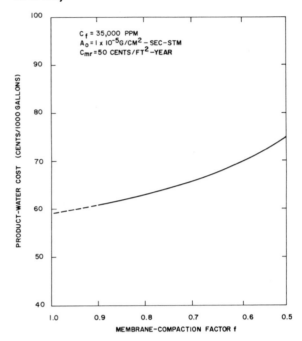

Fig. 6–10   Product-water cost for single-stage one-million-gpd plant as function of f.

g/cm^2-sec-atm, and $f = 0.5$. Second-stage product-water costs for these conditions, various feed salt concentrations, and $C_{mr} = \$.50/ft^2$-yr are given in Table 6–10, with the assumption that there is no charge for feed water.

Figure 6–11 presents additional data in graphical form for second-stage water cost as a function of pressure and R for the specific case noted. Optimum pressures appear to be around 1000 psi and R ratios around 5. However, it may well be that brackish water or second-stage plants using entirely different pumps, module containers, and membrane type will have an optimum pressure considerably below this.

Present Status of Plant Design

Sufficient engineering data exist at this time to allow realistic design of low-pressure brackish-water plants of sizes up to at least 1 million gpd, albeit with some overdesign and extra contingency allowance. Membrane-containing units capable of working at these pressures and flow volumes are apparently available in three of the basic configurations.

Before detailed engineering designs of large seawater plants of 1 million gpd can be made, more information on the long-term effects of pressure on membrane water flux and salt rejection is necessary. The

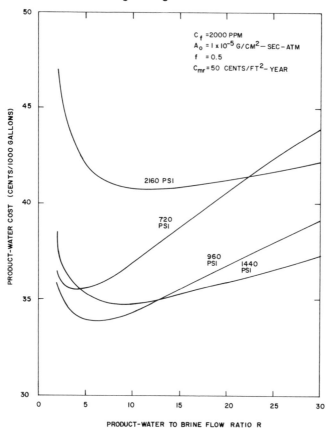

C_f = 2000 PPM
A_0 = 1 x 10^{-5} G/CM^2 – SEC – ATM
f = 0.5
C_{mr} = 50 CENTS/FT^2– YEAR

2160 PSI

720 PSI

960 PSI

1440 PSI

PRODUCT-WATER COST (CENTS/1000 GALLONS)

PRODUCT-WATER TO BRINE FLOW RATIO R

Fig. 6–11 Product-water cost for second stage of one-million-gpd plant as function of *p* and *R*.

parametric study discussed indicates that in order for a large reverse-osmosis plant to compete with other desalination processes, a membrane with sufficient salt rejection to allow single-stage operation and a membrane with higher initial water flux and/or a smaller membrane-compaction factor is needed. More information on material-corrosion aspects would be useful, although this lack can be overcome at the expense of increased capital and/or maintenance costs. These several areas of deficiency and uncertainty represent today's major challenges for membrane research and engineering development that relate to seawater desalination by reverse osmosis.

Symbol List

Symbols first appear in equation indicated, or in text shortly preceding or following this equation.

A	membrane constant, g/cm²-sec-atm	Sec. 6.3
A_0	zero-time membrane constant before compaction, g/cm²-sec-atm	Sec. 6.3
c_f	concentration of salt in feed water, ppm	Sec. 6.3
C_{mr}	membrane-replacement costs, cents/ft²-year	Sec. 6.3
c	salt concentration in solution, ppm	Sec. 6.3
D_h	equivalent hydraulic diameter defined as 4 × area/wetted perimeter, ft	6.3
D_2	salt-diffusion constant, cm²/sec	Sec. 6.2
F_1	flux through membrane, g/cm²-sec or lb mass/ft²-sec	Sec. 6.3
f	measure of membrane permeability loss with pressure	Sec. 6.2
g_c	gravitational constant = 32 lb mass-ft/lb force-sec²	6.2
H	product-water-side backing material pressure-loss constant defined by Eq. 6.3, ft⁻³	6.2
h	distance from membrane surface to centerline between membrane surfaces, cm	Sec. 6.2
K	symbol defined by Eq. 6.2, lb force/ft⁴	6.1
L_0	distance in product-water-side backing material from line of no product-water flow to outlet	6.6
p	system pressure, psi	Sec. 6.3
Δp	pressure difference, psi	6.1
Δp_m	net pressure difference across membrane, psi	6.2
R	ratio of product-water flow rate to exit brine flow rate	Sec. 6.3
R_0	outer radius of product-water-side circular disk of porous membrane-backing material, ft	6.1
r_0	inner radius of product-water-side circular disk of porous membrane-backing material, ft	6.1
v'	withdrawal velocity through membrane, ft/sec	6.2
w	thickness of porous backing-material layer or brine-side spacing in stacked-plate or spiral-wound approach, ft	6.3
α	$D_2/v_2'h$	Sec. 6.2
β	fractional porosity	6.3
σ	tortuosity factor	6.3
π	osmotic pressure, psi	Sec. 6.3
$\Delta\pi$	net osmotic pressure difference across membrane, psi	6.2
μ	viscosity, lb mass/ft-sec	6.2
Γ	a measure of concentration polarization as defined by Eq. 5.20	Sec. 6.2

References

1. McCutchan, J. W., S. Loeb, P. A. Buckingham, and A. W. Ayers, *Preliminary Economic Study U.C.L.A. Reverse Osmosis Process for Brackish Water Desalination*, UCLA Engineering Department Report 63-62, 1963.
2. Lonsdale, H. K., U. Merten, R. L. Riley, K. D. Vos, and J. C. Westmoreland, *Reverse Osmosis for Water Desalination*, Office of Saline Water, Research and Development Progress Report No. 111, PB 181696 (May 1964).
3. Bray, D. T., and H. F. Menzel, *Design Study of Reverse Osmosis Pilot Plant*, Office of Saline Water, Research and Development Progress Report No. 176, (1966).
4. Bray, D. T., U. Merten, and M. Augustus, *Reverse Osmosis for Water Reclamation*, Bulletin, California Water Pollution Control Association, October 1965, p. 11.
5. Loeb, S., and S. Manjikian, *Ind. Eng. Chem. Fundamentals* 4, 207 (1965).
6. "Reverse Osmosis," Industrial Water Engineering, Vol. 1, No. 6, Nov./Dec. 1964, p. 22.
7. Smith, W., "Reverse Osmosis Gains in Water Desalting Stature," *Chem. Eng.* 71, No. 16, 72 (1964).
8. Keilin, B., and C. G. DeHaven, *Design Criteria for Reverse Osmosis Desalination Plants*, Paper SWD/28, Proc. First Intn'l. Desalination Symp., Washington, D. C., Oct. 3–9, 1965.
9. "Fresh Water from the Sea," *Water and Waste Treatment* 9, 147 (1964).
10. "Reverse Osmosis Unit Desalts Water for City Mains," *Chem. Eng.* 72, No. 16, 62 (1965).
11. Mahon, H. I., Proc. of Desalination Research Conference, *Nat. Acad. Sci., Publ.* 942, 345 (1963).
12. Hearings before the Subcommittee on Irrigation and Reclamation of the Committee on Interior and Insular Affairs, U. S. Senate, 89th Congress, First Session on S 24, May 18–19, 1965, pp. 197, 198.
13. *A Standardized Procedure for Estimating Costs of Saline Water Conversion*, Office of Saline Water, PB 161375 (March 1965).

7. Reverse-Osmosis Pilot Plants

E. H. Sieveka

Preceding chapters of this volume have been devoted largely to laboratory-scale and theoretical studies. The pilot plants described in this chapter are a direct outgrowth of this work and provide an essential link between the laboratory studies and final production plants. In reverse osmosis, the close coordination achieved between fundamental work and pilot-plant development is illustrated by the fact that many of the personnel engaged in theoretical and experimental membrane studies have also been responsible for the design and operation of the initial pilot plants.

With most new processes the first pilot plants leave the greatest impact on future designs and hence are of special interest. This, too, will doubtless be the case with reverse osmosis. Although the number of plants built to date is limited, nearly five years' work on these plants has provided a significant body of design and operating experience. This chapter will attempt to summarize the progress in reverse-osmosis pilot plants from their earliest years to the present.

7.1 Current Status

The general development state of reverse osmosis is indicated by the fact that commercial units are not generally available on the market as of this date. Operations have been of a pilot-plant or experimental nature. However, the advent of the commercial reverse-osmosis unit, in the conventional sense, is imminent. It is worthy of note that for practical purposes only one specific type of membrane has been employed in the pilot plants, namely, cellulose acetate. The work of Breton and Reid at the University of Florida[1] gave great impetus to the basic research on reverse-osmosis membranes but provided no practical basis for operating plants. Hence, the entire pilot-plant activity began overnight, so to speak, with the discovery at the University of California in 1960[2] of a membrane formulation making possible a practical reverse-osmosis unit. By the same token, the process started without a background of design concepts on which to draw for future plants. Hence, the period since 1960 has been marked by an effort to establish design configurations best suited to utilizing the newly developed membranes.

The various designs proposed differ primarily in the hydraulic configurations and the materials selected. Methods for supporting the membranes are a key to the designs, and in this area consideration has been given to expendable as well as permanent support materials. The several design approaches to reverse-osmosis equipment, plate-and-frame, tubular, and spiral-wound module, have been described in Chapter 6. These designs are the only ones for which pilot plants of reasonable size (1000 gpd or more) have been built and operated; only these will be considered in this chapter.

Membrane-fabrication techniques[2-5] have been developed concurrently with the pilot-plant work, since the economics of the process of necessity depends on how readily membranes can be fabricated. The handmade-batch procedures of the early period have evolved into continuous production methods. In brief, this experience has supported the currently accepted estimate of the cost of the cellulose acetate membrane as 25 cents per square foot.

In introducing the pilot-plant work, special note must be made of the relative success of the process when operating on sea- and brackish waters. All of the early membrane research, as well as the initial pilot-plant work, was devoted to seawater. However, pilot-plant experience in the intervening years has indicated that the greatest immediate promise for reverse osmosis lies in the brackish-water field where runs for extended periods with satisfactory salt rejection have been achieved. Pilot-plant operations on seawater have failed to achieve reliable one-pass operation giving salt concentrations within the potable range at flux rates that can be sustained for reasonable periods. Two-pass operation on seawater has been shown to be entirely feasible, but it is believed that one-pass operation is essential to the desired economics. Hence, as of this date, reverse osmosis must be considered as a process already suitable for brackish water but requiring further development before it can be so considered for seawater.

7.2 Pilot-Plant Operations

A review of reverse-osmosis pilot-plant activities is presented in the following paragraphs. The material on the pilot plants is presented under the name of the organization conducting the work, rather than under a design-type or subject heading. This format is believed to be appropriate since the general nature of developments has been strongly influenced by research activities of the respective groups, and because credit can more properly be given to the investigators in this way.

University of California

It followed naturally that some of the early pilot-plant work in reverse osmosis should be conducted at the University of California at Los Angeles because the original work resulting in a high-flux cellulose acetate membrane had been conducted there. Two UCLA pilot plants warrant discussion in this chapter: the 500-gpd plate-and-frame reverse-osmosis seawater unit and the tubular reverse-osmosis plant currently operating at Coalinga, California, on brackish water. Another UCLA test, of historical importance, is a six months' operation of the reverse-osmosis membrane on a natural brackish water.[6,7] This was conducted at Coalinga in 1963. Because of its very small size, the equipment used was not a pilot unit in the true sense, but the results provided for the first time a basis for the estimated membrane life of six months, a figure that is still frequently employed today.

Early pilot plant — plate-and-frame design. As early as 1960, consideration was given at UCLA to the design of a pilot plant. By 1962 a 500-gpd unit had been designed and built. This unit was intended for seawater operation and was of the plate-and-frame design. Although the current emphasis at UCLA is on the tubular design, a major contribution was made to the development of the plate-and-frame concept through this early work.

In November 1962, S. Loeb and F. Milstein[8] reported on the design, development, and testing of the unit. The pilot plant is shown in Fig. 7-1. The design was based on circular plates 16 inches in diameter, spaced 0.2 inch apart. The unit had 23 plates and thus 46 membranes. Total useful membrane area was about 56 ft². In the plate-and-frame assembly the seawater or brine entered at one side of the space between two plates and flowed in a spiral path to the center of the unit; here it passed through one plate to the next passage above, flowing spirally from the center to the opening in the next plate above, and so on. The flow arrangement was in series rather than parallel, and a baffle was

Fig. 7–1   UCLA plate-and-frame pilot plant. Dr. Loeb is at left.

provided to induce spiral flow. The product water was manifolded from the ports at the edges of the collector plates.

Two types of product collector plates were employed in this work: a porous and a solid plate. Early laboratory work had indicated that porous stainless steel provided an effective collector plate. However, stainless steel was too expensive for future production plants and a porous plastic (polyvinyl chloride) plate was therefore selected. The plastic was not satisfactory for O-ring seals, and an aluminum periphery was provided for the plates for this purpose. A cutaway of the porous collector plate is shown in Fig. 7–2.

The porous plastic plate was also not found entirely satisfactory, because of problems experienced with the sealing of the plastic to the aluminum pressure rings. Hence, a solid plate was developed which relied on a layer of nylon parchment, placed between the filter paper and the solid plate, to carry the product water laterally to the collecting holes or slots in the solid plate (Fig. 7–3). The number of product outlet points required and the permissible width of the slots was an important design consideration.

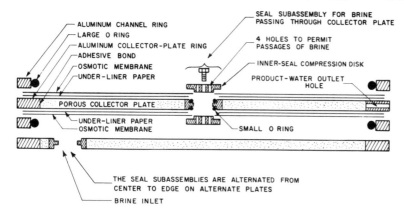

ALUMINUM CHANNEL RING
LARGE O RING
ALUMINUM COLLECTOR-PLATE RING
ADHESIVE BOND
OSMOTIC MEMBRANE
UNDER-LINER PAPER

POROUS COLLECTOR PLATE

UNDER-LINER PAPER
OSMOTIC MEMBRANE

SEAL SUBASSEMBLY FOR BRINE
PASSING THROUGH COLLECTOR PLATE

4 HOLES TO PERMIT
PASSAGES OF BRINE

INNER-SEAL COMPRESSION DISK

PRODUCT-WATER OUTLET
HOLE

SMALL O RING

THE SEAL SUBASSEMBLIES ARE ALTERNATED FROM
CENTER TO EDGE ON ALTERNATE PLATES

BRINE INLET

Fig. 7–2   Porous collector plates for UCLA plate-and-frame unit.

The pilot plant was equipped with a constant-volume pump that supplied 1500 gpd of feed water, and thus provided for a 2:1 brine-discard:product-water ratio at the design production rate of 500 gpd. Preliminary runs indicated that control of particulate matter in the feed water would be a serious problem; the feed water was therefore passed

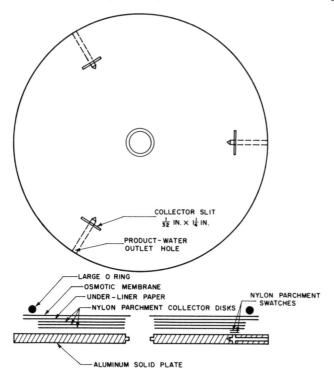

COLLECTOR SLIT
$\frac{1}{32}$ IN. × $1\frac{1}{4}$ IN.

PRODUCT-WATER
OUTLET HOLE

LARGE O RING
OSMOTIC MEMBRANE
UNDER-LINER PAPER
NYLON PARCHMENT COLLECTOR DISKS

NYLON PARCHMENT
SWATCHES

ALUMINUM SOLID PLATE

Fig. 7–3   Solid collector plate for UCLA plate-and-frame unit.

through cartridge filters with a nominal 10-μ rating. No other feed-water pretreatment was provided.

The only extended run made with the UCLA 500-gpd pilot plant assembled as described here was a 24-day run on seawater conducted at Port Hueneme, California. Operation was at 1500 psi. Initially the product water contained 1600 ppm total dissolved solids (TDS), and the salt content increased gradually to 2000 ppm during the first two weeks of operation. At this point, it began to increase rapidly, reaching a maximum of 9000 ppm before the unit was shut down and flushed out with distilled water. The flushing operation removed a large amount of solid matter from the unit, and when operation was resumed, the product TDS was down to less than 3000 ppm, where it remained for the last few days of the experiment. Water-production rates for the unit began at just under 700 gpd, and remained in the 500-to-600-gpd range during the bulk of the run.

A comparison of the performance data of the pilot plant with those for individual samples of the membranes used revealed that throughout the run the product salinities were much higher and the water fluxes somewhat lower in the pilot plant than in smaller test cells. In the latter part of the run both of these effects were probably attributable in large measure to the solid matter found deposited in the membrane unit on disassembly, but the variance in the initial results had to be ascribed to some deficiencies in design or assembly. In any case, the unit showed reasonably satisfactory mechanical and hydraulic performance and, while its desalination performance was not quite as good as had been hoped, the successes achieved were of inestimable value in demonstrating the feasibility of constructing larger reverse-osmosis equipment.

Following the Port Hueneme experiments, the 500-gpd unit was used in two pilot operations on synthetic brackish water.[9] The general arrangement was similar to that already described, except that only five plates (10 membranes) were used in the first run, and seven plates (14 membranes) in the second. This reduction in membrane area (to about 12 ft² in the first case and 17 ft² in the second) was made possible by the use of more permeable membranes. The solid-plate concept was again used, but with some of the aluminum plates replaced by plates of Plexiglas and PVC. The brine and product water were recombined and recycled.

Operating pressure in both runs was 600 psi. The first lasted for 16 days but was interrupted twice for a total of six days. About 300 gpd of product water was produced during the operating periods, with a feed of 1200 gpd of a 4300-ppm NaCl solution. The NaCl content of the product water ranged from 400 to 800 ppm.

The second run lasted 42 days and was interrupted twice for a total of 4 days. The product rate varied between 450 and 300 gpd during the course of the run. Part of the variability was attributable to temperature fluctuations and to periodic additions of a bactericidal agent which appeared to affect performance, but the data show a steady decline in membrane flux that is only partly masked by these other factors. The feed solution contained 5000 ppm NaCl, and the average concentration in the product water was somewhat less than 500 ppm.

These generally rather satisfying results on a synthetic brackish water were used by McCutchan, et al.,[10] in the economic study of larger reverse-osmosis plants already referred to in Chapter 6. On the basis of the experience gained, flux rates of 20 gpd/ft² at 600-psi operating pressure, a membrane life of six months, a brine channel thickness of ¼ inch, and the solid-plate arrangement were selected for this study. The basic unit around which the plant was designed was a 3-foot diam, 75-plate (150 membranes) cell, having a product rate of about 20,000 gpd. Electric power requirements were estimated at 12 kw-hr/1000 gal.

Coalinga pilot plant — tubular design. The success of their first unit in treating a synthetic brackish water led the UCLA group to design and build a larger unit for field trials.[11] It was completed and installed at Coalinga, California, during 1965, and as of this writing is the largest reverse-osmosis plant known to be in operation. It is also the first reverse-osmosis plant to supply its product to a city water supply system, since some of its production is used to supplement the city's present supply.

It is significant that the UCLA group chose to go to a tubular design in this plant, rather than continuing with the plate-and-frame arrangement discussed earlier. To describe the unit briefly, it operates at 600 psi and treats a brackish feed water of about 2500 ppm TDS. A detailed analysis is given in Table 3–4. The feed-brine rate is 10,800 gpd from which a nominal 5000 gpd of potable water is produced. The pressure vessels for this plant consist of 112 tubes, 10 feet long and 1-inch diam, assembled in series. For convenience, the tubes are stacked in four levels, as shown in Fig. 7–4. The pressure tubes are conventional copper pipe, and their assembly is shown in Fig. 3–8. The cellulose acetate membrane is formed into a tube that fits inside the copper pipe. When the membrane tube is ready to be inserted, it is wrapped with two layers of nylon net material and one layer of filter paper, so that when the assembly is completed the filter paper and nylon net will form a layer between the membrane and the wall of the copper tube. The purpose of this arrangement is to provide a lateral flow path for the product water to small holes placed 3 inches apart along the length of the tubes.

In the pilot plant, as initially installed, loose-fitting plastic sleeves were wrapped around each copper tube to collect the product water. This was ideal for experimental purposes since each tube could be

Fig. 7–4   UCLA tubular pilot plant. This view shows the pilot plant in early test operations. Only the lowest tier was completely tubed, and only the first four tubes in that tier were actually in production.

monitored separately. In a production plant a collection basin below the unit, or some other design, would doubtless be considered.

The plant was placed in operation with half the tubes in place on June 4, 1965. The production rate stayed relatively constant at about 4500 gpd until about July 1, after which time the rate dropped steadily, decreasing to about 2000 gpd at the end of July. The decrease in production was tentatively attributed to the deposition of particulate matter, largely ferric hydroxide, by microbiological organisms. On August 2, chlorination of the feed brine was started and appeared to arrest further decline in the production rate.

On August 11 the remaining tubes were installed. The installation was made without stopping production from the original tubes, since valving of the plant is so arranged as to make this possible. This flexibility is one of the advantages of the tubular design. Chlorination was provided for the remaining tubes installed with the hope of preventing the loss in production rate experienced with the initial tubes.

The most recent report on the operation of the Coalinga plant[11] indicates that, with 112 tubes installed, production after August 11 increased to 5500 to 6500 gpd. The production rate remained at this level throughout August and most of September, with a feed-brine chlorination of about 2 ppm. Several membrane failures occurred during this period, and since no failures were observed prior to chlorination, chlorination at this level was stopped on October 3.

On September 27–28 the tubes in two of the four tiers were removed, and those in one of these tiers were replaced with fresh tubes. Initial production with three tiers operating was 6500 gpd. After chlorination was stopped, the production rate again dropped off steadily to a low of 2750 gpd on November 4.

The decreases in production were attributed to the gradual deposition of ferric and manganic hydroxide on the membrane surface. Analyses indicated that the feed brine was about 50% saturated in dissolved oxygen. An oxygen scavenger was therefore added to the feed water to remove the dissolved oxygen and maintain the dissolved iron in the more soluble ferrous oxidation state. Dosing with catalyzed sodium sulfite for this purpose was started on November 4. This scavenging procedure not only arrested further decline in the production rate but actually resulted in increased production. This latter result may be accounted for on the basis that the ferric iron in the precipitated ferric hydroxide was being reduced to ferrous iron and removed in this more soluble form.

During the period from June 17 to December 15 the total desalinized water production of the Coalinga unit was 773,500 gallons, an average of 4260 gpd for the 181-day period. The dissolved solids content of the water was 170 to 330 ppm, and total offstream time was about 100 hours. Operation of this pilot plant is expected to continue for some time.

Havens Industries

The tubular design for a reverse-osmosis system was first introduced by Dr. Glenn G. Havens of Havens Industries, San Diego, California. His work was started in 1961, shortly after the successful development of the cellulose acetate membrane by Loeb and Sourirajan[2] had been announced. Havens' basic configuration is much like the tubular UCLA configuration already described, but he uses a porous Fiberglas tube instead of the metal tubes later utilized by the UCLA group. In this case the tube itself serves both as the porous-membrane support and the pressure vessel. The tubes are filament-wound from S994 filament produced by Owens-Corning Fiberglas Corporation, and resin bonded. They are reasonably light in weight, have high tensile strength, and are highly corrosion resistant. The Fiberglas tubes are expected to have a life of many years and are expected to be relatively inexpensive. Quantitative cost and life information on the membrane-lined tubes is not available.

Information was released in 1964[12] on a pilot plant then in operation on seawater. The unit was being test-operated at the South Bay Power

Fig. 7–5   Havens' tubular pilot plant. Dr. Havens is holding a bundle of the Fiberglas tubes.

Plant of the San Diego Gas and Electric Company in San Diego. A photo of the tubular unit is shown in Fig. 7–5. The membrane-separator section of the pilot unit was made up of tubes 8 feet long and $\frac{1}{2}$ inch in internal diameter. The unit was operated in two stages to reduce the 35,000-ppm salinity of seawater effectively to a product salinity of 200 ppm. The first stage operated at 800 psi and reduced the salinity to 2000 ppm, while the second stage used this 2000 ppm water as feed and operated at 500 psi. Chemical analyses of the seawater and the product from the first and second stage are shown in Table 7–1.

At the time that information concerning the unit was released it had reportedly been in operation for approximately six months and was producing 250 to 300 gpd of product water. Flux rates were approximately four gpd per tube for the first stage and seven gpd per tube in the second stage. These figures also correspond directly to gallons per square foot per day, since an 8-foot tube supports approximately 1 ft^2 of membrane. For production plants, it was assumed that the tubes would be mounted in modules of 100 tubes, which were estimated to occupy a volume of approximately 8 ft^3 each. On this basis, the tube volume for a 1000-gpd seawater unit operating in two stages would be approximately 32 ft^3. Power requirements for systems of this type (two stages) operating on seawater were estimated at 20.4 kw-hr per 1000 gallons with energy recovery and 27.8 kw-hr without energy recovery.

The information released by Havens in 1964 referred entirely to

Table 7–1 Water Analyses[12] for Havens' Pilot Plant*

	Seawater	After 1st stage of purification	After 2nd stage of purification
Conductivity	68,300.	3,300.	425.
pH	8.0	7.5	7.3
Calcium — Ca	416.	5.6	0.6
Magnesium — Mg	1,340.	18.5	1.6
Sodium — Na	10,400.	560.	76.
Potassium — K	390.	30.	4.4
Bicarbonate — HCO₃	415.	7.3	4.9
Sulfate — SO₄	2,360.	12.	3.0
Chloride — Cl	19,000.	960.	122.
Nitrate — NO₃	0.08	0.0	0.0
Boron — B	4.5	3.1	2.8
Silica — SiO₂	0.9	1.1	0.2
Iron — Fe	0.0	1.3	0.0
Ortho-phosphate — PO₄	0.06	0.0	0.0
Total alkalinity — CaCO₃	340.	6.	4.
Total hardness	6,560.	90.	8.0
Dissolved solids	37,220.	1,720.	216.

* Units are presumably μmho/cm for conductivity, and ppm for all constituents after pH.

seawater operation. It is understood, however, that since that date additional attention has been given to brackish waters and various improvements have reportedly been made both in the design and fabrication techniques.[13]

Aerojet-General

Design of 1000-gpd plate-and-frame pilot plant. The pilot-plant work at Aerojet-General Corporation dates back to 1962 when work was started on a 1000-gpd unit based on the plate-and-frame design.[3,4] This plant and subsequent pilot plants developed at Aerojet represent the most extensive contribution yet made to the plate-and-frame concept. A photograph and process flow sheet for the original 1000-gpd unit are shown in Figs. 7–6 and 7–7, respectively. The unit was trailer-mounted and consisted of 45 membrane-support plates utilizing membranes of 16-inch diam. The effective membrane dimeter was 14¾ inches, resulting in 1.12 ft² of membrane area per plate. Hence, 45 plates with a membrane on either side provided 90 membranes with a total area of 100 ft². The plates were grouped in three sections or modules so that product could be collected separately from each section and individual flow and other measurements could be made. The cellulose acetate membranes were bonded to the support plates with a strip of adhesive (93%

Fig. 7–6   Aerojet 1000-gpd plate-and-frame pilot plant.

Pliobond, 5% cellulose acetate, and 2% acetone) $\frac{1}{8}$ inch wide at the periphery of the membrane. Teflon tape, 1 inch wide, was used around the periphery of the membrane seal as reinforcement.

The unit was of tie-bolt construction with carbon steel vessel heads and was designed for pressures up to 1500 psi to permit operation on either sea- or brackish waters as required by the experimental program. The design capacity of 1000 gpd with 100 ft^2 of membrane obviously assumed a design flux of 10 gpd/ft^2, which in actual operation was expected to be higher or lower, depending on conditions. An 8-gpm piston-type pump was provided to pressurize the feed. This pump capacity was chosen to provide a brine channel flow of 1 ft/sec parallel to the membrane. The original unit was provided with a 10-μ filter on the feed-water line.

The seal between the plates was achieved with an O ring. The saline feed flowed back and forth across the plates parallel to the membrane surfaces until it completed its path through the unit. Ports for transfer of the flow from plate to plate were provided near the periphery of the plates. The product was collected on the low-pressure side of the membrane flowing through the porous support plate to its periphery where holes were provided to manifold and collect the product. In actual assembly, a layer of filter paper was placed between the membrane and the support plate.

The material chosen for the first support plates was sintered bronze. It was recognized from the beginning that, although satisfactory for

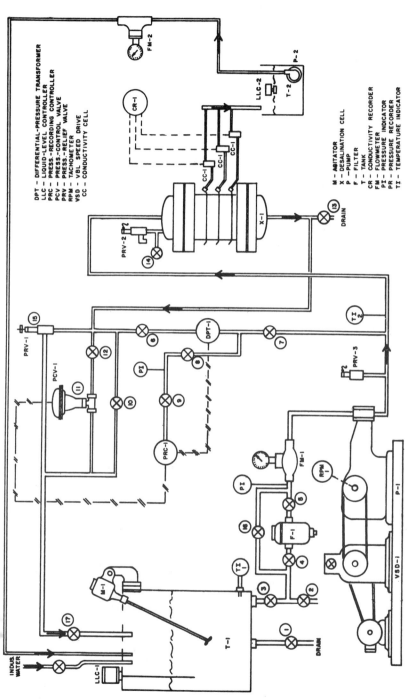

Fig. 7-7   Process flow sheet for Aerojet 1000-gpd pilot plant.

experimental purposes, this was entirely too expensive for use in production units. Substitute materials were immediately investigated and resulted first in the development of a glass-fiber-epoxy-bonded porous support plate having both superior flow characteristics and lower cost. This was followed by a still lower-cost plate reported to have excellent hydraulic characteristics, the grooved phenolic plate. This phenolic plate was made of solid material, as opposed to the previous porous materials. Test operations in the 1000-gpd pilot plant showed that the plate gave results as good as or better than those obtained with the porous epoxy plate. Test plates of the grooved design were made using various groove depths and groove spacing. Selection of groove width was guided in part by previous experience indicating that a membrane supported by filter paper will bridge a $\frac{1}{32}$-inch hole at 1500 psi. Dimensions found suitable in a test plate were grooves 0.010 inch wide and 0.030 inch deep, spaced 0.10 inch apart.

Very early in the program it became apparent that the grooved plate would present a variety of molding and fabricating problems. Further development produced the slotted phenolic plate as an alternate to the grooved plate. This plate could be molded readily and was also improved hydraulically. In the final design, a $\frac{1}{8}$-inch-thick plate is made in two identical halves, each $\frac{1}{16}$ inch thick. Each plate contains Λ-shaped parallel grooves or slots that are 10 mils wide at the top and 45 mils wide at the bottom. In assembling the plates, the two halves are joined with the wide grooves together, rotated so that the grooves in the two plates are at right angles, and permanently bonded together. The product water flows through the interior grooves to the nearest product-water outlet. The design, as conceived for future plants, would provide for collection of the product at the center of the plate. Likewise, the feed would flow from the outer rim to the center and then axially through the center of the several plates as the waste stream. The plates would have elevated rims around the periphery and center to provide spacing. A short gap would be provided in the outer rim to permit entry of the feed, which would then flow through a circular baffle to the center. This plate design is shown in Fig. 7–8, where one of the halves is represented schematically and details of the vital cross sections are given.

The general design described above with a central flow manifold for the product and waste streams was envisioned for future plants with larger plate diameters and with single pressure vessels instead of the tie-bolt construction. In replacing the glass-fiber-reinforced plates in the 1000-gpd pilot plants with the slotted phenolic plates, it was necessary to adapt the design to the tie-bolt construction and to retain the same general plate configuration as that in the previous plates. This was successfully achieved while retaining the general features of the plate design shown in Fig. 7–8. Field experience at Aerojet with the slotted phenolic

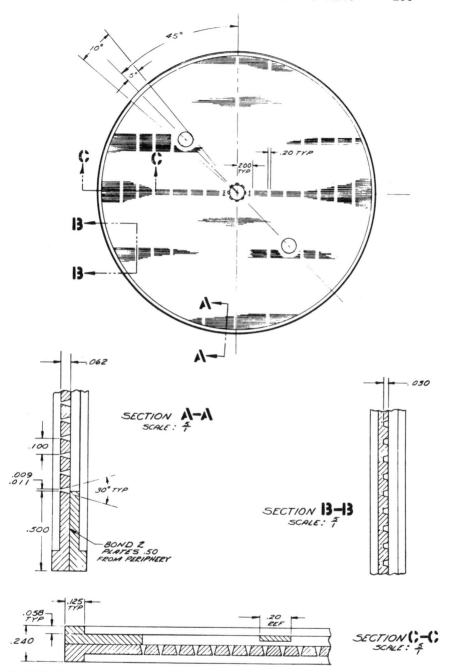

Fig. 7–8   Membrane-support plate for plate-and-frame unit. Generalized design of a slotted phenolic plate.

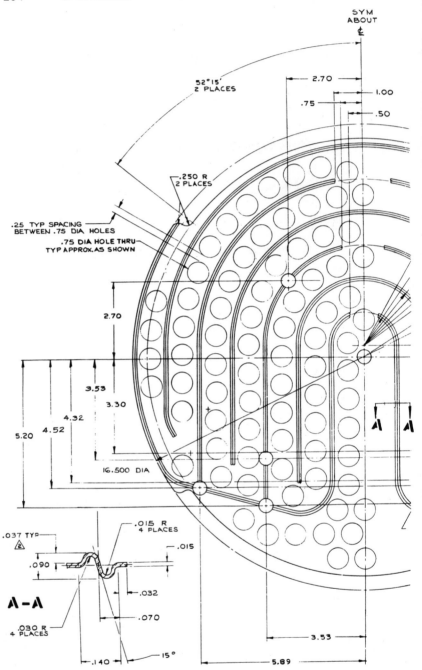

Fig. 7–9   Baffle for 1000-gpd pilot plant.

plate in the 1000-gpd units has demonstrated the merits of the design and its serviceability. Concurrently with the plate development, baffles were also designed for the 1000-gpd units that had initially operated without baffles in the feed-water channels. These baffles, shown in Fig. 7–9, were made of vacuum-formed polystyrene sheet. The stream is split into two halves, above and below the baffle, and it is further divided into a left and a right quarter. A flow path of from 30 to 40 feet is provided. Feed-stream velocities are increased by a factor of about six over that of the unbaffled design.

Test operations. Pilot-plant operations at Aerojet have been pursued with equal emphasis on sea- and brackish waters. It became evident early in the test program that test results would not be obtained rapidly with only a single test unit. Hence, three additional units of the same design were added. Two units were housed in a trailer at the brackish-water site and two in a trailer at the seawater site. Brackish tests were first made at a well at the Irvine Ranch (Santa Ana, California) and later at Laguna Beach, California. A successful test run was conducted at the Irvine Ranch, where the original pilot unit was run continuously for 106 days before it became necessary to vacate the site because of highway construction. Actually, the test operation was continued to $5\frac{1}{2}$ months at the Laguna Beach site. Figure 7–10 shows the flux rates and product-salt concentration for the 106-day period. The flux remained stable at 10 gpd/ft² during the last 10 weeks of operation, and the salt content of the product was nearly constant at 250 ppm. The unit was

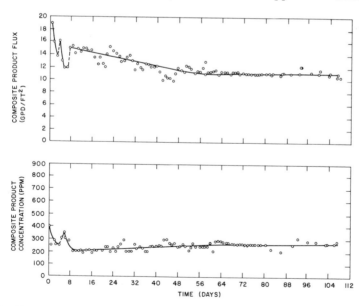

Fig. 7–10   Water flux and product salt concentration during Irvine Ranch test.

Table 7-2   Analysis of Feed and Product Streams.
Irvine Ranch test well

	Well-water feed (ppm)	Product (ppm)
Total dissolved solids	4900.	250.
Total hardness	1600.	65.
Ca^{++}	350.	15.
Mg^{++}	200.	9.
Na^+	1000.	100.
HCO_3^-	220.	19.
SO_4^-	1700.	12.
Cl^-	1350.	140.
Fe	0.1–1.7	<0.1
Mn	0.8	<0.1
NO_3^-	2.8	0.7
F^-	0.5	<0.01
B (as H_3BO_3)	0.02–0.16	0.05–0.09
SiO_2	13.	<0.1
pH	7.5	6.5

operated at 750-psi pressure, and the only pretreatment received by the well water was filtration through a cartridge-type filter. The analysis of the Irvine Ranch well water and the product produced during the test are shown in Table 7-2. This was the first time that a plant of as much as 1000-gpd capacity had operated continuously on a natural brackish source for more than three months. This test did much to establish the estimate of six months' membrane life more firmly.

Operations at Laguna Beach were a continuation of the Irvine Ranch run. However, difficulty was experienced almost immediately because of iron present in the well water at 4.7 ppm (see analysis, Table 7-3). It was found necessary to remove the iron to very low levels to assure good operation. This was achieved by simple aeration, brief detention, and filtration through a diatomite filter. As a consequence, a diatomite filter was made a regular part of the equipment. Some tests were also made to prevent precipitation of the dissolved iron by use of a sequestering agent, such as citric acid. The tests were limited in scope but appeared to indicate that the dissolved iron had not been completely sequestered by a citric acid dose of 5 to 20 ppm applied to the feed. Satisfactory results were obtained, however, in removing iron previously precipitated on the membranes by use of a 2% citric acid wash.

It was observed that manganese present to the extent of 0.7 ppm apparently produced no precipitation in the unit, and chemical analyses indicated that it was quantitatively rejected by the membrane. This is an interesting observation but requires verification since it is based on a single field test.

Table 7–3   Analysis of Feed and Product Streams.
Laguna Beach test well

	Well-water feed (ppm)	Product (ppm)
Total dissolved solids	4075.	375.
Total hardness	1650.	80.
Ca^{++}	230.	10.
Mg^{++}	250.	12.
Na^{+}	830.	110.
SO$_4^{-}$	1350.	20.
Cl^{-}	800.	110.
Fe	4.7	<0.1
Mn	0.7	<0.1
NO$_3^{-}$	2.5	0.7
F^{-}	1.2	0.05
B (as H$_3$BO$_3$)	0.8	0.4
pH	7.1	6.9

One operating technique employed by Aerojet during the field-test work consisted of periodic relaxation of the pressure. It had been observed that the flux rate increased to its previous level each time the pressure was dropped and reapplied. The 106-day field test at the Irvine Ranch was operated in this manner with the pressure reduced four times a day for periods of 10 to 15 minutes each.

Pilot-plant operations on seawater demonstrated that membrane-support plates and other components of the unit function satisfactorily at the high pressures required (1500 psi). Likewise, the membranes themselves did not show mechanical or physical failure at these pressures, nor was any difficulty encountered with the adhesives used to seal the membrane to the phenolic plate. However, as in the experience of other investigators, no degree of effort to date appears to have overcome the problem of inadequate salt rejection, which has prevented attaining a 500-ppm product on a continuous basis with one-stage operation. As is characteristic of cellulose acetate membranes under these pressures, flux rates dropped rapidly with time. The test results are too varied to be summarized briefly; however, they were characterized generally by runs that began with fluxes of possibly 10 gpd/ft² and product salinities between 500 and 1000 ppm but, after as little as two weeks' operation, showed flux decreases to a few gpd/ft² and product salinities of 1000 to 2000 ppm or more. The tests demonstrated that potable water of 500 ppm can be produced in one-pass operation but failed to demonstrate how this can be sustained at reasonable fluxes in a production unit.

In the pilot-plant work, various membranes were tested. In addition to the conventional magnesium perchlorate membranes, the zinc chloride and triple salt types have been studied. In the latter case the mem-

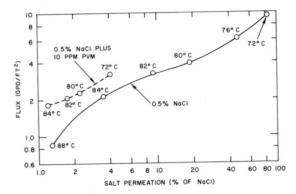

Fig. 7–11   Performance of triple salt membranes at 750 psi, with and without poly-vinylmethyl ether feed additive. The temperatures indicated are those at which the membranes were heat-treated.

brane salt is a combination of magnesium perchlorate, magnesium bromide hexahydrate, and zinc bromide; hence the name "triple salt." PVM (polyvinylmethyl ether) was frequently used in the pilot-plant work to achieve better salt rejection by the membrane. The performance gains achieved by this technique in concurrent laboratory experiments are illustrated in Fig. 7–11. PVM appears to be a useful feed additive, which makes possible higher salt rejections at a given flux.

Design criteria and economics. As a guide to scaleup of the small pilot plants to units of larger capacity, various design and economic studies have been conducted by Aerojet concurrently with the field testing of the 1000-gpd units. Details of this work are contained in progress reports,[1,2] and a recent summary is provided by Keilin and DeHaven.[14] Although the purpose of the latter paper was to optimize the process for low-cost desalination, the design data and criteria are of particular interest in this chapter since these data are indicative of the status of the process development.

As a basis for making calculations on a plant design, assumptions were made that seem reasonable in view of current technology. Actual plants will be expected to vary with circumstances and improvements in technology. These assumptions included a product-to-feed ratio of 0.5, a product rate of 1 million gpd, and an average flux of 10 gpd/ft², automatically fixing the total membrane area at 100,000 ft². Corollary assumptions necessary to fix unit conditions include a plate thickness of 0.1 inch and a membrane spacing of 0.1 inch. With this information, the contact time of the feed stream with the membrane can be determined and the appropriate path length for given velocities can be calculated. As an example, an inlet feed-stream velocity of 2 ft/sec with 0.1-inch spacing and a product-to-feed ratio of 0.5 requires a path length of 200 feet.

Based on the assumed 100,000 ft^2 of membrane, a generalized design for a flat-plate unit has been outlined. It is assumed that five cylindrical pressure vessels would be required. Thus, the unit size is considerably larger than that chosen in the earlier study of McCutchan, et al.[10] Generalized specifications for a single separator unit are given in Table 7–4.

Table 7–4   Specifications for 20,000-ft^2 Plate-and-Frame
             Separator Unit

Plate thickness	0.1 inch
Membrane spacing (gap height)	0.1 inch
Cell diameter	36 inches
Cell length	30 feet
Pressure rating of cell	1500 psi
Membrane area per plate	11.7 ft^2
Number of plates per cell	1740
Membrane density	97 ft^2/ft^3
Plate weight	5.9 lb each

Cost estimates were prepared for both the slotted phenolic and the glass-fiber-reinforced epoxy plates. The latter was estimated to cost $1.50/ft^2, and the former $0.77/ft^2 of membrane area.

Similar cost estimates were made on the pressure vessels and a chart prepared to show the change in cost with vessel diameter. In brief, the estimate indicated that the pressure-vessel components, namely the head, the flanges, and the shell, would contribute $0.036, $0.125, and $0.133, respectively, to the cost per square foot of membrane.

The design criteria chosen by Keilin and DeHaven[14] assume that the unit would be operable up to 1500 psi. Pressures to be used in actual situations will vary with the salinity of the feed water and are subject to considerable change as different optimizations are indicated. However, the pressures used by Aerojet in the existing pilot plants, probably indicative of current practice, are 750 to 800 psi on a 5000-ppm brackish water and 1500 psi on seawater. Total power requirements are directly related to the percentage of product recovered from the feed and the extent to which the energy of the waste stream is reused. For design purposes, targets of 80% product recovery for brackish waters and 33$\frac{1}{3}$% for seawater operations have been established. With the high product recovery and with the lower pressures normally applied in brackish waters, it is evident that the power recovered from the small waste stream may be of marginal significance. However, with seawater operations at higher pressures and lower product-recovery ratios, this energy recovery may be significant. The power recovered from a seawater plant may be worth as much as 10 cents per 1000 gallons.

In reviewing the design criteria of Keilin and DeHaven,[14] it should be

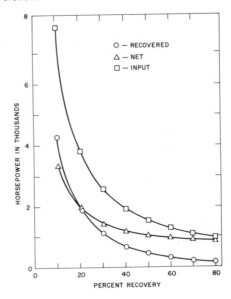

Fig. 7–12   Power requirements for one-million-gpd reverse-osmosis plant. An 80% over-all conversion efficiency in pumps and turbines is assumed. (From Office of Saline Water Research and Development Progress Report No. 213.[4])

remembered that these data represent practical conditions under which brackish-water plants (5000 ppm) could operate today. For seawater, from a practical standpoint, these data are not immediately applicable since the membranes available are not yet suitable for seawater in one-pass operation. The flux rate of 10 gpd/ft² assumed in the design criteria is fully applicable to brackish waters today, and higher fluxes may actually be attainable. However, for seawater the latter figure is not realistic with currently available membranes. (Two-stage operation to achieve the desired salt rejection is, of course, possible, as demonstrated in Havens' experiments.)

A convenient plot expressing power relationships for reverse-osmosis systems based on the Aerojet work[4] is given in Fig. 7–12. It is well to remember that the efficiencies assumed can change the net power figures a great deal. The data of the figure were calculated on the basis of 80% over-all energy-conversion efficiency in pumps and turbines. On this basis, operation at 1500 psi and 33⅓% water recovery would result in 41 kw-hr/1000 gallons input power and 21.5 kw-hr/1000 gallons recovered from the waste stream for a net of 20.5 kw-hr/1000 gallons. However, if 70% conversion efficiency is assumed, the input would be 47 kw-hr/1000 gallons and the recovered power 19 kw-hr/1000 gallons for a net of 28.7 kw-hr. The latter figure compares closely with the 28 kw-hr given by Keilin and Watson.[15] Again assuming the 80% efficiency number, operation at 800 psi, and 80% water recovery, input power is 9.1 kw-hr/1000 gallons, recoverable power is only 1.4 kw-hr/1000 gallons, and the net requirement is 7.7 kw-hr/1000 gallons.

General Atomic

Pilot-plant design. Pilot-plant work at the General Atomic Division of General Dynamics Corporation has been conducted exclusively with units based on the spiral-wound concept.[16] Figure 7–13 is a schematic drawing of such a module. The modules used in pilot-plant work to date have been approximately one foot long and $2\frac{1}{2}$ to 3 inches in diam. Modules of this size contain 4 to 8 ft² of membrane area. While a variety of materials have been used both as brine-side spacers and as product-water-side backing materials, the current materials of choice are an 0.026-inch-thick Vexar polyethylene screen on the brine side, and a 0.020- to 0.030-inch-thick layer of fine glass beads sandwiched between two layers of felt on the product-water side. This product-water-side material is made by first spreading the beads on one piece of the felt and bonding them to it with adhesive, and then adding the second felt layer. Reasonably extensive experiments with woven and felted synthetics without glass for the product-water-side material have shown these to lose permeability at an excessively rapid rate because of creep phenomena at system pressures above 200 psi.

The method of assembling these modules into systems of larger size is illustrated in Fig. 7–14. A group of six to twelve of the modules is connected together at their central tubes, and the assembled group is slipped into a single pressure vessel. The central product-water tube is connected

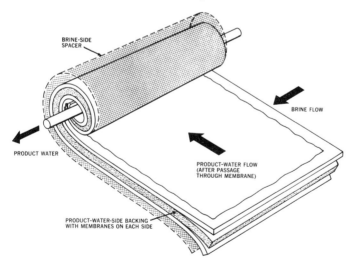

Fig. 7–13 Schematic drawing of spiral-wound module.

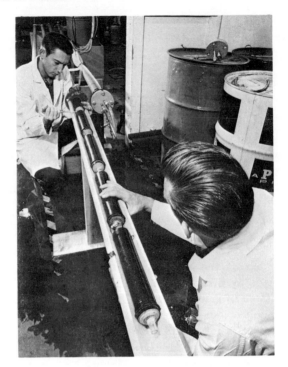

Fig. 7–14   Series-connected spiral-wound modules.

to a penetration in one or both end fittings. The feed water passes through all the modules in a given pressure tube in series, becoming more concentrated as it passes from module to module.

Four test loops with nominal capacities in excess of 1000 gpd have been constructed at General Atomic. Two are designed for operation at about 400 psi, and one of these is shown in Fig. 7–15. The figure shows a loop equipped with two $2\frac{1}{2}$-inch inner-diam, 15-foot-long glass-reinforced-epoxy pressure tubes, and two $2\frac{1}{2}$-inch inner-diam, 12-ft-long stainless steel tubes. The shorter tubes have a capacity of ten 5-ft² modules, and the longer ones one of twelve such modules. The configuration shown was used for a test series in which up to 2000 gpd was produced from a synthetic 2000-ppm brackish water, but more commonly each of these low-pressure loops is equipped only with two of the epoxy tubes.

Figure 7–16 shows one of the two loops capable of operating over a range of pressures up to 1500 psi. This system has six internally coated carbon steel pressure vessels, each of which will hold six 8-ft² modules. These tubes, the pump, the sump tank, and all accessory equipment are mounted on a single frame for easy transportability. The second high-pressure loop is generally similar in construction, but is established

Fig. 7–15   Low-pressure (400-psi) reverse-osmosis system.

in a laboratory and equipped with single-module containers to facilitate single-module testing, as well as with the larger vessels.

Field testing. The bulk of the field-testing program carried out by General Atomic has been conducted with the portable loop depicted in Fig. 7–16. It has been operated at seven different sites to determine the problems to be expected under a wide variety of feed-water conditions. Detailed reports on operations at four of the sites are available.[17–19]

The first of these sites[17] was on the Potomac River at Washington, D. C. The unit was operated on a 24-hour basis for ten days, using an inlet pressure to the pressure tubes of 600 psi.

The membranes used in these experiments (and in most of the other General Atomic field tests) are of the highly selective variety similar to those characterized as "seawater" membranes in Chapter 3 and designated "Type A" by General Atomic. Some of the reasons for making this choice in experiments in which many types of contaminants are to be encountered will be discussed in connection with the experiments at Pomona, California. With the high membrane quality, the total dis-

Fig. 7–16   High-pressure (1500-psi) reverse-osmosis system.

solved solids content (TDS) of the river water, which was already reasonably low, ~333 ppm, was reduced to ~10 ppm. Greatest interest in these tests was in the removals obtained on various contaminants of special significance in treating polluted waters. A summary of pertinent analytical data is given in Table 7–5. It is noteworthy that nitrates, phosphates, and organics were all reduced to very low levels of concentration.

Bacteriological samples were also taken during this test and, neglecting the first sample taken (which was apparently slightly contaminated by residual materials in the system), all product-water results for coliform bacteria were <3-negative, expressed as most probable number of bacteria per 100 ml. Tests made on the feed water gave results ranging from 1500-positive to >11,000-positive. It is, of course, to be expected that no bacteria will penetrate the membrane; but the question is whether or not large-scale systems will be sufficiently leak-tight to prevent bacteriological contamination of the product water from a highly contaminated feed water. The results are encouraging.

Table 7–5   Potomac River Test Chemical Analysis Summary[17]

	Feed-brine mean (ppm)	Product (ppm)	Rejection (%)
Total dissolved solids			
10-day composite	369.	16.	95.7
Mean — 5 daily samples	333.	9.5	97.0
Chlorides			
10-day composite	31.5	<1.0	>96.8
Mean — 9 samples	29.6	<1.1	>96.2
Phosphates			
10-day composite	0.015	0.000	—
Mean — 9 samples	0.072	<0.011	>84.6
Nitrates			
Mean — 7 daily samples	0.164	0.016	90.4
Chemical oxygen demand			
Mean — 9 samples	11.3	0.44	96.1
Total organic carbon			
10-day composite	4.0	<1.0	>75.
Mean — 19 samples	6.9	<1.5	>78.

The second test was performed at Little Ferry, New Jersey, in cooperation with the State of New Jersey and the Bergen County Sewer Authority. Here the unit was operated for approximately three days on secondary sewage effluent available at the site, and for approximately four days on water drawn from the Hackensack River. Operation was again at about 600 psi except during one of several "special experiments" which will not be discussed further here.

The record of these experiments[18] contains extensive analytical data, which we will not attempt to summarize in detail. Suffice it to quote that during operation on the secondary sewage effluent which contained 1200 to 2300 ppm TDS, "the concentration of all components in the delivered product water . . . was well within the recommended maximum values established in the Potable Water Standards for the State of New Jersey."[18] During the operation on the Hackensack River, on the other hand, the TDS of the product was deemed too high to meet potable standards, the analyses generally showing 750 to 1000 ppm TDS.

The high dissolved solids contents obtained during operation on the river water are hardly surprising in view of the fact that the Hackensack at Little Ferry is a tidal river, and analyses of the feed water indicated 15,000 to 25,000 ppm TDS. It is apparent from the discussions of membrane properties given in earlier chapters that 600 psi is a marginal operating pressure at best under these circumstances.

The Little Ferry tests were punctuated by at least two incidents in which the membrane modules became plugged, probably due to failure of the diatomaceous-earth filtration system used. It was found possible to restore the unit to satisfactory operation after each of these incidents by reverse flushing of the pressure tubes. This is potentially a factor of great practical importance, since there had been some concern that the relatively fine feed-water passages used in this design concept might be subject to fouling which would be excessively difficult to reverse.

In the tests performed with this unit at Washington, D. C., and Little Ferry, water recoveries were generally in the range of 25 to 30%. The first effort to achieve much higher recoveries was made during the next tests[19] at two sites near Kittanning, Pennsylvania. At both sites the feed water was acid mine drainage, containing 1300 to 2000 ppm TDS.

The performance of the equipment on these water sources was quite similar to those reported for the Potomac River water and the Bergen County sewage effluent. The acid was well retained, product water with a pH of 4.85 and a total acidity (measured to a pH 8.2 end point at 60°C) of 2.5 ppm (as $CaCO_3$) being obtained, for example, from a feed having a pH of 2.75 and a total acidity of 280 ppm in the same units. Iron was also well retained, feed concentrations as high as 189 ppm (as Fe_2O_3) being reduced to $\sim$0.1 ppm by the highly selective membranes.

Flux decline, presumably due to sliming by ferric hydroxide, was observed in these tests in the modules exposed to the incoming feed at the second site. Interestingly, this problem was much less severe in the latter modules which were exposed to the more concentrated brine. This is believed to be due to the higher solubility of ferric iron in the more concentrated acid of the brine. No similar problem was encountered at the first site. Washing with a complexing agent proved a useful technique for recovering much of the flux decline caused by the iron, and precautions to avoid aeration and thereby oxidation of ferrous to ferric iron are suggested as desirable measures in future experiments.

But the most interesting result of the mine-water tests may be the high water recoveries achieved. With all six pressure tubes connected in series to provide maximum brine velocity, recoveries as high as 95% were maintained for extended periods (about 12 hours at a stretch) without difficulty. The exit brine was reportedly supersaturated in calcium sulfate during these high recovery tests.

More recently, this same test loop was operated on brackish well waters at Ft. Stockton, Midland, and Kermit, Texas. Reports on these operations are not available at this writing but should be in the near future.

One other field test made by General Atomic deserves brief mention here, even though the production rate ($\sim$100 gpd) was lower than that of the other experiments discussed in this chapter. This was a test performed at Pomona, California in cooperation with the Sanitation Districts of Los Angeles County, using secondary sewage effluent as feed.[20] Operation was at 200 psi.

Table 7-6 shows typical analytical data for the feed and product

Table 7-6 Pomona Test Chemical Analysis Summary[20]

Test	Feed Water*	Product from module 12-18-6 (5A1)†	Product from module 1-6-3 (5A1)†	Product from module 1-29-1 (3B1)†	Product from module 1-22-1 (5C1)†
Alkalinity, ppm CaCO₃	213	15	13	100	15
Ammonia nitrogen, ppm N	17.6	3.4	3.4	12.0	6.1
Total nitrogen, ppm	20.6	4.6	4.6	13.0	6.8
Specific conductance, μmho/cm	1044	51	56	489	175
Chloride, ppm Cl	98	3	5	73	26
Total hardness, ppm CaCO₃	213.2	1.4	1.4	40.6	5.2
Total phosphate, ppm PO₄	28.0	0	0	1.8	0
Potassium, ppm	13.8	0.9	1.4	9.1	3.8
Sodium, ppm	88.2	5.1	8.0	62.2	21.8
Calcium, ppm CaCO₃	141.5	0.5	1.4	30.7	2.4
Magnesium, ppm CaCO₃	71.5	0.9	0	9.9	2.8
Total dissolved solids, ppm	531	20	20	250	90
Sulfate, ppm SO₄	70.6	0	0	11.9	0
ABS, ppm	3.0	<0.1	<0.1	0.8	<0.1
COD, ppm O	38.8	1.9	0	4.8	2.7
pH	7.50	6.60	6.50	7.00	6.30

* Chlorinated and diatomaceous-earth-filtered secondary effluent.
† Pressure = 201 psi, temperature = 64°F, time in use = 650 hr for 12-18-6 (5A1), 1-6-3 (5A1), and 1-29-1 (3B1), and 175 hr for 1-22-1 (5C2).

waters using three different module types, 5A1, 3B1, and 5C1. The letter in the type designation indicates whether the membrane has a high (type A), low (type B), or intermediate (type C) ability to retain sodium chloride. The product water from the type A modules is clearly of quite high quality, while the other two module types yielded smaller degrees of contaminant removal. The initial fluxes of the less selective membranes (about 10 gpd/ft² at 200 psi for type C) were, of course, substantially higher than those of the most selective material (about 2 gpd/ft² at 200 psi for type A).

Two possible reasons for preferring the less permeable high-selectivity material on waste waters, even though large reductions in TDS are not needed, are made apparent by the Pomona results: First, the removal of nitrogen-containing compounds and of organics that contribute to chemical oxygen demand (COD) is substantially less complete than TDS removal in all cases. The desire to achieve good results on these less abundant contaminants may force the selection of membrane materials far more selective than needed to reduce TDS to acceptable levels. Second, flux data collected in the experiments indicated that the type A membranes are much less susceptible to flux loss during operation in the sewage effluent than are the B and C types. Thus, pretreatment requirements may be less stringent in the case of high-selectivity membranes than in that of the more permeable types.

7.3   Conclusions

The pilot-plant tests conducted to date have shown that technically successful units having a production capacity of one to a few thousand gallons per day can be built around all three of the design concepts under intensive study. A comparison of the data obtained in pilot-plant operations with those obtained by the same groups in laboratory-scale work shows that large membrane areas incorporated into practical systems can be expected to perform just as well as small membrane areas in laboratory equipment so long as the system design provides for suitably permeable membrane-backing materials and adequate brine circulation.

Field operation on a variety of water sources has demonstrated that reverse osmosis may well have the applicability to such water problems as concentration of acid mine drainage and recovery of usable water from municipal waste streams, as well as the more commonly considered desalination of brackish well water and seawater. The versatility of the process stems largely from its generality, the membrane being highly permeable to very few substances other than water. Pilot-plant experience on seawater has confirmed that the reverse-osmosis membranes of today are not yet adequate to the task of single-stage desalination of seawater but that two-stage systems are feasible.

One problem that has arisen in the field operations has been encountered in almost all the test programs: It is the problem of membrane fouling by iron-containing deposits. It is not certain that all the increased flux declines (as compared with what is observed in the laboratory) are traceable to iron, but certainly this is the only substance implicated in a number of instances. The fact that the difficulty has been encountered in all three system types suggests that it cannot be alleviated through mechanical design. At least three routes to overcome the problem seem to be feasible: The iron can be removed from the feed stream, for instance by aeration and filtration; the iron can be kept in the ferrous state and carried through the apparatus; or perhaps relatively selective membranes that are least subject to fouling can be used and cleaned periodically with complexing agents. The choice in a particular case will depend upon the concentration and oxidation state of iron in the feed stream and upon economic factors.

The next step in pilot-plant development has recently been announced by the Office of Saline Water. Research and development contracts have been let to Aerojet-General and to General Atomic which include the construction of pilot plants of 50,000 gpd and 10,000 gpd, respectively, designed for brackish-water operation. These unit sizes have been chosen because they will constitute tests of logical building blocks for much larger plants based on the plate-and-frame and spiral-wound-module concepts. Successful operation of these pilot plants should lead, as a next step, to plants large enough to permit a meaningful demonstration of reverse-osmosis economics.

References

1. Breton, E. J., Jr., and C. E. Reid, Office of Saline Water, Research and Development Progress Report No. 16, April 1957.
2. Loeb, S., and S. Sourirajan, UCLA Department of Engineering Report 60-60 (1960).
3. Aerojet General Corporation, Office of Saline Water, Research and Development Progress Report No. 86, January 1964.
4. Aerojet-General Corporation, Office of Saline Water, Research and Development Progress Report No. 213, September 1966.
5. Manjikian, S., S. Loeb, and J. W. McCutchan, Paper SWD/12, *Proc. First Intn'l. Desalination Symp.*, Washington, D. C., October 3–9, 1965.
6. Loeb, S., and S. Manjikian, UCLA Department of Engineering Report 64-34 (1964).
7. Loeb, S., and S. Manjikian, *Ind. and Eng. Chem. Proc. Des. and Dev.* 4, 207 (1965).
8. Loeb, S., and F. Milstein, UCLA Department of Engineering Report 62-52 (1962).
9. Loeb, S., and S. Manjikian, UCLA Department of Engineering Report 63-37 (1963).
10. McCutchan, J. W., S. Loeb, P. A. Buckingham, and A. W. Ayers, UCLA Department of Engineering Report 63-62 (1963).
11. Loeb, S., in UCLA Department of Engineering Report 66-1 (1966).
12. *Water and Waste Treatment*, September/October 1964, p. 147.
13. Havens, G. G., private communication.
14. Keilin, B., and C. G. DeHaven, Paper SWD/28, *Proc. First Intn'l Desalination Symp.*, Washington, D. C., October 3–9, 1965.
15. Keilin, B., and E. R. Watson, paper presented before Division of Water, Air, and Waste Chemistry, American Chemical Society, Detroit, Michigan, April 4–9, 1965.
16. Bray, D. T., and U. Merten, Annual Report to Office of Saline Water under Contract 14-01-0001-426, August 1965, Office of Saline Water Research and Development Progress Report No. 165.
17. Schultz, J., Final Report to Office of Saline Water under Contract 14-01-0001-761, January 1966, to be published as Office of Saline Water Research and Development Progress Report.
18. Wilford, J., and F. R. Perkins, Report of General Atomic Reverse Osmosis Unit Test in New Jersey, released by New Jersey State Department of Health and New Jersey Department of Conservation and Economic Development, January 1966.

19. Riedinger, A. B., and J. Schultz, Final Report to Office of Saline Water under Contract 14-01-0001-752, March 1966, to be published as Office of Saline Water Research and Development Progress Report.
20. Bray, D. T., U. Merten, and M. Augustus, *Bulletin of the California Water Pollution Control Association* **2**, No. 2, 11 (October 1965).

8. Current Activity in Reverse Osmosis

George F. Mangan, Jr.

The activities of the Federal Government in the field of saline-water conversion began in 1952 when Congress passed Public Law 448, 82nd Congress (Act of July 3, 1952), which is referred to as the Saline Water Act of 1952. This original act authorized the appropriation of $2 million for a 5-year research program to be administered by the Secretary of the Interior. The stated objective of this program was to develop economically feasible processes for converting seawater and other saline water to fresh water of a quality suitable for municipal, industrial, agricultural, and other beneficial purposes.

After the program had been in effect 3 years, it became apparent that a 5-year program was not long enough to accomplish the objective and that the funds authorized were not adequate for financing the research work. In addition, certain changes and expansion in the authority granted in the original act were needed. These needs led to the enactment in 1955 of Public Law 84-111 (Act of June 29, 1955). This act extended the period of research to 10 years and increased the amount authorized to be appropriated from $2 million to $10 million. It also made possible the use of the facilities of existing federal scientific laboratories to conduct research and technical development work and provided for full cooperation with the Defense Department, the Atomic Energy Commission, and other federal agencies.

In 1958, the Secretary's authority was again expanded by enactment of Public Law 85-833 (Act of September 2, 1958), which authorized the construction and operation of not less than five experimental demonstration plants for the conversion of seawater and brackish water. This act provided for three seawater-conversion plants to be located on the East Coast, Gulf Coast, and West Coast, respectively, two of them to have a capacity each of at least 1 million gallons per day. It provided, in addition, for two brackish-water plants to be located in the northern Great Plains and in the arid area of the Southwest, with one of the plants designed to produce at least 250,000 gpd.

The first of these demonstration plants was constructed at Freeport, Texas. This is a long-tube vertical evaporator designed for the conversion of 1 million gpd of seawater. The plant is presently in operation.

The second seawater-conversion plant was constructed at Point Loma, near San Diego, California, to demonstrate the multistage flash-distillation process. In February 1964, in the national interest, this plant was transferred to the Navy and moved to the Guantanamo Naval Base in Cuba.

The other seawater conversion plant has been built at Wrightsville Beach, North Carolina, for demonstrating the freezing process. It is designed for a capacity of 200,000 gpd, but several serious problems have been encountered in its operation.

The first of the brackish-water plants is located in Webster, South Dakota. It is a 250,000-gpd plant demonstrating the electrodialysis process. This has been a successful operation, producing valuable data on membrane processes.

The second brackish-water plant was constructed at Roswell, New Mexico, to demonstrate the vapor-compression-distillation method of conversion. The plant designed to produce 1 million gpd was completed in 1963. It has not yet operated at its design capacity nor for any extended period of time because of numerous problems that have arisen.

In 1961 the saline-water research program was again extended and expanded by Public Law 87-295, the Anderson-Aspinall Act. This act of September 22, 1961, provided for the expenditure of $75 million for the 6-year period fiscal year 1962 through fiscal year 1967. Emphasis of the expanded program was focused on basic research rather than on development work. While recognizing the need for pilot plants and demonstration plants as the program progressed, the predominant view of Congress at that time favored a program of basic research in the hope of a real breakthrough in the cost of desalination.

8.1 The Program of the Office of Saline Water

In 1955 the Secretary of the Interior established a formal organization to pursue the Department's activities in saline-water conversion more effectively. This organization later became known as the Office of Saline Water; it has been the principal federal agency working in saline-water conversion since its formation. The activities of the Office are summarized in a series of reports, the most recent of which is the *Saline Water Conversion Report for 1964*.[1] The financial support and encouragement of membrane research for the reverse-osmosis process by the Office of Saline Water has been in direct proportion to the funds made available by Congress to the saline-water-conversion program. After the work of Reid and Breton at the University of Florida,[2] supported from 1953 to 1955, the Office of Saline Water funded only two additional studies related to reverse osmosis during the period 1955 through 1961.

With the emphasis on basic research as a result of the passage of the Anderson-Aspinall Act, research activity on the reverse-osmosis process accelerated rapidly. In 1962 the Office awarded four contracts for reverse-osmosis-related research, in 1963 five contracts, in 1964 nine contracts, and in 1965 thirteen contracts and grants. A summary of dollar expenditures and contract awards by the Office of Saline Water for reverse-osmosis research and development is shown in Table 8–1.

Table 8–1   Contracts Awarded for Reverse-Osmosis Research by the Office of Saline Water

Fiscal year	Number of contracts and grants awarded	Total (dollars)
1953	1	18,080
1954	0	0
1955	2	72,777
1956	0	0
1957	0	0
1958	0	0
1959	0	0
1960	2	67,030
1961	0	0
1962	4	383,585
1963	5	384,400
1964	9	970,046
1965	13	1,496,723

The work of Breton and Reid at the University of Florida[2] and that of Loeb and Sourirajan at the University of California[3] made it apparent that much research and development effort will be necessary before the reverse-osmosis process can be brought to a state of practical utility. Despite some discussion of pore sizes and shapes, and an empirical hypothesis of the role of perchlorates in the membrane-fabrication procedure, very little was known about membrane structure, chemical and physical properties of the membranes, and the relationships of those properties to the mechanism of water transport and salt rejection.

System limitations, such as membrane lifetime, optimum pressures of operation, boundary-layer limitations, pressure effects on construction materials, or plant-design considerations on which to base cost estimates were also largely unexplored. The complex physical nature of the membranes fabricated by Loeb and Sourirajan and the critical factors arising in each step of the fabrication procedure indicated that an empirical approach in the search for an optimum membrane would have a very low probability of success.

In 1962 the Office of Saline Water began to increase its financial support of fundamental research in reverse osmosis. The program was initially directed toward developing an understanding of the mechanism by which the membrane separated salt from water. The experimental program involved studies considering the relationship of the chemical and physical properties of cellulose acetate to its effectiveness in water transport and salt rejection, with the Loeb and Sourirajan membrane as the basic model. It included investigations of

  The role of membrane salt
  The microstructure of semipermeable membranes
  The role of post-membrane-formation treatments
  The relationship between water content and flux
  The chemistry of film formation and characterization of the
      surface layer
  The development of phenomenological equations describing
      the flow of water and salt through osmotic membranes
  Boundary-layer effects
  Engineering analyses of reverse-osmosis desalination plants

By 1963, the results of the Office of Saline Water basic-research programs were sufficiently encouraging to justify a development effort toward design, construction, and testing of reverse-osmosis bench-scale pilot plants. In 1963 and 1964 the Office of Saline Water awarded contracts to the Aerojet-General Corporation for proceeding with a plate-and-frame pilot plant, to the General Atomic Division of General Dynamics Corporation for a spiral-membrane pilot-plant module, and to Dorr-Oliver, Incorporated, for a reverse-osmosis module employing membranes sandwiched between plastic plates with channels of capillary dimensions scored on their surfaces. Because of the lack of similarity to any known process, no single plant design has yet been considered or accepted as the optimum design. As of 1965 there are no pilot or demonstration plants in existence of sufficient size to produce definitive cost data that can be used with confidence to project the economics of large-size plants. At the present state of the art economic projections are useful only as a measure to point out those components of the system that should receive additional development effort.

Increased effort in desalting activities, including the reverse-osmosis process, was prompted in July 1964 by a request from President Lyndon B. Johnson to the U. S. Department of the Interior and the Atomic Energy Commission for a program that would significantly advance large-scale desalting technology. The conclusions and recommendations resulting from the studies undertaken in response to that request are set out in a report approved by the Secretary of the Interior and the Chairman of the Atomic Energy Commission on September 22, 1964, submitted to the President on that date, and released to the public on October 26, 1964.[4] It advocated expansion, extension, and acceleration of the saltwater-conversion research and development activities being conducted by the Department of the Interior. Among the specific recommendations made by the Secretary of the Interior was "that we substantially increase our research effort to develop entirely new desalting techniques, to improve distillation processes, and to develop the promising reverse-osmosis process." The proposed program for improving the reverse-osmosis process recommended placing primary emphasis on membrane research and development. It was suggested that the program include research on

> Developing an understanding of how the process works
> Factors affecting membrane lifetime
> Improvement of cellulose acetate membranes
> Alternative membranes which combine suitable permeation
>   properties with greater durability
> Problems of membrane production on a larger scale

Also recommended was the acceleration of the design of system equipment for the reverse-osmosis process. It was suggested that an experimental plant capable of producing 25,000 gpd of converted water could be designed with the then existing technology. The first prototype plant was to be operated on brackish water, to be followed at a later date with a larger prototype plant for seawater operation.

A five-year program in reverse osmosis proposed by the Office of Saline Water was described further at open public hearings held by the Subcommittee on Irrigation and Reclamation of the Senate Interior and Insular Affairs Committee on May 18 and 19, 1965, and by the Subcommittee on Irrigation and Reclamation of the House Interior and Insular Affairs Committee on May 20 and 21, 1965. The program presented to the committees by the Department of the Interior was in terms of goals which the Department hoped to attain during the 5-year period. Of the proposed $200 million program, the sum of $26,550,000 was requested for activities related to membrane processes. The membrane program outline presented to the committees suggested the following program schedule:[5]

A. *Membrane Development*

Investigations seeking improvement in the properties of cellulose acetate membranes and the search for alternative membranes with properties superior to cellulose acetate will be accelerated.

B. *Module Design and Module Construction Techniques*

The membrane module is the key component of a reverse osmosis plant. Its properties largely determine operating parameters, and its costs are the greatest source of uncertainty in present cost projections. For this reason, a major program on module development and the development of techniques for manufacturing membrane modules is suggested.

C. *Design and construction of Two 50,000 Gallon-per-Day Prototype Pilot Plant Modules*

Each of these modules will embody different design features and will serve primarily to test the feasibility of the design and the manufacturing techniques used in fabricating the modules. The design of these plants will be such that they can be used for both brackish and sea water applications.

D. *Design and Construction of Two 250,000 Gallon-per-Day Test Bed Plants*

These two plants will be specifically designed for operation on brackish water. The operation of the pilot plants, and experimentation with them, would be directed toward the investigation of the validity of the criteria used in designing them and to provide definitive data for engineering design of larger plants.

E. *Engineering Design of a One-Million-Gallon-per-Day Experimental Brackish Water Test Bed Module*

At this point in the development program, the design showing the best operating performance through the 50,000 and 250,000 gpd test states will be selected for further development.

F. *Construction of the One-Million-Gallon-per-Day Experimental Brackish Water Test Bed Module*

G. *Operation of the One-Million-Gallon-per-Day Experimental Brackish Water Test Bed Module*

It is expected that during operation, critical areas for plant improvements and cost reductions will become apparent. It is too early to preduct just what these areas will be, but an allowance for further development work is included in the suggested program in order to immediately exploit those findings which may lead to significant cost reductions.

H. *Sea Water Program*

Concurrent with the development effort on the brackish water applications of reverse osmosis, design and test effort to develop an optimum system design for sea water application of reverse osmosis will also be conducted.

I. *Selection of Design Criteria for Sea Water Plant*

The 50,000 and 250,000 gallon-per-day prototype modules used to obtain test data for the design of the brackish water test bed plant will be modified and adapted for sea water operation. The data obtained from operation of those prototype modules plus the operating experience gained from the one-million-gallon-per-day test bed brackish water plant will be used to develop the design for a one-million-gallon-per-day sea water test bed plant.

J. *Study of Feed Water Composition Variables on Membranes and Plant Performance*

The chemical composition of sea water throughout the world is relatively constant. Except in the vicinity of harbors and river outlets where organic pollution may be encountered we do not foresee major problems arising which would lead to the need for expensive preconditioning of feed water. Brackish water, however, presents us with a number of potential problems. The composition of brackish water varies widely among different sources and is even known to vary in different wells in the same aquifer. In brackish water, one may encounter heavy metals at a much higher concentration than in sea water, suspended matter such as colloidal clay, organic matter, sulfur and other materials which may adversely affect reverse osmosis membranes. We propose to determine the effect of those contaminants on membrane performance and to develop means for their control in order to insure optimum membrane performance.

A chronological schedule for the proposed reverse osmosis development program is shown in [Fig. 8–1]. It calls for start-up of a one-million-gallon-per-day brackish water test bed plant in 1972. We believe that goal is attainable if funds are made available for the program.

K. *Brackish Water Test Facility*

The proposed membrane program deals primarily with engineering development and much of the program involves construction, testing, and operation of bench scale equipment, pilot plant modules and complete experimental test bed plants.

The membrane processes hold most promise for initial application to the conversion of low and moderately saline waters. For this reason, the first goal in the membrane program will be the development of the most efficient and economical process for the conversion of inland brackish water supplies.

To attain that goal, it will be necessary to test proposed processes and system designs and to obtain operating and economic data for each of the advanced design concepts selected for intensive development. Since processes and designs will be competing with each other, it will be necessary that the test modules and the processes embodied in them be operated under standard conditions.

To insure that standard conditions are provided, we are requesting funds for the establishment of an inland brackish water test site to provide adequate facilities for the simultaneous operation of between six and twelve pilot and test bed plants. The daily feed water requirements for those plants will vary between 50,000 and 2,000,000 gallons per day and facilities will need to be provided to handle the disposal of up to 1,000,000 gallons per day of brine.

In 1965 Congress amended the Saline Water Act by enactment of Public Law 89-118 (Act of August 11, 1965), which authorized the expenditure of $90 million from 1962 to 1972 inclusive to carry out the recommended expansion and acceleration of the program. With the authorization granted under this act, the activities of the Office of Saline Water related to membrane research and development are expected to be greatly increased in accordance with the statement quoted. Of course

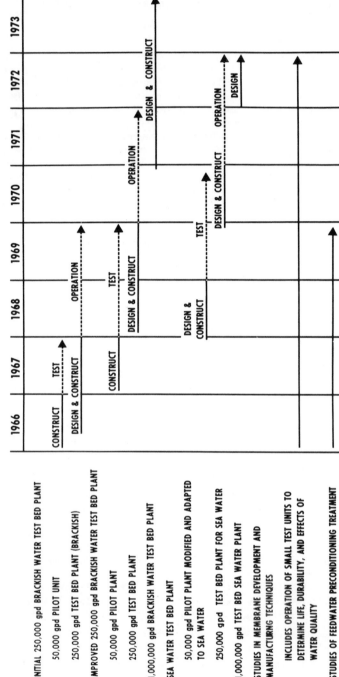

Fig. 8–1 Reverse-osmosis development-program schedule.[5]

the direction the program takes in the future depends to a great extent upon the results obtained as the research progresses. However, the search for superior membranes will undoubtedly be expanded, and system design and pilot-plant activity should be rapidly accelerated. The initial emphasis of the accelerated membrane program will be on the development of a reverse-osmosis system for brackish-water conversion, to be followed by the development of a seawater-conversion capability.

8.2 Programs of Other Groups

State of California

One of the significant developments in the late 1950's which gave impetus to the current surge of activity in membrane desalination processes and particularly in the reverse-osmosis process was the perfecting of a technique by Loeb and Sourirajan at UCLA for casting cellulose acetate membranes possessing good salt rejection and a high water-permeation rate.[3] It was this discovery which put the reverse-osmosis process for seawater and brackish-water desalination within the range of economic feasibility.

The work of Loeb and Sourirajan evolved from the seawater-conversion research program of the University of California which has been in progress since 1951–1952 on both the Berkeley and Los Angeles campuses. It was initiated at the request of the California State Legislature and has been financed primarily with funds appropriated by that body.

The emphasis of research on reverse osmosis at the University of California has been directed primarily toward an understanding of the fundamental mechanisms of the process. However, the work has also included the two pilot plants described in Chapter 7. The UCLA group has designed and constructed a 5000-gpd pilot plant for installation in Coalinga, California, where it is being used to demonstrate the applicability of the process for converting brackish water to water of a quality suitable for municipal use.[6]

U. S. Public Health Service and Federal Water Pollution Control Administration

Early in 1963 the Division of Water Supply and Pollution Control, U. S. Public Health Service, awarded a contract to the Aerojet-General Corporation for a feasibility study to demonstrate the potential of the reverse-osmosis process for the recovery of potable water from secondary sewage-treatment plant effluents.

Experiments were designed to study the effects of varying membrane-permeation rates and applied pressures. Secondary effluent from the treatment plant of the community of Azusa, California, was used as a feed for the laboratory test cells.[7] The experiments demonstrated that it is possible to recover between 80 and 90 percent of product water averaging less than 80 ppm total dissolved solids (TDS), less than 0.3 ppm detergents (ABS) and less than 10 ppm oxygen-demanding substances (COD) from a sewage effluent averaging 600 to 800 ppm TDS, 5 to 10 ppm ABS, and 80 to 120 ppm COD. No studies were conducted to determine the bacterial and viral properties of either the feed or product water.

It was also revealed that flux rates declined and some membrane deterioration occurred. No attempt was made to isolate the factors responsible for the degradation of the membrane. The experiments were significant, however, and demonstrated a potential application of the reverse-osmosis process in raising the quality of low-grade water. In addition, it was shown that the reverse-osmosis process could remove both inorganic and organic material not removable from waste water by conventional means of secondary sewage treatment.

More recently, the General Atomic Division of General Dynamics, in cooperation with the County Sanitation Districts of Los Angeles County also conducted a series of exploratory tests further to explore the potential of reverse osmosis as a new means of water reclamation.[8] These experiments were run by District personnel at the Sanitation District's Pomona laboratories. General Atomic designed and built the experimental loop and supplied the membrane modules used. The modules tested contained membranes of three different degrees of permeability and selectivity. The results were impressive. In every case the product water from each module tested had substantially lower contents of all contaminants studied than had the feed water. Reductions in total dissolved solids ranged up to a factor of 25 for the high-selectivity membranes, reduction in chemical oxygen demand ranged from a factor of 4 to one of 30, and total nitrogen and phosphate were sharply reduced in all cases.

Decreases in flow rate with time were encountered with the high-permeability membranes while product flow rate and quality from the high-selectivity modules studied were maintained throughout the experimental runs. The flow-rate losses observed in the higher-flux modules were recoverable by means of suitable cleaning and backflushing procedures. Further investigation of those operations is planned. These activities led, in late 1965, to the formulation of a reverse-osmosis research program to be conducted jointly by the Federal Water Pollution Control Administration and the County Sanitation Districts of Los Angeles County. This program will include the installation and operation of a several-thousand-gpd reverse-osmosis loop at the Pomona water reclamation plant.

Atomic Energy Commission

A basic research program carried out at Oak Ridge National Laboratory under an interagency agreement between the Office of Saline Water and the Atomic Energy Commission is designed to develop information pertinent to desalination on equilibrium and transport properties of solutions, phase relationships, equilibrium and transport phenomena at phase boundaries and surfaces, and separation methods, including reverse osmosis.

The reverse-osmosis studies deal principally with (1) development of equipment and methods for study of the transport of water and salts across membranes under pressure, (2) boundary-layer phenomena, (3) experimental and theoretical studies with uncharged membranes, (4) development of new reverse-osmosis membranes with particular emphasis on ion-exchange membranes, (5) evaluation of inorganic membranes, and (6) theoretical studies of salt filtration with microporous ion-exchange active materials.

Other studies have dealt with (1) the theoretical analysis of concentration polarization in flowing systems, (2) development of a concentration-polarization method for testing membranes, and (3) boundary-layer studies whose object is the development of techniques for increasing mass transfer and decreasing concentration polarization. These studies have resulted in a series of publications in the scientific literature.

The Office of Saline Water is continuing to provide financial support and encouragement to the Oak Ridge National Laboratory saline-water research program.

Other Federal Agencies

Water problems are getting wider recognition and broader consideration in public and private circles today than in any other period in history. Among recent significant developments in the field of water resources was the enactment of the Water Resources Research Act (Public Law 88-379) in 1964, and the enactment of the Water Resources Planning Act (Public Law 89-80), the Federal Water Pollution Control Act (Public Law 89-234), and the amendments to the Saline Water Conversion Act (Public Law 89-118) in 1965.

The Water Resources Research Act (Public Law 88-379) provided for the establishment of a water-resources research institute at a land-grant college or state university in each State and in Puerto Rico. It authorized $75,000 in the first year, $87,500 in the second and third years, and $100,000 each year thereafter to assist all participating States in establishing and carrying on the work of a competent and qualified water-resources research institute, center, or equivalent agency. In addition, the Act authorized the appropriation of $1 million in 1965, $2 million in 1966, $3 million in 1967, $4 million in 1968, $5 million in 1969 and each succeeding year thereafter, for matching on a dollar-for-dollar basis money made available to institutes by States or other non-federal sources for specific water-research projects undertaken by those centers.

In April 1966 Congress amended the Act by Public Law 89-404, which authorized additional funds to be appropriated in the amount of $5 million for fiscal year 1967, $6 million in 1968, $7 million in 1969, $8 million in 1970, $9 million in 1971, and $10 million for each of the fiscal years 1972 through 1976 inclusive. The appropriations are to finance contracts, grants, matching or other arrangements with educational institutions, private foundations or other institutions, with private firms and individuals, and with local, State, and federal Government agencies, to undertake research into any aspects of water problems related to the mission of the Department of the Interior which may be deemed desirable by the Secretary of the Interior and are not otherwise being studied.

The Water Resources Planning Act (Public Law 89-80) provided for the establishment of a Water Resources Council composed of the Secretary of the Interior, the Secretary of Agriculture, the Secretary of the Army, the Secretary of Health, Education and Welfare, and the Chairman of the Federal Power Commission. The Council is required to conduct a continuing study and prepare an assessment biennially, or at such less frequent intervals as it may determine, of the adequacy of water supplies necessary to meet the requirements in each water-resource region in the United States. It will also maintain a continuing study of the relation of regional or river-basin plans and programs to the requirements of larger regions of the nation and of the adequacy of administrative and statutory means for the coordination of the water- and related land-resources policies and programs of the several Federal agencies, and it shall appraise the adequacy of existing and proposed policies and programs to meet such requirements; also it shall make recommendations to the President with respect to Federal policies and programs.

The Water Resources Planning Act also provides for the establishment of river-basin water- and related land-resources commissions for the coordination of federal, State, interstate, local, and nongovernmental plans for the development of water and land resources in its area, river basin, or group of river basins. The membership of the river-basin commissions will consist of both federal and State representatives.

In order to stimulate increased participation by the States in water- and related land-resources planning, the Act also provides for financial assistance in the form of matching grants to the States to assist them in developing and participating in the development of comprehensive water- and related land-resources plans.

The Water Pollution Control Act (Public Law 89-234) created a Federal Water Pollution Control Administration within the Department of Health, Education and Welfare to provide technical services and to administer Federal grant programs with State and interstate agencies and municipalities in connection with the prevention and control of water pollution.

The Act requires that States adopt by June 30, 1967, water-quality criteria applicable to interstate waters and a plan for the implementation and enforcement of the water-quality criteria adopted. In the event the States do not adopt and enforce acceptable water quality standards the Act provides mechanisms for the Secretary of Health, Education and Welfare to set forth and enforce standards of water quality applicable to interstate waters or portions thereof within such States.

On February 23, 1966, President Lyndon B. Johnson forwarded a message to Congress entitled, "Proposals for the Preservation of America's Natural Heritage." In it he proposed means to achieve the promise of "clean rivers, tall forests and clean air — a sane environment for man." In the area of water resources the message recommended a Clean Rivers Demonstration Program to be undertaken with federal financial assistance. It was proposed that the program begin with a few basins in States and communities already prepared with basin-development plans and to extend its activities as additional basin organizations were formed and their plans drafted. Federal assistance was proposed for the initial construction of local treatment works. Thereafter, local communities would be expected to collect revenues from users sufficient for the operation, expansion, and replacement of the facilities.

In order to construct the initial facilities it was proposed to eliminate the dollar-ceiling limitation on grants for sewage-treatment facilities in the Clean River Demonstrations — but only in the Demonstrations — and to provide special funds to finance both planning and project costs in Clean River Demonstrations. It was also proposed that the Department of the Interior assume leadership in the clean-water effort and that a reorganization plan to transfer to the Department of the Interior the Water Pollution Control Administration now housed in the Department of Health, Education and Welfare be submitted to Congress. In addition, the President proposed the establishment of a National Water Commission to review and advise on the entire range of water-resource problems — from methods to conserve and augment existing water supplies to the application of modern technology, such as desalination, to provide more usable water for our cities, our industries, and our farms.

Also included in the President's message were recommendations that federal assistance to State water-pollution control agencies be doubled, that the Water Pollution Control Act be amended to allow the Federal Government to take stronger measures to abate pollution, and that additional funds be provided for research on new systems of disposal, the improvement of water treatment technology, and to study the effects of pollutants on plants, animals, and human populations.

8.3   Reverse Osmosis in the Water Picture

Research on the reverse-osmosis process was encouraged initially and continues to be encouraged by the promise this process holds for low-cost desalination. Engineering studies such as those described in Chapter 6 indicate that even with present membrane and equipment limitations the reverse-osmosis process approaches cost competitiveness with other desalination processes.

One of the features that contributes to the attractiveness of the reverse-osmosis process is its low energy requirement in comparison with other desalination processes. The basic heat-energy requirements for several saline-water-conversion processes with present technology are given in Table 8-2.[9]

Table 8-2   Basic Energy Requirements for Various Water-Conversion Processes

Processes using heat	Energy required (BTU per gallon of product water)
Multistage flash distillation	1020
Long-tube vertical distillation	1020
Processes using electricity*	
Vapor-compression distillation	610
Freezing	610
Reverse osmosis	510
Electrodialysis†	250

* The energy values given for the "electrical" processes are the thermal energies for the appropriate electrical power generation at 33 percent plant efficiency.

† The electrodialysis process is applicable to the conversion of brackish water only, and this figure is therefore not directly comparable with the others.

In addition to the low energy requirements, the reverse-osmosis process can operate at ambient temperature. This low-temperature operation minimizes corrosion and tends to avoid scaling problems such as those encountered with desalination processes requiring high temperatures for their operation. Probably the most appealing facets of the process are its conceptual simplicity and its potential usefulness in a variety of separation applications. Recent experiments have been made on the potential use of the process for the recovery of acid mine waters, and the removal of organic materials from aqueous solutions has already been demonstrated in the Public Health Service program as well as in the program of the County Sanitation Districts of Los Angeles County.

Further evidence of the potential of the reverse-osmosis process for low-cost desalination was given in the March 23, 1964, report of the Task Group on Nuclear Power and Saline Water Conversion to the Director, Office of Science and Technology.[9] It summarized the findings, conclusions, and recommendations of the task group appointed by the Director, Office of Science and Technology, to study large nuclear-powered seawater-conversion plants. Included in the report was an estimate of the cost of converting seawater in a single-purpose 1,000-million-gpd reverse-osmosis plant extrapolated from pilot-plant data. The estimate, as it appeared in the Task Group report, is shown in Table 8–3.

Table 8–3   Production-Cost Estimate for 1,000-million-gpd Reverse-Osmosis Water-plant, Based on Technology Estimated to be Available by 1980.

Membrane flux: 14 gpd/ft²
Capital cost: $430 million
Plant operating-factor: 330 stream days per year (based upon
                             single-purpose operation)
Energy required: 24 kw-hr/1000 gallons of water produced.
Total power required: 1000 MWe

		$/stream day
Fixed charges at 7% per year		91,200
Interest on working capital at 5% per year		1,200
Operating Costs:		
Labor	15,000	
Electricity at 2.1 mills/kw-hr	50,400	
Supplies and maintenance material	6,500	
		71,900
Total costs		164,300
Net water cost		16.4¢/1000 gal
Net water cost from plant based upon technology available for 1975 operation		21¢/1000 gal

The Task Group report also pointed out that further development and plant-operating experience with the reverse-osmosis process would be required before it could be considered as *the* desalination process for the 1980's. The report advised that it is important not to neglect the development of single-purpose saline-water-conversion processes, as there may be areas where by-product power may not be desirable or marketable.

The reverse-osmosis process has potential usefulness for numerous applications other than sea- and brackish-water conversion. The system has already shown promise for the renovation of sewage effluents and acid mine waters. In addition, reverse osmosis may have applications in the treatment of industrial and radioactive wastes, the processing of industrial water, and applications in the mining, food, pharmaceutical, and chemical industries.

The widespread adoption and application of the process awaits only an adequate demonstration of its reliability over a reasonable period of time under a variety of operating conditions.

References

1. *Saline Water Conversion Report for 1964*, United States Department of the Interior, Office of Saline Water, Government Printing Office, 1965.
2. Breton, E. J., Jr., and C. E. Reid, Office of Saline Water Research and Development Progress Report No. 16, April 1957.
3. Loeb, S., and S. Sourirajan, UCLA Department of Engineering Report 60-60, 1960.
4. *Program for Advancing Desalting Technology*, United States Department of the Interior, Government Printing Office, 1964.
5. Hearings before the Subcommittee on Irrigation and Reclamation of the Committee on Interior and Insular Affairs, House of Representatives, Eighty-Ninth Congress, First Session, on H.R. 7092, Government Printing Office, 1965.
6. *Saline Water Research Progress Summary*, Water Resources Center Desalination Report No. 2, UCLA Department of Engineering Report 66-1, 1966.
7. *Summary Report, Advanced Waste Treatment Research*, U. S. Department of Health, Education and Welfare, Public Health Service, Report AWTR-14, Public Health Service Publication No. 99-WP-24, 1965.
8. Bray, D. T., U. Merten, and M. Augustus, Bulletin of the California Water Pollution Control Association **2**, 11 (1965).
9. *An Assessment of Large Nuclear Powered Sea Water Distillation Plants*, Office of Science and Technology, Executive Office of the President, Government Printing Office, 1964.

Index

Date Due